BLEWETT GOLD

HISTORY OF THE

PESHASTIN MINING DISTRICT

Kent ... Always good to see you ... at the FHS picnic or other places. Here is the latest (maybe the finale) ... got one more going, but it's not a "for sure" project. So I got to have my way (solo) with this read ... hope you find some stuff of interest for you enjoy - Stay well - Later, Vic

NORTHWEST UNDERGROUND EXPLORATIONS

VICTOR PISONI

Happy Trails,
Vic Pisoni

NWMP LLC   Northwest Mining Publishers, LLC

D1571879

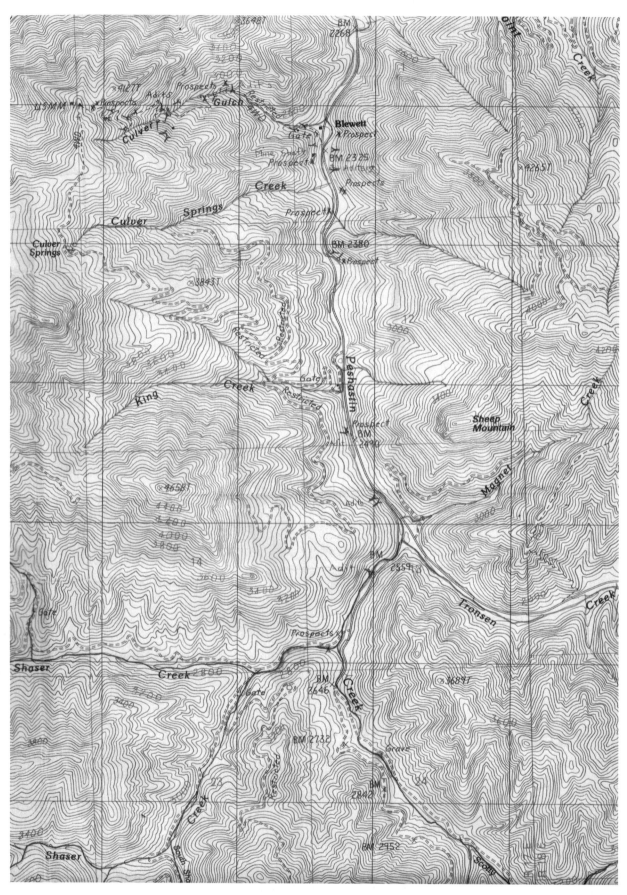

Blewett Quadrangle Washington 7.5 Minute Series (Topographic map) showing the town of Blewett and southward

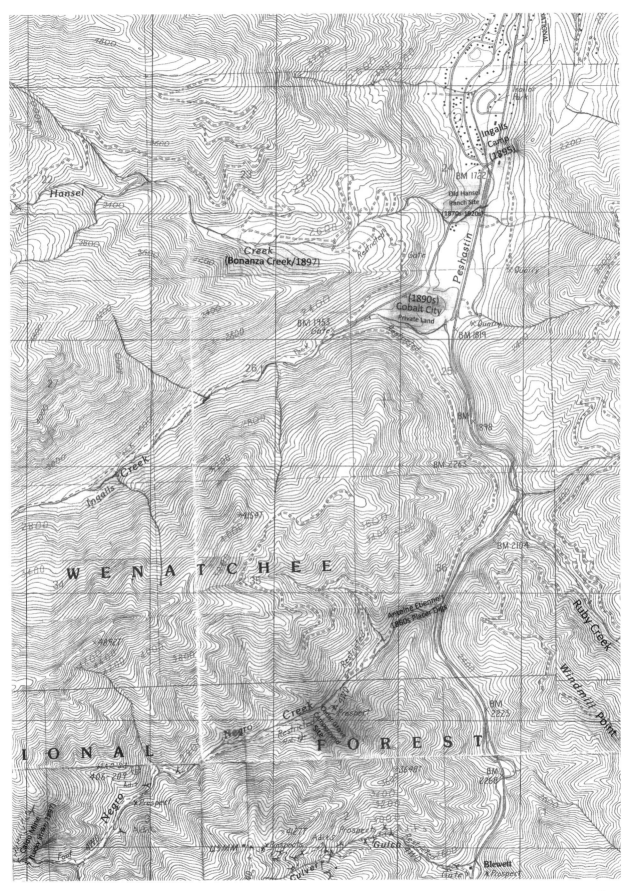

Blewett Quadrangle Washington 7.5 Minute Series (Topographic map) showing the town of Blewett and northward

Northwest Mining Publishers, LLC
P.O. Box 386
Monroe • WA • 98272

Disclaimer

In utilizing this publication, it is and should be understood that mines, mining, and mining claim locations can be dangerous, with numerous natural and artificial hazards.

By accepting and using this publication and the information contained herein, the user agrees to relieve the authors and Northwest Underground Explorations, its officers, and/or assignees from any liability from the use of any information contained in this publication. The user also accepts responsibility for any liability incurred by family members or guests incurred from the use of any information contained herein.

The authors and Northwest Underground Explorations do not encourage or condone trespass on private or otherwise restricted properties without express prior and proper permission from the rightful owners of said property.

10 9 8 7 6 5 4 3 2 1
Printed in the United States of America
LCCN 2014939080
ISBN 978-0-9822558-6-5

Production coordination:
 Sheryn Hara, Book Publishers Network
Editor: Julie Scandora
Indexer: Carolyn Acheson
Cover and interior design:
 Melissa Vail Coffman

OTHER BOOKS IN THIS SERIES:
Discovering Washington's Historic Mines
Volume 1, The West Central Cascade
Mountains

Discovering Washington's Historic Mines
Volume 2, The East Central Cascade Mountains
and the Wenatchee Mountains

Discovering Washington's Historic Mines
Volume 3, The North Cascade Mountains

Discovering Washington's Historic Mines
Volume 4, The Western Okanogan

Discovering Washington's Historic Mines
Volume 5, The Okanogan Highlands and
Ferry County

Discovering Washington's Historic Mines
Volume 6, Stevens and Pend Oreille Counties

Front cover photo: From a Washington
Meteor Mining Company prospectus
1905. (Chris Bell photo collection.)
Back cover photo: (Wesley C.
Engstrom photo collection)

Blewett gold : history of the Peshastin mining district / Northwest Underground Explorations ; Victor Pisoni. -- Monroe, WA : Northwest Mining Publishers, c2014.

p. ; cm.

ISBN: 978-0-9822558-6-5
Includes glossary, bibliographical references and index.

Summary: This book is a revealing visit into the historic gold-mining town of Blewett, Washington. The spirit of the town, its miners, and mining activities in Culver Gulch are brought to life in "Blewett Gold". About half of the information in this book is from unpublished data and the personal remembrances and photographs of past Blewettites. The Blewett Mining District is, presently, a downsized section of the original Peshastin Mining District, which established on May 1, 1894, in the East Central Cascade mountains. The district's focal point is a marker on the east side of US 97, at Mile Post 174.--Publisher.

1. Gold mines and mining--Washington (State)--Blewett--History. 2. Mines and mineral resources--Washington (State)--Peshastin--History. 3. Mines and mineral resources--Washington (State)--Blewett--History. 4. Mines and mineral resources--Washington (State)--Chelan County--History. 5. Abandoned gold mines--Washington (State)--Blewett. 6. Historic mines--Washington (State)--Peshastin. 7. Historic mines--Washington (State)--Blewett. 8. Historic mines--Washington (State)--Chelan County. 9. Blewett (Wash.)--History. 10. Peshastin (Wash.)--History. I. Pisoni, Victor. II. Northwest Underground Explorations. III. Title.

TN24.W2 B54 2014
338.2/09797--dc23

2014939080
1406

Dedicated to

The miners and folks from Blewett's past

AND IN MEMORY OF GREG CADY

One of the founders of Northwest Underground Explorations; longtime friend, trail pounder, and co-author in volumes No. 1 and No. 2 of the *Discovering Washington's Historic Mines* six-volume series. Greg will be kept in our circle of remembrances and lively conversations of good times past ... RIP.

Contents

Introduction

Researched, compiled, and written by Victor (Vic) Pisoni in conjunction with Northwest Underground Explorations. This book was edited by Vic Pisoni, Phil Woodhouse, Daryl Jacobson, and Wayne Massing. Phil and Daryl are credited with technical and other written informational insights and graphics placed in this book by way of their professional inclusion as fellow co-authors and Northwest Mining Publishers, LLC, business partner associates, and longtime (older than dirt) friends.

Acknowledgments

IN THE BEGINNING...

NORTHWEST UNDERGROUND EXPLO-RATIONS (NWUE) began as a gathering of like-minded mining history buffs, initiated by Daryl Jacobson and Greg Cady at the helm. I met them in 1988. We went searching for an underground working that was abandoned long ago, and I was the one to discover its vaguely noted location.

There was nothing I did that was calculated in a professional tunnel-seeking way. I was just annoyed at the tight tangle of underbrush and decided to walk up knee-deep Lewis Creek. I saw what first appeared to be a dark shadow to my right on the bank of the creek. As I approached, it revealed its secret place to view. It was the portal of the mine that we were trying to locate. There was no tailings pile because the adit's blasted tailings' debris had been dumped directly into the creek and washed away each year by the increased volumes of rushing waters caused by spring's surging snowmelt.

From that point on, I was hooked. The same year, I met fellow mines explorer Phil Woodhouse, the author of the book Monte Cristo. Phil, Daryl, and I were on a research-ing trip to the Monte Cristo Mining District. Phil is the go-to guy on all things related to the history of *Monte Cristo*. Through all our accumulated history, research, and writing

From the left are Daryl Jacobson and Phil Woodhouse in 1988. During this year, the author met Daryl and Phil, and we began exploring mine sites, accumulating data and pictures for *Discovering Washington's Historic Mines* six volume book series. Phil authored the book *Monte Cristo* (first edition 1979). It is a comprehensive and skillfully authored presentation, and it continues to be instrumental in initiating excitement among Northwest Underground Explorations members and individuals or groups seeking historic mining site adventures. (Photo by Vic Pisoni.)

skills, Daryl, Greg, Phil, Bill Petersen, and I put together volume one of our six-volume series on *Discovering Washington's Historic Mines*. Dave Rygmyr, owner of the Oso Publishing Company, contracted with us to publish and sell the volumes one through three. Phil, Daryl, and I bought the rights from Oso Publishing Company to our first three books in the series and *The Everett and Monte Cristo Railway* book. We formed Northwest Mining Publishers, LLC. Volumes four, five, and six, plus *Blewett Gold* are the results of our author-publishing partnership.

Membership in Northwest Underground Explorations began to increase because of interest in exploring abandoned mines. We have grown to the point where a Northwest Underground Explorations website has been activated. As of this writing, there are over 330 signed on as members at http://finance.groups.yahoo.com/group/NWUNDERGROUND.

Since 2003, the Northwest Underground Explorations website has gained members that have made inquiries pertaining to the organization's available information and member-posted photos. Many of these members now have gathered into core groups of friends that head out into the mountains, forests, and deserts seeking the experience of locating historic mine sites. Once a site is located, pictures of old mining artifacts, building remains, and miner-anthropology related evidence can be used as documentation for future published reports or to be included in subject-related books. Mineral-seeking club members, other rock-hounding individuals, plus folks active and interested in the metal-detecting aspects of understanding historic sites and their geological/mineral connection have made contributions via photos and field notes that are posted on the NWUE website.

Books now available are: *Discovering Washington Historic Mines Vol. 1* (ISBN 978-0-9822558-0-3), *Vol. 2* (ISBN 978-0-9822558-1-0), *Vol. 3* (ISBN 1-931064-15-16), *Vol. 4* (ISBN 0-9822558-3-7), *Vol. 5* (ISBN 978-0-9822558-4-1), and *Vol. 6* (ISBN 978-0-9822558-5-8). *The Everett and Monte Cristo Railway* book has been reprinted in soft-cover (ISBN 978-0-982258-2-7). The railway book reveals the history of the railroad connection between the mines in the historic Monte Cristo Mining District site and the industries in Everett that were associated with its mineral production and mine-related needs.

These books are published by Northwest Mining Publishers, LLC, and are currently available at bookstores; or contact nwminingpublishers@frontier.com.

SPECIAL THANKS

First and foremost, my personal thanks to Phil Woodhouse (Ancient Miner) and Daryl Jacobson (Jake) for their professional insight, suggestions, and recommendations during my effort in authoring this book as we went through the first few rounds of document editing. The quality of this historic Blewett Mining District presentation, involving their author-skills, resulted in a decidedly improved read.

Extended appreciation and thanks go out to **Lee Walkling** (head librarian at the DNR library in Olympia, Washington. Lee retired in 2012), and **Connie Manson** (former head librarian)

Amongst others who receive special thanks for unpublished but valuable information and photographs via personal family connections with the Peshastin and Blewett Mining Districts are past resident family members and friends. An in-depth look into the personal lives of those who lived and mined the area was graciously offered by **Dr. Charles Ballard** of Tarzana, California, and his cousin, **Phyllis Barthol-Cramer** who, up to the age of five years old, lived in the mining town of Blewett until 1942. (Phyllis's uncle **Cliff Davenport** came to the Blewett mines early enough to know and work with some of the original "first arrivers." He saw them either depart the area or die in Blewett. Cliff himself became an old-timer at Blewett and remained a resident miner for a considerable amount of his adult life). Thanks go to **Dorothy Davenport-Barthol, Phyllis Barthol-Cramer, Joyce Davenport-Rosenberger**, and **Virginia Davenport-Carpenter** who were also part of the resident population in the town of Blewett. Phyllis, Dorothy, Virginia, and Joyce greatly enhanced my look into the heart of the Blewett resident miners and their families through personal involvement and hundreds of pages of insightful, unpublished historic information with family and mining pictures related to those activities throughout the Peshastin (Blewett) Mining District.

To **Wesley C. Engstrom** and **Carole Fackler-Engstrom**, many thanks for their personal involvement in helping with volume two of *Discovering Washington's Historic Mines* (the Swauk and Blewett Mining Areas chapter of the book) and shared research publications. Northwest Underground Explorations has benefited greatly through Wes's vast personal history files, which contain family-related mining information. From Wesley and Carole Engstrom, NWUE has received and shared much historic data in compiling various books containing Washington's genealogy, mining, anthropology, and all aspects of pertinent history related to frontier life up to history-in-the-making, as it is presently.

Through Wesley, Northwest Underground Explorations' authors had access to several hours of interviews that he transferred from 12 hours of in-depth conversations about mining history, from cassette tapes to CDs, of Engstrom's Swauk miner friend **Ollie Jordin**, who was born in 1885. These interviews were conducted by locally famous Cle Elum High School history teacher **Fred Kruger** (now retired). Fred taped the historically fact-packed series in face-to-face meetings with Ollie during 1972, when Jordin was 87 years old. Prolific Swauk Mining District gold miner Ollie Jordin unloaded a treasure trove of mining history during those sessions. This valuable and newly released look into mining and miner's personal history was a boon to this book. Ollie worked with Karl Fackler at the Pole Pick No. 1 mine in Culver Gulch. Plus, Ollie brought to attention some of the other activities in the Blewett mining area. Ollie contributed many insights about how miners did things their way when normal mining practices didn't fit the needs of an unusual mine-related situation.

Carole Fackler-Engstrom has family mining ties to the Swauk Mining District/Liberty, Washington; Blewett Mining District/Culver Gulch, Blewett, Washington; and elsewhere. And some of the most important sources of data for this Blewett-based book came from the Fackler family's mining history background.

Many thanks to the Cashmere Museum and Pioneer Village Board of Directors, and Fred Harvey for his personal guidance and allowing my research (as a Cashmere Museum member) among the uncataloged stacks and table tops loaded with unpublished data that contained Blewett related information and photos, which appear in Blewett Gold.

Clint Black, *left*, and Tom Richardson. Both men are Blewett/Culver Gulch miners and mineral claim owners. (Photo by Vic Pisoni.)

To **Clint Black**, accolades as friend, historian, and fellow miner on his various mine workings projects. Clint was our go-to guy when we needed to physically research the many old historic mines up Culver Gulch or to collect data from his vast knowledge of the many Blewett/Culver Gulch mine workings.

And to **Tom Richardson**, many thanks for his insight and information gained from his Culver Gulch experiences as a youth. Today he owns the patented Pole Pick No. 1 claim located in Culver Gulch.

Then there is **Jim Holderhoff**, the former lone miner/resident up Negro Creek at the Caldo mine cabin (originally the Lucky Strike mine). Jim alone has more hands-on knowledge of the Negro Creek mines, second only to L. K. Hodges's (1897) accumulated and recorded research, whose newspaper reporting included some of the early mining activities covered in this book.

Notice: As of this writing, the old historic mining claims from the historic mill site at the bottom of Culver Gulch up to the head of the gulch are under active, recorded claim status. Trespass of private property, including removal of any mineral-bearing rock or "common" dirt, the removal or destruction of claim boundary posts and ORMC/claim notices, metal detecting for any reason, disturbing on-site mining equipment, or any of the secured structures is prohibited by law. *Trespass and damage has been a yearly occurrence on the Culver Gulch claims and is punishable by law.* Interfering with mining activities or harassment and obstructing in any manner of the owners on these mining properties or any mining property in the state of Washington is a felony. This is something to keep in mind should anybody consider instigating a challenge to the aforementioned warnings.

INDIVIDUAL ACKNOWLEDGEMENTS FOR HANDS-ON AND GETTIN' DIRTY

My serious interest in seeking-out mine claim sites began with my membership in the New West Prospectors Club in the mid-1980s. During a club outing in the Index area, I met **Daryl Jacobson** and **Greg Cady**, the organizers of what is now Northwest Underground Explorations. **Terry Carlson** was there that day in 1988, and throughout the following years, we have been on history-gathering treks as a team or with a group of NWUE members during the relocating of

Left to right: Northwest Underground Explorations members Todd Carlson, Terry Carlson (Todd's dad), Vic Pisoni, Chris Bell, Spencer Braun, and Jef Miller. This is the core group, who for several years searched the old historic mineral claims in the Blewett Mining District. We found and identified numerous mining artifacts, which were photographed and are written about in this book. (Photo by Chris Bell.)

hundreds of historic mine sites and exploring into the depths of numerous underground workings. And also kudos to **Fred** and **Lil Lovelace** who, in the several beginning, extreme hiking years with NWUE, lent their outdoor observation and indoor historic mine research skills to our cause. Others who have become involved in this book as core-group regulars to libraries, to museums, to individual old miner interviews, and/ or on bushwhacking trips are **Chris Bell**, **Spencer Braun** (Chris's nephew), **Todd Carlson** (Terry's son), and **Jef Miller**, who contribute their personal explorations and notes to our book-writing efforts. Todd and Jef, alone among our core-group, are technical rock climbers who often go up and over dangerous vertical rock formations. They also rappel down mine shaft workings to verify the underground structure of a mining site, mineral types, or what may be left of the (sometimes) 100-year-old mine workings.

So as you can see, after accumulating over ten years of information and friends with information and the eagerness of those mentioned above to pursue and explore all forms of mining history (and in particular Blewett information), this book is not the end result of my solo quest. This book about the Blewett Mining District history is more the harmonic conjunction of countless documentations and articles of all sorts and hands-on involvement by those who have contributed to this Blewett project. Those folks are the helpmates mentioned above in my acknowledgments and, again, my thanks to all of you.

Disclaimer

To anybody using the data within this book, it is to be understood that mines and all the varieties of hazards and lethal dangers on or near any mining claim, active or inactive, can, and will, under certain misuse of common sense or failure to heed posted warning, cause physical harm or worse.

By using the information herein, the user is solely responsible for his or her actions and relieves the author and Northwest Underground Explorations of any liability due to his or her decision to act on any of the information herein and any and all harm incurred by the user's actions on any of the sites and/or locations identified in this publication. The user and any friends or family members who may have incurred, by their personal decisions and actions, any personal injury leading to thoughts toward a libelous action incident, **may not** hold the author responsible for use of the information of this book's data.

Furthermore, the author does not encourage or condone trespass on private property or any other restricted land without getting expressed permission from the legal owners of said property.

Warning

To add emphasis to this warning, the following case in point confirms the seriousness of this disclaimer: A few years ago a group from Northwest Underground Explorations made note of a car parked at the entry of one of the gulches in the Blewett area. It had been there for three days. The local law office was notified, but apparently there was reason for hesitation to do anything about the situation. After a few more days, NWUE again notified the authorities of the abandoned car. Search and Rescue went to check out the area. They ran out of daylight and called the search off until the next day.

Several members of NWUE went beyond the point where the Search and Rescue party traveled. At dusk, they arrived at an open and very deep shaft that was on a private claim. At the edge of the collar was a man's pack. Search and Rescue returned to the shaft site the next day. Their rescue team rappelled and descended to an intersecting tunnel. In the tunnel near the shaft opening was the body of a man. He had died of hypothermia after his initial trespass and entry down the shaft.

ARTIFACTS

Taking any artifact from a posted historic site or within a national park boundary, will get you a fine and possible jail time. With a reward of $5,000 yielded to people who turn in violators (upon conviction in a court of law), it's not worth the risk to pick up an artifact memento as a reminder of an outing to a particular historic site. You will probably be found guilty. This is especially true if the judge hearing your case is environmentally minded. So snap a photo of the artifact and leave it for others to appreciate.

METAL DETECTING

Metal detecting is allowed in certain designated areas, but you need to get the latest information on what the law requires pertaining to this activity. Check with the federal, state, or local department that controls the ground you would like to search on. It could be US Parks, DNR, or US Forest land. Do your pre-trip information gathering because it is your responsibility to know what you can and can't do with that "metal-sniffer." Don't forget tribal lands and their rules if you want to keep your topknot out of trouble.

Wild Critters I Have Known in the Blewett/Peshastin Area

At the old historic Blewett mining town site area (elevation about 2,500 to 2,600 feet above sea level), there are no rattlesnake sighting reports available. And nary was a "buzz worm" (rattle-snake) seen during the numerous years in which field trips were made by Northwest Underground Explorations while bushwhacking through historic Blewett Mining District site areas. But, in conversation with (now deceased) old Blewett miner Bud Corbaley, we were told there were rattlesnake sightings close to Culver Gulch in the Ruby Creek and Negro Creek areas. Keep in mind that should you receive a venomous bite, a serum shot used to be about $500 each. Up to 15 shots may be required for a cure. You may survive the bite, but your wallet … not so much.

Other predators and their tasty critter entrees have been tracked up Culver Gulch, Negro Creek, Ingalls Creek, and all the other tributary creeks in the Blewett/Peshastin area. They include black bear, coyote, cougar, deer, the occasional elk, birds, bats, and many other smaller tidbits suitable for consumption by the aforementioned predators. This area has it all for every creature's enjoyment … one way or another. Keep an eye out for certain nasty spiders that bite; their discomfort factors present more than a few distractions of a painful nature.

One of the more elusive critters that have been encountered in the Culver Gulch area is the northern rubber boa. This snake is non-venomous. Several of us Northwest Underground Explorations members have seen these boas under matted, decaying leaves, in mine tunnels, and one was spotted hanging from the outside framework of a cabin roof. When NWUE member Terry Carlson pulled on the cabin boa's tail, it stretched out in the manner of a rubber Gumby toy. At a critical point, Terry released the boa, concerned that it would be harmed. The result was that the boa escaped into a hiding place in the cabin attic. Based upon the several boas we have encountered, we have found that the boas' colors range from brown to a light banana-yellow. The lengths of the critters we discovered were from 1-foot to about 2-feet long. It is difficult to determine the head from the tail of the Culver Gulch rubber boas without a close-up inspection, due to the similar tapering at both ends of its body.

BATS

Bats have been seen on various information gathering field trips in Chelan and Okanogan Counties. In certain areas within northern Chelan and Okanogan Counties' tunnel ceilings during the warm season; they have their young, keeping them in 3- to 4-foot-diameter nursery clusters among the colonies. **These must not be disturbed**. We have been surprised by what appear to be sentinel bats that have detached from the colony occupying the tunnel ceiling, fly to meet us, and confirm our presence. They have flown to within inches of our faces, turned suddenly 180 degrees, air-washing our startled looks with bat-wind turbulence, and disappeared back into the darkness. Upon regaining our composure from the sudden discovery of bats in any tunnel that we enter, we "beat feet" back to daylight. At least we got the courtesy of a warning. These insect eaters can have rabies, and a rabid sentinel bat could be in a biting mood. So stay clear of them. Why take the chance of having to go through a series of painfully injected serum shots?

The bats inhabiting the Culver Gulch tunnels have no breeding populations that NWUE is aware of, possibly due to the colder, wet interiors. About one out of 10 open adits has a lone bat. The loner bats appear to be of the Myotis bat family. It is against the law to harm or kill a bat. Check out the Bats Northwest Facebook on the Internet for more information about these critters.

And last, the hard to ignore, mainly because they can't be, the pack rat. Call them friend or foe, they are always around somewhere lurking in a dark tunnel or concealed in the security of the shadow land just beyond the reach of a glowing camp fire … *watching!*

Pack Rat… watching. This fearless Pack Rat's nest is located behind a ladder connecting two tunnel levels in the Black Jack mine. (Photo by Vic Pisoni.)

Geology, Landscape, and Weather

[**For a clearer understanding of the geological area** and mine locations in and near the Blewett Township, use the USGS 7.5-minute map for the Blewett Quadrangle.]

The big gold producing mines were within a mineral belt that is about 3 miles in length and 1 mile wide. It begins on the east side of Peshastin Creek on either side of the slopes of Windmill Point, trends westward, continues down through the Blewett town site area, crosses Peshastin Creek, and continues a bearing up Culver Gulch and over the divide down into Negro Creek and surrounding Negro Creek drainage slopes.

Throughout the entire mining district, isolated (minor) gold-bearing veins were discovered. However, the four major ore veins in Culver Gulch produced the highest capital rewards for the mining efforts involved.

The Hawkins Mountain batholith and plutonic rock evolved from the outcrops of the Peshastin formation, which dominates country rock structures, mainly with schist, serpentine, greenstone, etc. The serpentine rock at the head of Culver Gulch integrates into the workings that display signs of the Hawkins formation, as does the serpentine formation in the Tip Top mine workings near Windmill Point.

The dominating rock in the Culver Gulch mined areas is serpentine. Often the strike of a vein is discontinuous due to the various regional land mass movements that cause rock facings to strike-slip fault (slide past each other in opposite directions). These displace the vein structure to the point that miners, on occasion, could not relocate it after it "pinched out" or was displaced.

In regard to the ore bodies and their mineral characteristics, there are those that occur in well-defined fissure veins but are irregular in shape; all are contained in serpentine rock. Within the vein, there can be any mix of quartz, calcite, or talc, which carried the free gold. The common and most abundant minerals contained in the quartz, serpentine, etc. are gold, silver, copper, iron, lead, arsenic, and sulfur. Free gold occurring in the iron-stained quartz/calcite oxide zone, on or near the surface of the ground, shows as rusty and crumbling in texture. In the deeper mine workings, iron oxide-stained quartz/calcite rock was often found to be associated with a complex sulfide mix of gold, arsenopyrite, and pyrite. The gold was captured in the complex sulfides ore, which carried gold ranging up to several thousand dollars per ton. The gold-bearing sulfide ore needed to undergo a cyanide-process to free the gold from the sulfides. Some of the deeper digs also produced large flake-gold and visible wire gold.

CULVER GULCH VEIN SYSTEM

There are four main veins that are parallel to each other running east-west through the rock fissures in Culver Gulch. They became known as the North Star vein system, which runs through the North Star (Golden Phoenix claim), Pole Pick vein system, Peshastin vein system, and Ivanhoe (Gold Quartz) vein system. The Ivanhoe vein is the most northerly lead. The Peshastin is south of the Ivanhoe vein, followed by the Pole Pick vein. The North Star/Phoenix vein is the southern-most lead. The size of the individual vein's structure was predetermined by the geological events that created the open fissures into which the mineralized hydrothermal solutions were infused when the developing ore veins occurred. Even after the vein system was solidified into place, there was more earth movement that caused pressure on the veins. That pressure pinched them off or swelled certain areas along the system into lens-shaped or kidney-shaped ore deposits. Some ore lenses were huge masses and were called ore-shoots; they gave very high values in gold. The largest are two ore-shoots named for discoverer-miners John McCarthy and Thomas Parish.

One ore-shoot was accessed by Northwest Underground Explorations through our efforts of clearing a cave-in at the intersection of a main crosscut tunnel level. The ore-shoot workings were in a state of collapse. The mined-out, debris-filled area was estimated it to be about 20 feet deep, 35 feet wide, and 100 feet high. As of this writing, access to the area is once again caved and blocked by tons of boulders and rock debris. The workings in the serpentine rock tunnels disintegrate at a much faster rate than those of granite or other such harder geological formations.

Many of the ore veins mined in Culver Gulch show there was obvious local geological move-ment after the ore was deposited. This is indicated by way of smooth slicken-side surfaces in the serpentine/quartz where fracture zones have slid by each other under tremendous pressure. The rock is seen as grooved in the direction of movement. Where it is ground up by pressurized action, there often is clay-like gouge material accumulation containing talc where free gold is occasionally found.

NICKEL DIKES

About ½ mile up Culver Gulch, on the north side slope at 3,000 feet elevation, is a very reddish-orange-brown outcrop of rock. It is hidden from view from the gulch road until a higher point is gained on the south slope of the gulch. A gap in the high brush and trees allows an unrestricted view of the outcropping nickel dike formation. This low-percentage nickel deposit has three exploratory, coyote-hole-sized prospects that unknown miner/miners dug while lying on their sides/backs and stomach. The holes can be belly-crawled into, but reverse/exit belly-crawling is difficult; plus the longer one (30-feet) had a rabbit's nest at the end of the hobbit-like dig. It is possible that it could also become a snarling critter hole at some point, which was an after-thought once the investigating Northwest Underground Explorations (NWUE) volunteer had already committed himself deep-in and headfirst. With the extracting of said inquisitor from the rocky tube, we offered hindsight discussion about the investigation results and the possible fang-to-face puncturing scenario. If it sounds like a warning, it is.

The nickel dike deposit extends northward through the ridge dividing Culver Gulch and the Negro Creek area. It reappears on the south slope of the Negro Creek drainage. This nickel-dike deposit is one of several in the Peshastin Mining District. The biggest one explored by NWUE was at the head of Negro Creek and ran east-west for about 300 to 400 feet and was about 100 feet wide. It appeared to rise through the area's principle geology of serpentine rock as an intrusion from the Hawkins Formation. Further investigation by somebody possessing more than Geology 101 understanding of this particular find would have to verify this opinion.

MIDDLE EOCENE DIABASE DIKES IN CULVER GULCH

There are two prominent dikes that outcrop at the head of Culver Gulch. The largest outcrops at about 3,800 feet in elevation and is approximately 700 feet long. On the south side of the gulch at 3,400 feet elevation is a dike that runs west for about 1,000 feet but is not as thick as the larger dike. The importance of these dikes in relation to the mine workings is that they intruded into the in-place ore vein structure, and when the miners tunneled into the diabase rock, the veins broke up into blackened quartz stringer veins. Sometimes the fissure veins would split around massive blocks of rock and run parallel to each other; the separating diabase dike or peridotite/serpentine rock masses were called "horses." There are several places in the upper areas of Culver Springs Creek, which is located on the south side of the ridge separating Culver Gulch from Culver Springs Creek, where very narrow diabase dikes appear to geologically morph into quartzite veins.

GLACIATION

Culver Gulch got a break when glaciation was in its glory days. The miners of Culver Gulch had enough evidence of geological stress with which to deal, without having the burden of glaciation and its residual debris to struggle through in their digs. It is known glacial ice did form around some of the areas in the mining district. The Cascade Mountain Range, along with Mount Stuart, got a thick sheet of ice, and it ran thick and heavy in the peaks and headwaters of Ingalls Creek and covered the northern portion of Peshastin Creek, below its confluence with Ingalls Creek where a lot of sedimentary rock formations are located.

TIMBER AND VEGETATION

Before the mining activities in the Peshastin Mining District, the area was covered with tamarack, ponderosa pine, various other pines, red fir, other evergreen varieties, plus other indigenous trees.

The area in and around the town site of Blewett and Culver Gulch were sparsely covered by trees at the time of the beginning mining boom (as seen from old township photos of the 1880s). Those trees that were useable for mining, buildings, firewood, and logging-related activities were harvested and have since grown back. Today the ridges, slopes, and gulches now abound in more timber and low-growth ground cover than were present in photos taken over 130 years ago.

The vegetation consists of all the varieties one can see anywhere in the Cascade and Wenatchee Mountain Ranges. In Culver Gulch each spring, the ground shows its first colors with the appearance of the bright yellow, very prolific balsam root/sunflower plant.

CLIMATE

Generally, the weather in the Blewett/Peshastin area that has been experienced by members of Northwest Underground Explorations in the last 20 years of intermittent outings has seen highs up to 103 degrees a couple of times during summer and below 10 degrees several times during winter. A way to gauge Blewett weather is by the temperature in Wenatchee. It is a few degrees colder in the gulch in winter and about the same as Wenatchee in the summer, 80 degrees being the normal high most summers. There are no known, continuous weather-observation records for the town of Blewett/Culver Gulch from the 1860s through 1900. Bottom line: the Blewett area seasons receive heavy snow in the winter, spring rains, and dry summers.

Chapter One:
Early History

WASHINGTON TERRITORY'S FIRST GOLD DISCOVERY, 1853

The first recorded event for a placer-gold discovery in Washington Territory was made by General George McClellan's troops in 1853. He and his men were searching for new routes between the east side of the Cascade Mountains and the citizens of Olympia and Fort Steilacoom on the west side of the divide. Some of General McClellan's men found gold in either upper Wenas Creek or Manastash Creek (depending on whose information you chose). They built a long tom sluice box and washed out $4 in gold per day from the gravel and sands. Presently, the exact location of that gold discovery is undetermined.

The Naches Pass route was chosen to accommodate military travel, although the road was commonly called the "People's Road" and "Walla Walla to Steilacoom Pioneer's Trail." It didn't hold lasting favor as an immigrant or public route due to its rough, steep terrain. Snoqualmie Pass eventually became the main byway for homesteading pioneers traveling the improved Indian trail connection with the Kittitas Valley corridor from the east side to the west side of the Cascade Mountains.

QUALCHAN BACKS UP TRIBAL THREATS, 1854

Qualchan was the warrior son of Chief Owhi (also Ouhi) and nephew of Kamiakin. Qualchan and another Kittitas domain area Indian named Siah-han visited the great warrior Kamiakin for a "sit-down" about the white-man problem in tribal lands. Kamiakin wanted Qualchan as an ally in the perceived confrontations with the European invaders. Nez Pierce warrior Chief Pus-Winet was like-minded. Chief Pus-Winet sent Kamiakin a war horse with decorative trappings, rifle, and ammunition as an acknowledgement to the great warrior. Kamiakin expressed those same edicts to Qualchan as he presented him with the same gifts he had received from Chief Pus-Winet (this was a common tribal practice). It served the purpose of unifying Qualchan's allegiance to the Yakima/Nez Pierce in the looming war with the invading whites. Qualchan arrived at the meeting with Kamiakin aching for a fight with the intruding foreigners. The inspiring talk and prestigious gifts amplified Qualchan's bloodlust. It was the beginning of Qualchan's violent acts in the form of war parties, displayed in gratitude for the two chiefs' confidence in him.

The unsuspecting recipients of Qualchan's wrath were three white men who were first seen while Qualchan and Siah-han were headed outbound from the meeting with Kamiakin. The three foreigners were camped for a noon meal at Umptanum Creek on an old Indian trail/creek crossing and didn't notice the passing Indians. Ten miles down the trail, the two defenders of the tribal nations parleyed and formed a simple plan: kill the invaders. Qualchan anticipated that the war with the white man would soon develop. This pre-emptive opportunity proved to be an omen he understood.

But due to the three travelers' prearranged plan, or perhaps caution, they pulled out and headed off trail going toward the Yakima River. When the invaders didn't follow the trail into the valley as Qualchan and Siah-han expected, they backtracked until they cut trail on the three men, ambushed, and killed them. Thereafter, many tribal land intruders were slain by Qualchan in the years surrounding the Indian Wars that began in 1855.

Around 1855 to 1860, during tribal unrest and US troop movement, Army Lt. Bissell initiated a map that referred to pre-named Peshastin Creek as Pis-hostin Creek; then he simplified it to an army term and penned it into his field reports as Dragoon Creek. For a short time, some military travelers referred to it as Soldier Creek. There were many trails that could have been used to cross the area's list of mountain routes ending at present-day Leavenworth and Wenatchee. The access northward-southward through Swauk and Peshastin Creeks (Blewett) area is the route pertinent to this story.

The main Indian trail west of the Columbia River heading north out of the lands occupied by the Yakima Indian Nation went through today's Kittitas Valley east of Ellensburg. From here, it continued northward through Green Canyon, onward to the present Swauk Creek/ Liberty town area. It went over a low point on a ridge at the head of Lion Gulch and down Hurley Creek to its confluence with Swauk Creek, which was originally a seasonal tribal hunting and gathering camp. The camp was located west of Swauk Creek at the confluence with Hurley Creek. From there, the old Indian trail began to gain altitude along the similar direction of the original post-frontier Blewett Pass roadway, and northward toward present-day Peshastin Creek drainage to the Pisquouse/Wenatchi River.

YAKIMA INDIAN NATION MIND-SET DURING THE 1850s THROUGH 1870s

The Yakima tribesmen were just one of the many tribal populations that made every effort to keep the trespassing frontiersmen out of their country. They knew from past, bad experiences with non-tribal folks that if the intruders found gold, it was going to bring unacceptable consequences to their land. In some circumstances, the intruders were driven out of the tribal lands when found uninvited.

The Yakima Indians were different in their sense of having exclusive ownership rights to the land. It was an uncommon precept compared to the other Indians of the Northwest, but a stance they took, nonetheless. Anyone wanting to cross Yakima land had to get permission from them. It got to the point where evasive trespass by the frontiersmen was countered with the posting of Indian guards and scouting patrols to keep an eye on tribal borders. It didn't take long before the "Yakima's concern" was justified.

The deceptive Walla Walla treaty organized by Isaac I. Stevens in 1855 was soon broken by men who had no respect for any tribal/US government laws of the land. Soon the various far-ranging Indian Nations formed an agreement to detour and pursue the intruders. Some well-documented pitched battles often lasted for as many days as it took the shot-up, retreating companies of fleeing whites and their entourage attempting to reach the safety of the nearest fort, usually Fort Simcoe or Fort Okanogan.

So this was the plight that met the fevered white frontiersmen's imaginations driving the search for wealth in gold or looking to possess homestead land. This included whatever form of pursuing that dream they could come up with. Isaac Stevens (future governor of Washington State) didn't help matters by openly reporting on December 3, 1858, that gold was found during that year in a creek.

PESHASTIN CREEK PLACER-GOLD DISCOVERY, 1858

The first discovery of placer gold on Peshastin Creek was in 1858, 16 years before the vein/lode deposits were discovered and recorded up Thompson Gulch (presently named Culver Gulch). Captain Mortimer Robertson, an experienced California miner, was the man that is popularly credited with taking first gold out of the placer gravels and sands in Peshastin Creek.

Captain Robertson was in The Dalles, Oregon, in May 1858. He assembled a party of 76 men who had gold prospecting on their mind (two were Chinese miners). Captain Robertson's rank was the result of the group forming into a civilian company that elected captains, lieutenants, etc. in order to have a semblance of somebody in command and to direct disciplined travel. The company of men was determined to reach the Fraser (Thompson) River gold fields in Canada. The travelers consisted of men from California, Nevada, and Colorado. Mortimer took the title of "captain" as the contingent moved out on June 1, 1858. They moved 94 horses and pack animals at a slow pace getting from Oregon to Fort Simcoe in Washington Territory. Before they got to the fort, J. Whitley shot and killed himself—accidentally. The second and third fatalities took place after the company of miners left the fort, and two men of German extraction drowned in their attempt at crossing the Naches River. All central Washington Territory from the expansive land of the Yakima Indian Nation up to the US/Canadian border was Indian Territory. That land had more than a few hostile braves willing to kill the trespassing foreigners and plunder the impressive wonders of their supplies.

Eventually the company of prospectors made camp on Swauk Creek. The next day, June 17, 1858, they traveled down Weenich Creek (today's Peshastin Creek)—which was also noted by several travelers during other reported crossings along the creek by name variations such as Wee-witch, Wee-wich, or Oui-Owitch and Dragoon Creek. The company set up camp on the creek in the open, flat area of the future town of Blewett.

While camped there, Captain Robertson prospected from the creek, and in the first pan of gravel, there were two gold flakes. Mortimer was encouraged, so he and a few trusted men took shovels and pans and backtracked upstream. They panned samples from the Peshastin Creek placer materials for about 2 miles, which would have placed them close to the confluence where presently named Tronsen, Scotty, and Magnet Creeks flow into Peshastin Creek. At this, point three pans of bottom gravel were processed with a result of $1, $2, and $3 in gold dust and flakes. Mortimer and crew agreed to keep the gold discovery to themselves, thus not arousing local gold-seeking interest in the other members of the company who might want to stay in hostile Indian Territory.

CAPTAIN MORTIMER ROBERTSON VERSUS WENATCHI INDIANS, 1858

Today's town of Wenatchee was named after Wenatchi, an Indian chief and is one variation of his name that comes from the Pisquouse language of the Yakima Nation and signifies "boiling waters." According to the regional Salish dialect of other tribes, Wenatchi means "good place," and a romantic version is taken from the local Indian legend of the "Blood Daughter of the Widowed Moon," Wa-Nat-Chee is defined as "Robe of the Rainbow."

The setting for this running, horse-mounted battle between whites and hostile Wenatchi tribesmen was on and through turf where the town of Wenatchee is now located. At this time, there was not much tolerance of any non-Indian presence, with some groups of tribesmen declaring war-like intentions.

Previous to leaving for the Wenatchi/Wenatchee River, Robertson had a peace pow-wow with Chief Owhi. The chief assigned an Indian named Alex to accompany Robertson as interpreter.

The fight narrative starts on July 18, 1858. After their overnight stop at the duly noted Peshastin gold placer grounds, Robertson and his company of miners made their way to the confluence of the Wenatchi and Columbia Rivers, where they planned a route up the west side of the Columbia and onward to Fort Okanogan at the confluence of the Okanogan River and Columbia River.

On July 20, 1858, Robertson and the company of miners met with peaceful Chief Skamow (Owhi's son) at his camp on the Wenatchi River. Also at the meeting was Chief Quil-ten-nock of the Columbia tribe and another anti-intruder-minded brave, Quintimelah. They let it be known that if the company of miners continued into tribal land, the braves would fight them. And with that said, off went the 73 white guys with only 21 Sharps rifles belonging to the experienced Indian fighters. The rest, inferior in a firefight, had either handguns or shotguns. The slow-paced pack animals also put them all at a big disadvantage. The supply-encumbered detail got outbound about one mile from Owhi's camp, when a straggling miner, named George Romerick, on a badly traded horse was shot in his arm by one of the trailing hostiles. George fell off his mount. The man riding alongside George rescued him, but George lost his nag and three other horses along with his weapon, packs, etc. Quintimelah shot another man in the knee as the company retreated.

Next, Robertson's escaping men ran into Chief Skamow and his warrior band dressed in full battle array. As it turned out, peace-minded Skamow put up a white-man-friendly battle line pretending bloody intent that brought the pursuing hostiles to a halt. This allowed the miners enough time to make it back across the Wenatchi River under Skamow's tenuous guard. Even with this allowance of the uneasy ceasefire, the running battle with the miners and hostile Indian faction exploded back into action after the miners crossed the river. From that moment on, and for the next several days, a running gunfight ensued as the Robertson company retreated back toward Fort Simcoe.

At the Wenatchi River crossing, they gave and took gunfire from the daunting number of pursuing hostiles. Three more men were wounded. Robertson and his men were somehow able to repel the tribesmen, but 29 packhorses died in the fight. Quintimelah was killed along with Chief Tecolekun and three other braves. At that point, the battle let up for recovery of the dead and wounded tribesmen and to claim the spoils of the battle that the miners left behind.

The miners were on the run again, and then George Romerick, lashed to a borrowed mount, took another tumble on a steep slope. A brave overtook him, and George was relieved of his scalp. Four other men were wounded, Tom Keating, John Prouty, Tom Nelson, and a man named Piper. The run for Fort Simcoe was full-on again, but around four that afternoon, Qualchan and Quetalican (Chief Moses) and 14 Indians overtook them. One Chinaman and one white man were wounded, and six of the renegade braves fell as the battle lasted until dark. Mortimer's men continued southward through the night. At three in the morning, they stopped in the area where the town of Beverly is presently located. An hour later, they were getting fired upon from Indians among the rocks. One miner was shot in the thigh, and Qualchan (Owhi's warrior son) took a serious bullet wound in his side. One other brave was shot several times through his body. The miners continued their dash for self-preservation to Fort Simcoe throughout two days, marching during the night without food or water. An Englishman named Nicholas Jenkins died of fright before the beat-up and maimed company finally made it to the fort.

MAJOR MORTIMER ROBERTSON'S SECOND TRIBAL LAND CROSSING, 1859

By mid-July 1859, there were 250 men waiting at The Dalles, Oregon, to be led to the Fraser River mines; never mind that the Indians were still hostile. When men get gold fever, all bets are off as to how they will act to get it and this new contingent of men needed this emotion set under a controlling factor. Being the type to take command, Mortimer Robertson shifted into Major Robertson mode. Mortimer and the 250 men under his leadership made it safely to Fort Simcoe by the end of July. This time he didn't take the route leading to the restrictive passage on the old trail skirting Weenich (Peshastin) Creek. It was watched by hostile Indians observing all intruding travelers using the old Indian trail.

Instead, he led the company in a military-style formation over the longer and safer route near Priest Rapids on the Columbia River. Along the river, the company of men would be away from the Indian threat from the west. Robertson made it to the Fraser River mines in September, seemingly without any notable hostile Indian incidents.

With all the other consequences and involvements of history that Mortimer Robertson was involved in, he was not publically noted for his important activities of finding first gold in the placers of Peshastin Creek near the future town site called Blewett. Subsequent northbound mining expeditions used the Columbia River trail and avoided the Peshastin Creek/Wenatchi River route. In so doing, this Columbia River route delayed the discovery of the Peshastin Mining District's hard-rock mines.

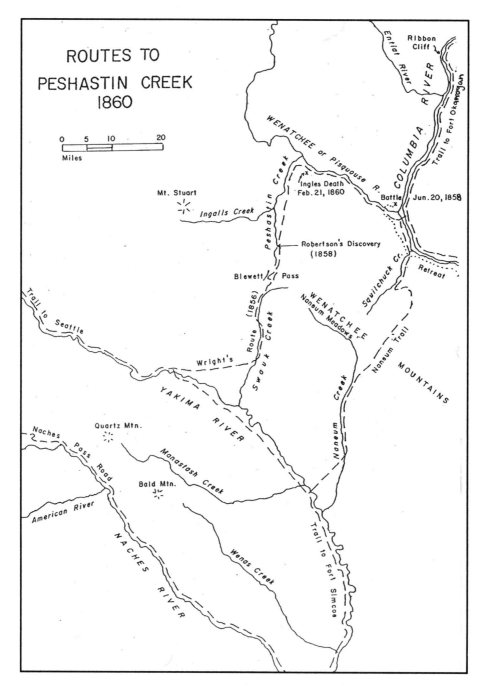

Routes to Peshastin Creek 1860. Captain Mortimer Robertson followed Wright's route from Fort Simcoe, northward along the Swauk Creek and Peshastin Creek trail to the June 20, 1858 battle site in the confluence area of Wenatchee River and Columbia River. Several days of running battle followed in the Robertson outfit's flight back to Fort Simcoe. (From *History of the Blewett Mining District* (page 52) by Daniel Y. Meschter [1980].)

Chapter Two:
Captain Ingalls's Lost Gold

CAPTAIN DEWITT CLINTON INGALLS'S LOST GOLD LOCATIONS

Captain Ingalls's two lost gold deposits were in two different locations that were encountered on different occasions. One was a lost hard-rock (lode) area in the elevated headwaters of Ingalls Creek. This is separate from his lost placer-gold location on Peshastin Creek.

Historians have the task of investigating this intriguing story of Captain Ingalls and his two separate lost-gold stories. At this point, a coalescing of facts is needed to unwind the origin of his name and rank. The real Captain Ingalls steps forward from the short list of men named Ingalls in quick fashion when only legally documented facts are compiled. Historians can count on one hand the references to those with an Ingalls surname in this region of Washington Territory in the 1860s time frame. After eliminating the unqualified Ingalls's names, Captain Dewitt Clinton Ingalls becomes the main focus in the search for the Captain Ingalls of the lost-gold locations.

Recorded documentation reveals that Captain Dewitt Clinton Ingalls was from Oregon City, Oregon. He was an original California forty-niner and credited by one source for having discovered the Coos Bay mines in present-day Oregon State. He was a skilled machinist, foundry man, blacksmith, farmer, and once operated a ferry, as Captain Ingalls, on the Willamette River for owner Andrew Jackson Knott. Ingalls's rank and title, once established in this way, would be carried throughout his lifetime. (Knott's name will come up later in direct association with D. C. Ingalls's attempt to rediscover his lost gold locations.)

The 1855–56 Indian War country included, what is known today as the Wenatchee Mountain Range, which contained the area that would later be known as the Peshastin Mining District. This is the time frame and region where Dewitt C. Ingalls is also noted for serving as a scout captain for the surveying party that was under the protection of the US Army. He was the lead man for the scouting contingent, which included friendly tribesmen and civilian whites.

CAPTAIN INGALLS'S GOLD LOCATIONS

We assume the first gold discovery by Ingalls occurred solo where he encountered three lakes. This area of gold-bearing, white quartz rock would later be the headwaters area for Ingalls Creek. This happened as he was ascending through the upper Wenatchee Mountain Range headwaters when he was separated from the surveying company and its US Army guard attachment. (The data source implies that he was lost, but his separation could have been self-willed. After all, scouting required him and his fellow scouts to forage into unknown areas to determine possible through-routes, solo or otherwise. Any woodsman worth his salt would have an after-search rendezvous area pre-determined, which did occur after Ingalls descended to Peshastin Creek.) Remember, nothing was lost at this point.

The second gold discovery was made afterward, somewhere on the Peshastin Creek placer gravels. This was when Ingalls traveled eastward, following his solo discovery of the lode gold in the three lakes area. Later, an inference indicates that after he arrived at the lower elevations in the Peshastin Creek area, he rejoined his Indian companion, Colawash.

It was at this time that Ingalls and Colawash found placer gold in Peshastin Creek. But due to possible Indian war-party presence in intensely hostile tribal country, the 200 heavily armed men of the surveying party and army attachment quickly traveled through the Indian-occupied area under the strength of their battle-capable company.

INGALLS ATTEMPTS TO RELOCATE HIS PESHASTIN CREEK PLACER-GOLD DISCOVERY SITE, 1859-60

After the Indian war and the threat of roaming war parties subsided, Ingalls went to Colawash's home. There he tried to entice Colawash to return with him to the gold placer on Peshastin Creek. Colawash declined the offer.

Ingalls began to enter Peshastin Creek solo, but for some unidentified reason, he became discouraged and returned (possibly because of signs of hostile Indian presence). There is no paper trail identifying the reasons for his actions, so any conversation beyond this point is speculation.

Next, in 1860, Ingalls recruited a group of interested friends in a gold-seeking fellowship (which included John Hansel) with the intent of finding Ingalls's evasive Peshastin Creek placer gold. At this point, it should be noted that John Hansel had been asked via a letter from Ingalls, previous to this trip, to join him on a search to locate the gold at the area of the three lakes. So it could be considered that the group of men was going on a quest to locate both of Ingalls's lost-gold discovery sites. The following is a series of interesting angles in which one can contemplate and make a personal conclusion.

CAPTAIN D. C. INGALLS'S LETTER TO JOHN HANSEL

This story stands alone, as opposed to the lost placer gold that was discovered by Ingalls and Colawash during passage along the banks of Peshastin Creek and the confluences of its tributary creeks.

Captain Ingalls was trying to find an easy passage/trail that would allow swift movement of military personnel across the Wenatchee Mountain Range. During the surveying expedition, Ingalls was in association with a Wenatchi/Wenatchee River area brave named Colawash. Since Colawash was a local tribesman familiar with the area and Ingalls was not, Ingalls (using common sense) engaged him as a guide.

The Wenatchee Mountain Range is located south of and parallel to the Mount Stuart Range area. At some point, Captain D. C. Ingalls was traveling solo on a trail (no mention of Colawash). While riding along a lofty ridge, Ingalls saw three lakes far below him. There was a crescent-shaped lake reflecting as light green, located between two round lakes of a dark-blue color. Dangerously steep slopes surrounded the lakes, except for a length of traversable, sloping ground leading to the shoreline of the centrally located crescent lake.

Night was approaching, so rather than dry camp on the ridge, Captain Ingalls opted for a water accessible lakeside camp. After he reached the lakes, he noted that there was about 600 feet of ground separating the three bodies of water that were connected by streams (the line of direction was not noted). While Ingalls was camped there, he explored them by high-banking along the streams from one lake to the next. The outlet of the lower lake flowed through a gap in a rock-faced area that would have been reached only by swimming to it.

The underlying rock in the dark-blue lakes located on either side of the crescent lake was of a granitic nature. At the center of the green-colored, crescent-shaped lake was a contact zone of green serpentine-talc mix. The exciting feature of the crescent-shaped lake was the beach along the inside curve of the crescent-shaped shoreline. It was scattered with rotten/decomposed quartz float that was thickly studded with visible gold. Ingalls estimated there was at least 10 tons of the gold-studded quartz on the beach at the time of his discovery. He wrote of the possibility that there could be a ledge of the same gold-bearing rock above the lakes. As evidence of the find, he took several small half-egg-sized samples of the gold-laden quartz float.

Ingalls broke camp the next morning and eventually made his way down to and along the creek that now bears his name. Ingalls mapped his route so he could find his way back to the gold discovery at the three-lakes. After Captain Ingalls returned to the rendezvous site on Peshastin Creek with the expedition company, he and Colawash went prospecting along Peshastin Creek. The two men scouted the creek area and found several small gold nuggets and other substantial indicators of gold-rich placer deposits. They were in hostile Indian country and didn't linger for further investigation because if they were found out by the hostiles, their lives would have been forfeited. So they were compelled to abandon the placer gold find for the time being and rejoin the others.

After the surveying expedition was over, Ingalls wrote a letter to his friend John Hansel and sent along a sample of his gold find. He asked Hansel to join him on a return trip to the lakes where the gold was located. Ingalls made reference to a map, along with a description of where he had stashed it near the mouth of Ingalls Creek.

It was 1860 when Ingalls's second attempt was made to relocate the site of the Peshastin Creek placer-gold discovery. Ingalls visited Colawash first, in February 1860, hoping he would accompany the captain back to the gold, but old Colawash flat-out refused to be moved by any of Ingalls's rich offers, preferring a warm fire to comfort his old bones as opposed to a difficult, upper-elevation snow trek through icy, swollen creeks.

Captain Ingalls's gold prospecting activities along Peshastin Creek adds another variation to where and who has the first call on the placer gold discovered along its water course. Ingalls and Colawash may have left those gold placers for other gold prospectors, who were uninformed of Ingalls's discoveries. Those prospectors who followed may have mistakenly thought they originally discovered the Peshastin Creek placer gold at the abandoned Ingalls-Colawash placer ground. But they too would have been aware of the Indian threat and wisely moved onward to the comparatively safer gold fields located north on either side of the US-Canadian border.

The question is where were the gold placer locations according to each of the first discoverers? They left no staked or marked areas; none that anybody can claim was ever recorded in those pre-mining camp years. Lack of legal records affords open speculation of placer locations.

THE FELLOWSHIP

Failing to recruit Colawash, Ingalls joined up that same February 1860 with John Hansel, Jewell Sinclair, Levi Knott, and Andrew Jackson Knott, who was Ingalls's old employer with the steamboat company in Oregon. John Nelsen and Robert J. Ladd were also part of the eight-man party. Ladd was married to Levi Knott's sister Elizabeth.

Levi Knott was a carpenter by trade from Olympia, Washington. He was in the Wenatchi area in August 1858, headed for the mines in the northern areas of the United States and Canada. Levi joined with Mortimer Robertson's first trip in the company of miners who were headed for the Fraser River gold mines. Levi had been with Robertson's men in the running battle with the hostile tribesmen during that trip along the Columbia River.

The Ingalls group was on a mission to locate the Ingalls-Colawash gold placer on Peshastin Creek and, as was formerly mentioned, possibly the quartz gold at the area of the three lakes. They began by traveling upstream on the Wenatchi River. A. J. Knott was in the rear, and Captain D. C. Ingalls was in front of him. The horse-mounted men were in single-file formation along the river's icy edge and thick-brushed riverbank. This maneuver was due to the 20 inches of snow on the ground above on the flatland that forced them to the more easily traveled river's edge. Ingalls was riding with his pick and shovel over one shoulder. The pick caught on a willow branch, and as it released, Ingalls called, "Watch out!" Knott was close behind and stooped low in the saddle as the branch passed over his head, striking the hammer of his rifle. Knott's movement put him in a position that caused a percussion that sent a lead ball through Ingalls's lower back and exited out the front.

Ingalls was shot about noon on February 20, 1860, and died about the same time the next day. The group of men traveled day and night bringing his wounded body back by a handmade, wood-hewed sled through 20 inches of snow. The emergency trip was over 16 miles of rough trail to the main camp on the east bank of what is today's Columbia River, opposite the mouth of the Wenatchee River. Captain D. C. Ingalls was buried next to the bank of the Columbia River at nine in the morning on February 23, 1860, near the main camp. A grave monument-board was etched, "Dewitt Clinton Ingalls; Died February 21, 1860." Dr. J. N. Bell and Mr. Turner were with the forty men attending the burial ceremony. The Ingalls-Knott group abandoned the Peshastin Creek and three-lakes gold digs trip and continued up the Columbia River with some men from the main camp who were bound for the Similkameen River mines.

The above information was in the signed, documented affidavit describing the accidental death of Captain D. C. Ingalls. The affidavit by Jewell Sinclair and others (formerly named above) was signed at the bottom. It said that they were in the company of Captain Dewitt Clinton Ingalls who was a former scout for the US Army, although "US Army" was not a correct notation, whether they realized it or not.

CAPTAIN INGALLS'S LOST GOLD ACCORDING TO KATE BAILEY

Kate Bailey, historian and journalist for the *Wenatchee World* newspaper had a different take on these events. Her popularly known "Captain Ingalls Lost Gold Story" features the gold-laden shore of one of the three lakes.

The history of the gold mines on either side of Peshastin Creek, Negro Creek, Ingalls Creek, or many feeder creeks can attest to the fact that for over 150 years placer gold in the form of dust, flakes, and nuggets has been mined from the Peshastin/Blewett Mining District. But the particular areas of interest related to the lost gold of Captain Ingalls are focused up in the various headwater areas approaching Ingalls Creek.

Kate's story of Captain Ingalls's lost gold is an interesting read and inspires visions of hidden wealth. But, in fact, the time frame would exclude any possibility of Captain Ingalls to be in certain parts of Kate's story. After her meeting with John Hansel, she wrote of Ingalls's letter in which Ingalls indicated it would be necessary to use his map due to the fact that the 1872 earthquake may have changed the landscape. Perhaps she meant to say that Hansel, rather than Ingalls, had "indicated" the need for the map; that change would clear away the apparent timing problem. D. C Ingalls died in 1860 and was not alive during that earthquake. So unless Hansel made the remark about the earthquake, it can be suspected that inaccuracy or perhaps an errant, but enhanced, deception took place.

Kate's authored story also wrongfully has Captain Ingalls shot and killed by an Indian. Kate stated she got her lost-mine information from reading Ingalls's letter and a "personal conversation" (in her words) with 60-year-old John Hansel in that 1897 meeting/interview (John died in 1917, so he was 58 at the time of the interview). Kate's data does not reflect the affidavit submitted, sworn, signed, and recorded by the authorities, of the men present when Ingalls was mortally shot.

It would also be understandable if Hansel wanted to muddle the true facts to throw like-minded lost-gold seekers off the track from what Hansel considered his rightful windfall of hand-me-down gold information. But the inaccurate information has nothing to do with the site-specific details of the Ingalls Creek lost-gold area. It could be an incorrect, but innocent, compilation of the facts, minus the professional scrutiny that was otherwise the norm of Kate's profession in her early years.

Kate claimed that she personally saw and read the letter in 1897, the one that John Hansel got from Ingalls. It was noted to be yellowed by time and still legible, although worn from handling. She also states seeing three or four crumbling bits of quartz about half the size of a hen's egg and that one-fourth of each piece was studded with gold.

Then there is the afterthought: How much did or could or would John Hansel's fireside story have been enhanced by alterations and additions to the facts during the 37 years that passed before Hansel related the story to an impressionable, young Kate Bailey in 1897? And how much did she remember or alter for the benefit of an enhanced and even more readable tale 54 years later when she wrote the newspaper story in 1951?

At the time of the meeting with John Hansel, Kate later related that John's eyes were black and clear and that his conversation was precise. He was of stocky build and had white hair.

JOHN HANSEL

John, his wife, son George W. Hansel, and his wife, Marguerite Burmeister- Hansel, ran a productive farm. His land included the confluence of Hansel Creek and Peshastin Creek, located on the west ½ of southeast ¼ of Section 24 (use the USGS 7.5-minute map of the Blewett Quadrangle).

Old John was noted to be remarkable in his youthful energy. When not tending to his property at the mouth of Ingalls Creek, he was known to mine at three placer claims on Hansel Creek. He also prospected the back country around the mountains at the headwaters of the many creeks and feeder streams that enter into Ingalls and Peshastin Creeks.

And as time allowed, John went in search of Captain Ingalls's lost gold. He states he never found the map that Ingalls buried at the mouth of Ingalls Creek.

There were other miners and treasure seekers who totaled up a lot of time during the late 1800s searching for Ingalls's lost gold. If the 1872 earthquake did bury the gold-bearing, depression-lakes area with cliff-side boulders and rockslides that adds more complexity to locating Captain Ingalls's lost gold.

The lakes at this point in time (2013) may be nothing more than seasonally wet depressions or a large dry cirque. And consider if the damming structure of the three lakes' spillway also collapsed during the seismic event and drained the lakes; this could account for the lack of any geological three-lake evidence on current maps.

John Hansel died at his ranch on May 17, 1916, at 78 years old and was buried at Leavenworth, Washington. His personal effects were lost or stolen after his death. Later, his son George (by himself) became a long-time resident of Leavenworth. In 1935, locals lost track of George's whereabouts.

The bottom line is, as far as anybody can speculate, Captain Ingalls's lost gold is still somewhere up in the mountains, westward of the headwaters of Ingalls Creek.

The high-country in this area presents golden opportunities when it comes to scenic hikes. A hike up the Ingalls Creek trail or along the high-country trails in the Navaho Peak area may inspire thoughts that you are on the very ground on which Captain Ingalls made his exciting passage.

CHARLES A. SPLAWN GOES LOOKING FOR INGALLS'S PESHASTIN CREEK GOLD, 1860

Charles Splawn visited Peshastin Creek in the spring of 1860 when he travelled through the area to see his friend and Ingalls's old scouting comrade, Colawash. Charles knew of the Colawash-Ingalls placer-gold discovery and Captain Ingalls's three-lake hard-rock gold location. Splawn specifically asked Colawash to guide him to the place Colawash and Ingalls had found their Peshastin Creek placer gold. This may have also been a planned move in seeking additional information about Ingalls's lost gold in the headwaters of Ingalls Creek. Once again, Colawash declined, but he did draw Splawn a rough map to assist him in locating Ingalls's gold-bearing placer area on Peshastin Creek. This is one of two maps mentioned in connection to Captain Ingalls's gold discoveries. Splawn pocketed the map and joined with a mining partner named Gilbert Pearl.

There was no information found to indicate Splawn did any immediate follow-up on the placer map. A. J. Splawn said that the gathering of Ingalls's lost gold data was in vain and the hard-rock gold location remained lost. As for the placer site, it can be assumed that eventually someone made a claim among the many placer discoveries along Peshastin Creek and its feeder streams and unknowingly on Ingalls's abandoned Peshastin Creek gold placer ground.

During 1860, Charley Splawn and Gilbert Pearl were noted working their way down the Columbia River from Fort Colville. While prospecting along the river, they missed finding a fortune in gold that was later mined at the future site in the Gold Bar placer gravel, located upstream on the Columbia River, past the mouth of the Methow River. Two other gold-bearing gravel bars/sandbars in other mining districts yielded exciting amounts of gold. They were also on the Columbia River and shared the name "Gold Bar Placer."

Later, when Splawn and Pearl passed through the placer grounds on Peshastin Creek, Splawn found a placer-gold prospect on slate bedrock. Splawn noted the location was at the lower extremity of Peshastin Creek, which could include the known gold placer grounds from Bonanza (Hansel) Creek and southward.

On a second trip north to placer mine for gold on the Similkameen River, Splawn was later joined by four departing Similkameen River miners. They accepted his offer to partake on an adventure for any gold found in the placer grounds on Peshastin Creek. No details of how or where the gold was placer mined could be determined. It is known that the group did carry some away from the Peshastin Creek placers. The map Colawash drew for Splawn was not mentioned regarding either trip.

While traveling homebound, they came across an express mail carrier named Tom Russell (Russell was once the sheriff of King County). Russell was returning from the mines up around the Similkameen River area. He was also heralding the news that Lincoln won the election for president of the United States. Russell was impressed when shown Spawn's gold and asked for samples, which he received and brought with him back to Seattle. The sight of the gold generated some excitement, and the resulting spin-off story of the gold discovery was exaggerated by Seattle area newspapers. These perpetrated and excited prospective placer miners to outfit in Seattle with the thought of gold nuggets reported to pay as high as $12. Nobody bothered to explain that the $12 size was an isolated exception.

Soon after Splawn's Peshastin Creek-generated gold rush broke out, there appeared news of bonanza gold strikes emanating from Idaho and British Columbia, Canada that received top-story status by the newspapers. This was sufficient reason for the Blewett area prospectors to stampede out of the Peshastin area and head for the new, more promising gold bonanzas the following spring. They left the placer ground behind for the new, in-coming crowd of Peshastin gold seekers. It didn't take long for the disappointed, early-on, get-rich-quick Seattle faction to head back to the West Coast area with their shattered covetous thoughts of getting easy gold.

Historic notes suggest that even during Splawn's gold placer mining activities, word got out about the new gold discoveries in other distant territory. Around the event of the aforementioned stampeding exodus, Splawn estimated 75 prospector/miners stayed the winter on Peshastin Creek gold placers. Many miners were on or near the flat ground where Ingalls Creek flows into Peshastin Creek and along placer ground upstream and downstream, including various feeder creeks and streams along the Peshastin water course. This was the time of his acclaimed finding of the first gold placers on Peshastin Creek.

Chapter Three: 1860—Seattle Is Bitten by the Peshastin Gold Bug

During 1860, D. C. Ingalls and Charles Splawn thought they had a somewhat secretive grasp on the placer-gold locations along Peshastin Creek. But during this time, there was an increasing amount of migrating, non-Indian frontier traffic and temporary camps populated with prospectors. They were gold panning as they passed up and down the trail. Prospecting took place from the north side of the divide between Swauk Creek and Peshastin Creek, and down to the Wenatchi River.

A packer named James Wyckoff made regular trips on the same route to the Similkameen River area mines and Rock Creek mines in British Columbia. Wyckoff made mention of the gold placer activities along Peshastin Creek and the Rock Creek mines to Seattleite L. B. Abbott, who repeated it in exaggerated tones. He was of a nature also to spin into the mix, but not separating the two-location facts, the gold-enriched stories that included the high-grade gold discovery news coming out of the Rock Creek, British Columbia, mines. Whatever his motive, it started a movement of bodies that had the Peshastin gold placers on many gold-bug-bitten minds.

Seattle merchants Plummer and Hinds had on display at their store rich gold specimens from Rock Creek, brought in by packer James Wyckoff. Plummer and Hinds sent a pack-train of goods to what they referred to as the Wenatchee mines (note the name change from Wenatchi to Wenatchee), which included the Peshastin area digs, and northward to Rock Creek, British Columbia.

Seattle buzzed with stories of easy gold to be had. Most of the men employed at the Yesler-Rand & Company sawmill headed for Peshasta/Soldier's Gulch (Peshastin Creek) forcing the mill to temporarily shut down.

This unnamed prospector, with a gravel and sand-filled gold pan, is shown placer mining at a creek located in the east central Cascade Mountains. (Grace Browitt Elkins photo collection.)

By this time, concentrated gold mining action ranged from the upper section of Peshasta (Peshastin) Creek down to Ingalls Creek. A contingent of miners from Oregon settled in as a mining camp at the mouth of Ingalls Creek. Meanwhile, gold fever continued the influx of gold prospectors into area. During this time, Peshastin Creek was made the creek's permanent name, and Wenatchee was evolving into common use, displacing Wenatchi.

In the mix was Joseph Foster, a state legislator from Seattle, transformed into a prospector. He was a mining-enthusiast friend of Charles Splawn. Unpublished notes indicate that Foster was on one or more of Splawn's prospecting expeditions.

Foster is also listed amongst those claiming to have discovered the Peshastin placer grounds. The accolades and credentials about who made the original placer-gold discovery start to pile up at this point.

Meanwhile, the Plummer and Hinds's pack-train returned from the Rock Creek, British Columbia, mines, accompanied by 25 men who stopped at the Ingalls/Peshastin Creek gold placers. Finding the gold in attractive quantities, the group dropped the remaining store supplies there. A Rock Creek miner named Dr. F. G. Kellogg was sent back to Seattle with the pack animals for more miner-friendly goods. Joe Foster and several groups of miners per unit ordered $200 to $300 in goods for the returning pack-train destined for their Ingalls Creek site. The new shorter distance to the Ingalls Creek mines made their trade much more cost-effective and a windfall compared to the long trek north to Canada.

Express-mail carrier Tom Russell stopped by the new digs at Ingalls Creek on one of his trips to the Rock Creek, British Columbia, mines. He was surprised to find his brother and four men named Low, Richards, Stratton, and Edward King. They were panning 3 to 10 cents in gold from each pan, with an occasional $1 pan. This was an era when $2 to $3 a day was good wages. As back-breaking as panning can be, a good gold-panning man can wash 150 to 200 pans of gold-bearing material a day. This could have led to a full miner's poke if the gold held a strong average.

Tom Russell sent his brother to Rock Creek in his place with the express mail, while he remained on the gold placer claim. Tom sent a letter via a coast-bound miner with notice that he was staying at the Ingalls Creek placers to mine gold. He also suggested to his friends that there was still room for more prospectors and encouraged them to head for the Peshastin/Ingalls Creek gold placers.

It wasn't long before the gold taken was becoming less encouraging profit-wise, and the Seattle miners drifted away from Peshastin Creek. The more industrious Oregon miners quickly filled the void left by the departed Seattle bunch.

OREGON MINING FACTION ON INGALLS CREEK AND PESHASTIN CREEK, 1860

Oregonian miners were now in the majority on Peshastin Creek. Mining records show Oregon transplants James Bothwell, brothers George and Frank Moulthrop, and H. Young working on a legally filed claim named "Bothwell Bar." Bothwell was the prominent name among the placers' digs at this time. Bothwell and Young went to Portland, Oregon, in mid-September of 1860 for supplies and brought back provisions to last through the winter.

Another group of five Oregon State miners was headed by A. J. Boyakin, with 13 more associates camped nearby. Their group was eating survival portions of food and was in dire need of re-supplying their camp. The Boyakin claim had a good thing going, with some men stating they were pulling out $4 to $6 in gold on a good day. So their program of living off a diminishing menu wasn't due to lack of money. The immediate concern was whether or not it was possible to remain there at the Ingalls Creek miners' camp throughout the winter. By October 5, 1860, an Ingalls Creek miner named George Hull returned to the area around the confluence of the Wenatchee and Columbia Rivers. He stated that there were still 50 men at the snow-free miners' campsite. The remaining 50 men planned to stay there throughout the winter. That decision would put them in position to start mining early in the spring.

The population of the winter camps (including the ranks of the Oregon faction) was beginning to decrease due to lack of grub and to the cold weather with incoming snow accumulation. Another count of gold seekers found more miners from Wenatchee at the mining campsites in October, compared to the head count that favored the Oregonians during the previous month. A few weeks after this observation was made, it was admitted that the bonanza that was anticipated was less than originally hoped.

A November 1860 updated report stated nearly all the miners at the gold placer camps farther up Peshastin Creek left due to the lack of staples to survive until the spring packers could arrive. By December 3, 1860, only 13 miners remained; they were mining near Bothwell's Bar. Snow was on the ground, and the Swauk-Peshastin divide (later known as Old Blewett Pass) had 4 feet of snow. James Bothwell, Frank and George Moulthrop, and several other miners survived the winter and were still on Bothwell's Bar in April 1861.

By 1861, Charles Splawn departed from his wandering gold placer days and married into the Thorp family. He and his wife settled down in Moxie Valley (east of the present-day town of Yakima, Washington).

In February 1861, Charles Splawn's old friend Alfred Henson, his wife, and five children were guided up Peshastin Creek by a Wenatchi tribesman named How-mil. They settled on a location where Henson established a supply post for the miners in the area. Also along in the party headed for the placer claims were George Barfield and John Gubser. Barfield and Gubser were assisting Henson while on their way back to test the gold placers on Peshastin Creek. Unfortunately, Henson's timing was not in synchronization with the demand for his goods, and his business venture failed due to the easy gold in the placers, along with his potential customers, running out.

About this time, new gold digs were discovered on the Colville tribal lands and other more gold-alluring Washington Territory areas. Then there were several individual incidents of white men getting killed related to treaty violations. It was a backlash reaction by angry braves on the lower Columbia. These ill-fated omens gained Henson's attention, and he pulled out of the placer-miner supply business. Alfred and his family relocated to Klickitat Country. Washington State's mining news in general faded to a whimper, and the newspapers began heralding news about the United States' Civil War.

This scene looks upon a donkey looking at a prospector "lookin' fer gold" – a lot of lookin' goin' on here. (From *Handbook for Prospectors and Operators of Small Mine* [1943].)

Chapter Four:
Antoine Etienne

NEGRO CREEK PLACER MINER, BIG ANTOINE, 1860s

Antoine Etienne figured in a brief gold-mining stint in the Peshastin Creek area. Big Antoine Etienne was the son of slave parents. Etienne was a common first name amongst the Deep South French population, but a search for Etienne as a surname was not in any database. His keen mind was noticed by his French "national" possessor, a plantation owner, and Antoine was placed among students attending school classes. As an adult, Antoine demonstrated his academic gifts in speaking various languages, including English, Greek, Latin, German, and French.

(A word about several slave name origins: Most slaves had only one name. If they had a last name, it was often the owner's European surname, another Christian-based identity, or classic European names. Some slave names were linked to the name of the African port of deportation upon crossing the Atlantic Ocean.)

During the US Civil War, Antoine gained his freedom via his service as an interpreter for the army. During his newfound freedom, he utilized his intellectual abilities by quickly picking up Indian languages. This led to an easy transition as he immersed himself among the like-minded tribal population who had a common distrust for the encroaching European frontiersmen. Antoine eventually made his way into the regions of Washington Territory.

At an unspecified date, Antoine was gold-placer mining a few miles up the Entiat River. By that time, he had a locally known dislike for folks of European lineage. He also had a reputation for causing them trouble on his own or in friendly company with any one of several tribal groups in the country. However, in a face-to-face talk with Andrew Jackson Splawn, a convincing and brutally honest review of Big Antoine's past aggressions was set upon. Antoine was given no alternative to the stern suggestion presented to him. This left Antoine in a position to no longer carry on with his harassing mood.

In the 1860s, Big Antoine Etienne was recorded in the traveling notes of goldfield-bound miner Robert Stevenson while he and his company of companions were passing through an Indian encampment at the confluence of the Wenatchee and Columbia Rivers. At that time, Antoine was married to a chief's daughter and living in the tribal village.

In Stevenson's group were two educated men that had graduated from universities, "Long" Tom Davis (nephew of Jefferson Davis of Southern Confederacy fame) and Bill "Skill" Schombrah. They decided to test Antoine's stated abilities and found that he was fluent in several languages. Etienne also impressed the white men with his in-depth knowledge of the classics, giving proof that he had a university-level education and resulting with "points well made."

Antoine's presence on Negro Creek has been vaguely established in the 1860s, about the same time as the other firsts among those early placer-gold finds along Peshastin Creek and its related feeder streams. The fact that he mined placer gold to the sum of $1,100 at the mouth of the creek could very well have had the effect of generating interest in those prospectors coming into the area around the same time. The fact that Nigger Creek was the first and only name applied to this water course at this time would indicate Antoine was there ahead of the white-man influx of gold seekers.

Pressure and distain for the new wave of white miners attracted to the area near him may have been the reason he allegedly headed upstream on Negro Creek. That is pertinent to the story that follows. Antoine's personal history after his presence on Negro Creek is that of an Oregon State-based orchardist, renowned for his much sought-after peaches, grapes, and cherries. As it seems fitting for orchard folks, he died at a ripe old, unspecified age in 1907 while on a trip to Vancouver, Washington.

NIGGER CREEK, NEGRO CREEK, ETIENNE CREEK

The creek's original name, Nigger Creek, was because of Antoine's placer-gold discovery and presence. Although offensive today, that name reflects the vernacular of its time and is the historical name quoted in the data researched.

More recently, there has been a movement to change certain historic words to soothe present-day conscience about terms that, although not politically correct, reflect our nation's past activities. Certain frontier verbiages have already been politically sanitized and misrepresent the early growing pains of US frontier history, the way life really was.

It is true that early American history has left a trail of moral wrongs, but it is still history the way it happened. Today's face-lifting, "nip tuck" history, rewritten in polite, modern platitudes, often has little bearing on the true facts. The way it was is deliberately deleted. And so, during the 1960s, Nigger Creek was officially renamed Negro Creek.

In the following text, the name Negro Creek will be used in all references of the era starting from 1860 to the end of the Negro Creek written data, a fair and respectful accolade to the achievements of the man Antoine Etienne.

BIG ANTOINE ACCORDING TO MINER "NEGRO CREEK" JIM

A group of us from Northwest Underground Explorations interviewed miner Jim Holderhoff in 2002, while he was living 2¾ miles up Negro Creek in the Caldo cabin (old Lucky Strike claim) as property groundskeeper. Jim informed us that he and his dad mined up and down the creek together for many years.

Jim repeated a story told to him about the acclaimed location of Big Antoine's hard-rock mine and underground workings in the north slope above Jim's cabin. We were led up the steep slope following a comparatively recent (1960s) bulldozer road to the site. On a walking and talking tour by Jim, we were informed the adits and surface trenches were Antoine Etienne's underground digs and upper cabin site. Later information proved Jim's story about Antoine's hard-rock activities were unfounded (Antoine was a placer miner, and no record shows he was ever a hard-rock miner). The digs Jim spoke of were originally developed by Charley Striker in the 1800s. The mining claims were lost to memory for a time and then rediscovered. The Caldo mine's group of claims are the latest in development on and near the original underground workings.

Note: As of 2013, the claims are under new owner/possessor claims status.

There is no evidence of more than several black miners in the hard-rock mining districts of the Wenatchee Mountain Range. This is in comparison to the large population of black miners that was working in the Roslyn, Washington, coal mines when the European miners went on strike in 1888.

In 1896, gold miners William McKasson and John H. Corbin, of African ancestry, had mineral claims in the upper part of the Cle Elum River. Their best gold-producing claim was located one mile above China Point on the Cle Elum River. It had a blue flag, on which a battle axe was stitched in gold thread, indicating the name and location of their property. They made a living panning gold off the bedrock. Aside from these noted references, there are no other records indicating that any black miners were found plying the area as prospectors or in any other hard-rock-related jobs.

Chinese miners sluicing away high placer bench gold deposits with a Monitor nozzle. (From *Idaho, an Illustrated History* [1976].)

Chapter Five:
Foreign Miners

CHINESE IN NORTHERN AMERICA, 1850s

Most folks reading about the Chinese presence that started in the California region don't know the origin of their forced, mass movement. The Chinese/Celestials (meaning "children of the sky" or something similar, as the term Celestials was used in 1852) from China's Kwangtung Province were suffering due to widespread economic depression. The result was the Taiping Rebellion. An emigration of about 25,000 Chinese reached California by the end of the year.

But to pay for their long sea voyage, the Chinese émigrés had to borrow the price of the ocean voyage and agree, by contract, to work for the money lender. Deductions were thereafter taken from future earnings. The first wave of Chinese that came to America after the California gold strike soon formed one big company, and then smaller groups were formed. They were driven hard as indentured servants to the managing motherland tongs (who were, essentially, economic warlords) and under the stern eye of an overseer for those organized labor gangs of Chinese. The Celestials adapted quickly and were either working for the railroads or actively placer mining for gold. Fine particles of gold overlooked by the stampeding non-Asian miners were then patiently gleaned by the Celestials after the former mining contingent abandoned their gold-rush digs.

CHINESE MINERS

The Chinese were the most numerous group among foreign-born miners and could be found in every mining region of the old west. They were seen mining the placer ground throughout central Washington, mainly along the gravel bars on the Yakima, Wenatchee, and Columbia Rivers. They made a number of appearances throughout the Swauk Mining District via placer-mining activities. In some places, the Chinese miner did get to the placer gold first, but not often. The Chinese miners would meticulously pan the smaller gold particles from abandoned placer claims. In some cases, the Chinese would take more gold value out of the abandoned placers than the previous, impatient miners.

CHINESE FUNERAL

An interesting fact was made known in April 1894, related to the funeral of Jung Foo, who was killed by countryman Lee See. The funeral scene was more like a bon voyage than a backdrop for sorrow. Foo's very decorative coffin was transported in a horse-drawn wagon-hearse, accompanied by equal numbers of oriental and white friends and acquaintances. They all arrived at an old cemetery, followed by a wagon loaded with a generous supply of oriental cooked chicken, duck, pastries, and Asian you-name-its. These were placed on Jung's grave so that he would start his spiritual journey on a full stomach. After the ceremony for Jung Foo, the main crowd left.

Local tribe members who had seen similar funerals before were appreciatively present but kept their distance from the burial activities. Eventually, only they remained at the grave site, and before the grave turf could begin to settle, the patient tribal folks were having a darn good square meal. And, it could be said that they were just as pleased over the Chinaman's farewell celebration as was the Jung Foo fellowship. To the tribe folk, it was another in a series of Chinese-sponsored, free, stomach grubstakes, a cuisine-type gold strike, but with a comparatively shorter-lived duration. After they consumed their sumptuous meal, a snoozing tribute to the disciple of Confucius may have been consummated in the comfort of a shade tree or teepee.

CHINESE BONE BOX

In the aftermath of sufficient time for the flesh to decompose from the bones and form the skeletal remains of brother Foo, they would be disinterred, placed in a bone box, and shipped back to his home in the Flowery Kingdom.

It was the Chinese sacred belief not to let the deceased one's bones turn to dust in a foreign country. There were six companies from China that sponsored all Chinese who worked through them in the United States. If anybody was poor and couldn't afford the "bone ticket" to the motherland, the company would foot the bill, on loan, in exchange for … what, perhaps more indentured servitude?

Chapter Six:
Serious Beginnings

YAKIMA COUNTY IS ESTABLISHED

On January 21, 1865, Yakima County was created. Then, Kittitas County was created from the northern portion of Yakima County on November 28, 1883. Chelan County was partitioned from southern Okanogan County and northern Kittitas County in March 1899. So, it appears that the early Blewett miners may have been challenged to keep up with which county they would be filing and recording their mineral claims the next time the occasion came around.

PESHASTIN MINES, 1864 TO 1874

From 1864 to 1874, there was yearly mining activity along the gold placers on Peshastin Creek and the other Blewett area tributaries. During this time, there were occurrences of gold rushes still going on in Canada and states, such as Idaho, Nevada, Oregon, Utah, Colorado, and California. Most of the prospecting and mining, up until 1874, in and around the future Blewett town site/ Peshastin Creek region was of a transient nature. Stories of the Swauk placer-gold discovery were the focus of the public arena. This renewed hope for finding formerly undiscovered Peshastin Creek placer gold.

Renewed mining activities taking place on the Peshastin Creek gold placer claims resulted in the discovery of gold-bearing quartz veins that intruded into the massive serpentine formations associated within what would become the Peshastin Mining District. The first and richest digs were in Thompson Gulch (later renamed Culver Gulch), located west of the future historic Blewett mining town site in Yakima County (Kittitas County had not yet been formed).

EARLY PESHASTIN CREEK MINING CAMP AND THOMPSON (CULVER) GULCH

The Blewett town site area from the 1860s to around the late 1870s was flat ground that was the most convenient mining camp area set-up on upper Peshastin Creek. It was located across from the trail entrance heading up Thompson (Culver) Gulch to yet-to-be-discovered hard-rock claims. It was generally known as one of several "way camps" in the 1860s with no particular name but carried the connotation of mining camp. As mining activities increased, in the 1870s, the name Peshastin Camp came into use next, and "way camp" was discontinued. The pack trail traversing north and south between today's Swauk and Peshastin/Blewett Mining Districts slowly widened as it gained attention as a popular byway and mining camp destination. It would later become the original Blewett Pass Highway. By 1879, the first rudimentary, seasonal wagon road was intermittently passable. Peshastin Camp evolved onto "Culver Mining Camp" in the 1880s to early 1890s and was the oldest mining camp in the Wenatchee Mountain Range.

THE TOWN OF BLEWETT IS ESTABLISHED, 1894

The Culver Mining Camp name once again morphed into the name of the dominant powers-that-be, and the mine campsite became known (for one year, in 1893) as the Warner Mining Camp. William and Edward Blewett bought the Warner mill and accumulated mining properties in 1894, and Warner Camp became Blewett Camp to reflect the new ownership. This site became the mining town of Blewett that same year with a permanent post office affixed to it. The first postmaster was E. C. Sterling.

BLEWETT MINERS AND CLAIM LOCATIONS – THE FIRST 20 YEARS

Among the early, dominating Culver Gulch hard-rock miners of the early 1870s were John Shafer, Ezra Brusha, Ira Canaday, Samuel Culver, James Lockwood, Harry Savage, John Alden Shoudy and sons John Jr. and Dexter, Tom Johnson (an established Ellensburg, Washington, merchant and brother-in-law to John A. Shoudy), Tom's brother John A. Johnson, Wilmer Cooper, Harbin Cooper, John Olden, John Hill, Peter Wilder, James Wilder, Marshall Blinn, Thaddeus Neubauer, and Anton Neubauer. Other miners were George Henton, William Donahue, John Ernest, S. C. Davidson, Daniel Shaser, G. W. Parish, Edward King, Jacob (a.k.a. John) Somers, T. S. Wood, T. John Vinton, brothers Joseph and Ed Warner, Henry Bash and his brother William, Edward and William Blewett, and Cliff Davenport. All these men, plus many miners of a transient nature, participated in staking and recording claims as individuals or, with many of the above men, as mining partnerships.

Trading and selling of the early claim properties happened quickly. Because of the often vague records on hand to review, it is sometimes an unclear progression of who owned what and when these actions took place. Miners who leased claims from other miners and mining companies were part of the problem because they high-graded and produced small fortunes that went unreported. More than a few of the early 1870s prospectors who poked around the Culver/Blewett digs were already mining south of Blewett Pass in the Liberty area of the Swauk Mining District due to the Goodwin brothers' 1867 gold discovery on Swauk Creek and the ensuing gold rush. Some of the Swauk Mining District miners who held mineral claims in both mining districts were John Shoudy, his sons John Jr. and Dexter, Mose Splawn, George Henton, Richard Price, Zeb Keller, John Black from Ohio, Walter A. Bull, John L. Lyons, J. P. Cumminsky, Gus

(Bull) Nilson, Torkel Tweet, William (Billy) Johnson, Tillman Tripp from Missouri, William M. Elliott, Carl Rydberg, David Livingston, Howard C. and Ness Jensen, plus many others.

Real estate investor Howard Walters was sole owner or part owner in 150 separate mineral claims located in the Peshastin, Swauk, and Cle Elum Mining Districts. The problem with this kind of monopoly is that it slowed down the ability to develop meaningful mining activities. Not much work could be accomplished when the owner/owners were spread thin throughout these mining districts. The mining properties existed as potential capital-producing investments but were compromised by this faulty business premise. Too much time was wasted maintaining ownership via yearly assessment work and resulted in limited mineral production. Also, too many individual claims were held back under speculation that property would soon rise in value due to some nearby successful mine. It also discouraged other prospectors from entering a mining district that had the apparent rich ground already claimed.

MINERS WITH CLAIMS RECORDED IN THE BLEWETT AREA, 1880s

Mining claims were set down in writing as the miners told scribes in the office. From the manner in which the information was inked into the records, the claim recorder seems to have penned what he thought the miner said or meant, resulting in a lot of muddled claim-location information to sort through. All mineral claim locations in what was destined to become the Peshastin Mining District (Chelan County) was, at this time, recorded in Kittitas County.

Some of the recurring mine claim owners named in the mineral recordings from 1880 through 1889 included, 43-year-old Jacob Somers from Maryland, John Shoudy (Shoudy introduced the paperwork that got Kittitas County established in 1883), George Henton, Ira Canaday, Wilmer Cooper, James Lockwood, E. W. Lockwood; 1883—T. S. Woods, William Donahue, S. C. Davidson, Nes Jensen, Tom Johnson; 1884—E. A. Grunden and John Ernest (60 years old, from Pennsylvania); 1886—Torkel Tweet; 1887—J. P. Cumminsky (25 years old, from Pennsylvania); 1888—T. John Vinton. By 1889, most mining claims of any value were taken.

This is a typical representation of a five-man mining crew... thinking what? "Can hardly wait to get back into that hole for three bucks a day". (Vic Pisoni photo collection.)

Chapter Seven:
Early Hard-rock Miners

The following accounts of Blewett miners are examples from the many men who were outstanding among the gold seekers.

JOHN SHAFER

John Shafer was the first miner to record a hard-rock quartz claim in Thompson (Culver) Gulch. It was the Culver mine, located near the head of Thompson Gulch. The Thompson Gulch name location was used in the earliest recorded claim filings as a location reference. At that point, there was a period of vague mine trading and name changes whose transactions evade documentation. Under those circumstances, the Culver mine property also became locally referred to as the Shafer mine property (there was no Shafer claim in the record book until later, and it was a different Shafer claim location and owner). Soon after these name exchanges, Thompson Gulch was dropped in favor of the permanent Culver Gulch title.

SAMUEL CULVER

Hot on the heels of the Culver claim by John Shafer was 38-year-old Samuel Culver from Pennsylvania with the Pole Pick, which was on ground down the gulch from the Shafer-owned Culver property. Then Samuel Culver added the Hummingbird digs to his list, located even farther down the gulch. The prospecting and claim staking activities were in high gear, as indicated by James Lockwood taking the Bob Tail (later the Wye Tunnel workings was developed on the property) and 32-year-old John Olden from Finland and 34-year-old Peter Wilder from Germany staking boundary lines and recording the Sandel. These claims were followed by John Olden and Samuel Culver claiming ownership on the Little Culver.

Gold-bearing rock, considered to be from the same system as the vein tapped at the higher elevations in Culver Gulch, was located at the bottom of Culver Gulch. It was on the west bank of Peshastin Creek where Jacob (a.k.a. John) Somers recorded the Black Jack mine.

Miners who stayed in the Blewett area after the initial claim recordings of the early 1870s are John Ernest, James Wilder, John Olden, John Hill, S. C. Davidson, Tom Johnson, and William Donahue. Details about these men follow.

JOHN ERNEST

Early Blewett miner John Ernest recorded the Alta Vista (Pole Pick No. 2) in 1874. An 1893 mining-claims map shows the Pole Pick No. 2 as the claim joined to the south line of the Culver. He and William Donahue were mining partners in several mineral digs. Ernest recorded the Evening Star with mining partner William Donahue in 1884. The Evening Star was joined to the south line of the Peshastin claim. Ernest had the Pole Pick No. 2 to himself in 1884. In 1886, Ernest and Gus Nilson recorded the Ernest-Nilson property up in the Summit Pockets area. Then Ernest had the Peshastin Range in 1888. In the early 1890s, Ernest was part owner in the Lucky Queen mine. Ernest was a prolific Blewett miner, and his mining activities will be noted in the following pages.

As a 20-year veteran of the Blewett area mines, 76-year-old John Ernest was still a physically active miner in 1894. He had an excellent memory and was a likeable man, always an entertaining talker, reader of many books, industrious, and of a sober manner (when sober). He was a bachelor with no relatives in the territory, other than his son Frank S. Ernest who was residing in Vancouver, Washington. John was born in Pennsylvania in the spring of 1818. As a resident/miner living in the town of Blewett, he was known to be frugal with his money. He lived alone most of the time, except when he had a house guest drop by and stay for a visit. In all things, John Ernest was acknowledged as a man of generous impulses.

On August 8 of that year, 1894, he was busy grinding ore in his arrastra, which was one of the first to operate in the mining camp back in the 1870s. As it turned out, John had a senior moment and took a tumble down amongst the ore and drag-stones grinding everything in the arrastra pit to particulates and powder. Miner/mine owner James Wilder's young twin sons, Ray and Roy, saw John topple into the arrastra grinding well. By the time the boys ran home and alerted their mother and returned with help, massive physical damage was done to John. When the water source for the 25-foot diameter waterwheel that powered the arrastra was finally shut down, John sustained a crushed arm, broken leg, ankle, and wrist. It was also noted he was banged-up around the shoulders and head.

John died five days later on Friday the13th, a number that John had frequently said was unlucky (for him, for sure). As a result, John Ernest occupied the first grave in the Blewett Cemetery.

JAMES WILDER

James and his wife Lucy were married in 1879. They started a family but lost the first three children born to them during a diphtheria epidemic in the state of Michigan. They left that state and settled in Seattle, Washington. Twins Roy Clayton and Ray Stuart Wilder were born in Seattle on November 8, 1891. Following the twins' births, James heard about the gold mines up Culver Gulch and moved his family to Culver Camp.

Previous to mining, his occupation was noted as "saloon owner." James eventually became one of the prominent miner/mine owners in the Blewett area. He is mentioned mainly with the mines of Culver Gulch and secondarily noted for his mineral claims up Negro Creek. So to

James Wilder, Blewett/Culver Gulch miner and mine owner, stands by the portal of the lower Ivanhoe tunnel. (Cashmere Museum and Pioneer Village photo collection.)

establish his presence at this early time is pertinent to his involvement in Blewett mining activities that started in 1892.

Other Wilder children born to James and Lucy at Blewett were Amber Glee (1893), Hazel B. (1895), twins Byron G. and Reginald (1897), and Mildred (1901). A family tragedy struck in 1896, when three-year-old Amber's clothes caught fire, and she died two days later. Amber Glee was buried in Ellensburg, Washington. In 1897, Baby Reginald died (cause not given) and was buried in the Blewett Cemetery.

Lucy Wilder was the mining camp Sunday school teacher. Also a midwife, she and Alice McCarthy delivered babies born in the Blewett area.

JAMES WILDER'S PROLIFIC MINING CAREER

Note that Peter Wilder's family relationship to James is unknown. Peter was up Thompson (Culver) Gulch in 1874. In 1880, Peter Wilder was actively operating his own arrastra located on Peshastin Creek.

James Wilder was one of the many miner/owners with multiple claims in Culver Gulch. His claims were concentrated in the upper Culver Gulch areas near the Shafer/Culver, Pole Pick mines, and the old Summit Pockets (ore deposits). He was also active on placer digs along Peshastin Creek. James recorded several mineral properties up Negro Creek, mainly on the southern drainage slopes that separated Negro Creek from Culver Gulch. He recorded 49 mining claims during his career in the Peshastin Mining District. The areas of his digs were up Negro Creek, Ruby Creek, and Culver Gulch area. Wilder was sole owner or in mining partnerships with other well-established local miners throughout this time. Wilder's above-mentioned mining activities were accounted for through his filed mineral recordings.

A review of Wilder's earliest Culver Gulch mining history showed James started as a professional miner at Culver Gulch in 1892. Some of Wilder's mining activities failed to show on record due to the mining claims he leased. His mining activities when he was hired to work for other miners were known but not recorded. When he leased or worked others' mineral property, newspaper articles sometimes falsely credited James as owner rather than lessee or manager of a mine. Similar mistakes also applied to other miners at the time, creating gray areas in mining data.

The Ivanhoe claim was one of Wilder's main focuses of his mining activities. In the summer of 1892, Wilder was in possession of the Hindoo (Ivanhoe) claim. James changed the Hindoo name to White Elephant. Copley Lloyd leased the White Elephant from Wilder and made a rich strike on a deposit of gold. Among the gold extracted by Lloyd from his leased White Elephant digs was a gold nugget worth $27 (gold was at $18.94 an ounce). After Copley's lease was up, Wilder worked the claim.

James recorded eight claims in 1892: the Twin Brothers (named for Wilder's sons), Providence, Wild Irishman, Capitol, Congress, Wilder (Ivanhoe/White Elephant), Cornucopia, Mountain Treasure, and the Roy and Ray. In 1896, Wilder had the Sulphuret No. 2 and the Amber Glee, which he leased from the Blewett Gold Mining Company. James relocated the Amber Glee in 1902, listing himself as sole owner. By 1910, James had advanced the workings in the Amber Glee, which consisted of a 200-foot drift with a 60-foot raise.

Wilder added four more claims to his mineral holdings in 1897, the Copper King, Gold Nugget, Rockefeller, and Wilder No. 2. The Golden Spear placer claim, Empress, X-Ray placer, and Indian placer were recorded by Wilder in 1898. In 1899, James came up with six more recorded claims. They were the Home Stake, Wilder No. 4, Leroy Extension, Rainy Day, Lucky King, and Empire No. 2, which were later referred to as the Wilder Group. Several references involved Wilder in groups of claims. This was also the year that he became the postmaster in Blewett. The new road in from the north allowed the mail and other commerce to be transported by wagon and stagecoach between the connected towns and railroad terminal in Kittitas County. He and his family lived in the town of Blewett for 11 years.

In 1903, Lucy insisted that the family move to Cashmere, Washington, where the children could get a more in-depth education. She got her way, and the family moved to a ranch near Cashmere.

James Wilder died in Cashmere on March 11, 1918, at 67 years old. Lucy died December 15, 1941, in Cashmere at the age of 85.

James's mining activities were numerous, and he had great influence creating or being involved in the many historic mining-related events at Blewett until 1917. His mine-related activities are noted throughout this book.

JOHN OLDEN (1830-1910) AND JOHN HILL (1855-?)

John Olden and his mining partner, John Hill, drifted into the Peshastin Mining Camp in 1874. The two men were neighbors in Chicago, Illinois. They lost their homes and families to the Great Chicago Fire that swept through and leveled the center of the district where they lived. Olden

John Olden stands in front of his cabin (1905). The mill superintendent's residence is partially shown to the right in the background. These buildings were located south of the 20-stamp mill and west of Peshastin Creek. (Chris Bell photo collection.)

lost his wife and several children to the blaze, and teenager John Hill's widowed mother died in the same manner.

Due to the circumstances of the traumatic event, 44-year-old Olden (who was 25 years older than Hill) took responsibility for 19-year-old Hill. They departed from the charred remains of their past homes in Chicago, headed west, and eventually came to Culver Mining Camp.

John Olden lived in Blewett for the next 36 years until his death in 1910 at 80 years old. John Hill was a miner in the Blewett area, but the only mining claim in his name was a Tronsen Creek placer, recorded September 6, 1899, as Indian Camp. It was located about ½ mile south from the confluence of Peshastin and Tronsen Creeks. John Olden's mining activities are addressed throughout the remainder of this book.

This horizontal arrastra (1905) is one of three that John Olden built. It was being used to grind ore at the rate of $50 to $100 in gold weekly. (Chris Bell photo collection.)

S. C. DAVIDSON

S. C. Davidson, along with Tom Johnson, was co-owner of the Johnson-Davidson (Pole Pick No. 1) claim in 1874. In 1883, Johnson had another claim, the Johnson (Pole Pick) claim to himself. The Pole Pick was joined to the east claim line of the Pole Pick No. 1 claim. After 1883, Davidson departed from Thompson (Culver) Gulch for places unknown.

TOM JOHNSON (1840-1908)

Tom Johnson was one of the first miners to record a hard-rock claim in the early 1870s. Tom's Pole Pick claim was located on the eastward property line of the patented Pole Pick No. 1 mine. In 1884, Tallman Tripp was the new owner of the Pole Pick. Tallman and his wife, Eva, used an arrastra to process the gold ore.

In 1877, Tom owned and operated his own stamp mill, which is verified by the following story. Tom Johnson's mining and other activities evolve throughout the following pages of this book.

TOM JOHNSON'S MILL ROBBERY-MURDER, 1877

The drift of this story was verified by two miners, John Olden and John Hill. In July 1877, James Lockwood and Harbin Cooper had a much heralded mining claim that was producing impressive amounts of free gold. It required miner/mill operator Tom Johnson's six-stamp mill to pound the free-gold quartz ore into a course flour-like consistency. Then mercury was applied onto copper plates to absorb only the gold into the mercury resulting as a silver-colored, putty-like consistency called "amalgam." Tom Johnson's stamp mill finished running a large amount of ore from the Lockwood-Cooper mine, and 1,000 pounds of concentrates in 25 canvas bags, which weighed about 40 pounds each, were locked in Tom's stamp mill building. The awaiting shipment would be moved out on wagons as soon as repairs on the road trending south over the ridge separating the Swauk Mining District from the Peshastin mining areas was finished. There was no northward road connecting Blewett to the Wenatchee area at this time. After the road was repaired, two of the three wagons used were to be loaded with canvas bags and used as decoys whenever gold shipments went out. Only the mill manager and owner Tom Johnson would know which wagon carried the sacks containing the gold. All sacks, fake or real, looked alike. The smelter-bound load of gold was locked inside the mill under the protecting eye of the mill foreman.

On the morning the gold was to be shipped out, the teamsters and guards had just finished breakfast and were in the stable harnessing the horses, hitching them to the three wagons, and saddling single mounts. As soon as dawn broke, they would head over to load the sacks of ore; their first rest-stop was scheduled at a campground about 12 miles south of Blewett.

(Some of the following events were reconstructed by witnesses and crude aftermath forensics via old west guestimates.) The stamp mill was loudly stomping away at a new run of ore, and the mill foreman hardly heard the movement of horses' hooves as they arrived at the mill under pre-dawn cover. Somebody who knew the signal whistled to alert the foreman that it was time to transfer the ore onto the wagons. The foreman freed the heavy lock from the reinforced door and swung it inward. However, instead of the prearranged group of company men; several strangers with pistols drawn pushed their way in. They speedily loaded only the sacks that had the gold in them onto a string of six pack animals. There were four men on saddle horses in the gang, and as they were leaving with the loot, a shot rang out. A .45 caliber chunk of life-ending lead was sent through the foreman's lung.

Needless to say, the sons of darkness fled north out of town with their heavy load of gold-laden booty as fast as the six weight-encumbered equines could go.

Why was the foreman shot? Later John Olden said most likely to avoid the foreman identifying them. Maybe it was an inside job, and the rest of the gang double-crossed the foreman, shooting him for the same reason.

The sound of the fired gun alerted the wagon guards and awoke a group of able-bodied men from the mining camp, including John Olden and John Hill. As quickly as a group of men could arm themselves and mount up, they were in hot pursuit. The miners and guards saw their tracks headed north and figured the robbers would eventually head westward over the Wenatchee Mountain Range for Stampede Pass. With renegade tribesmen raising mayhem and death on the east side of the state, it was too dangerous to travel east, down the Wenatchee River, and cross the Columbia River into hostile territory.

If the pursuing Blewett miners were correct in assuming the robbers took a route northward and then westward toward Stampede Pass, they would have had to head north along Peshastin Creek and take a westbound trail up Negro Creek or Ingalls Creek. Using either of these exits would require them to cross over the Wenatchee Mountain Range. They could descend the west slopes of the mountain range and follow the Cle Elum River to Roslyn, Washington, and cut westward again toward Stampede Pass.

The assumption was that the pursuing group of Blewett volunteers would catch up with the slower moving string of pack-animals and murdering thieves somewhere north on the narrow, brushy tote trail alongside Peshastin Creek, between Culver Gulch and Negro Creek. But after several miles, the pursuing group realized they should have seen the fleeing lynch-party candidates much sooner than the point at which that realization entered their minds.

So slowly back-tracking and carefully examining all the cut-offs entering the less used way trails, they finally came to a brush-screened trail only ½ mile south of the Peshastin Mining Camp. It trended east up a slope and away from Peshastin Creek and eastward to the crest of the ridge. From there, the fleeing gold-thieving mob went north. So much time was wasted due to the tracking mistakes that the pursuers called off the chase until the next day.

The next morning, the trail of the death-dealing robbers was picked up and followed north on the ridge, to the east of Peshastin Creek. Then the robber's trail headed west again, downslope to Peshastin Creek and onto the flats at the mouth of Ingalls Creek.

What the miners found at the mouth of Ingalls Creek was not the group they were pursuing but, instead, just the opposite. A scouting party of US Cavalry was camped there. The officer of the scouting party relayed to the pursuing men that four riders with a six-horse pack-string came through their camp the night before and explained they were coming from their claim back up in the hills. The officers said the four men stated they had made a very good clean-up of gold and were headed into safer country. They stayed with the soldiers overnight and left early the next morning.

The group of pursuing miners followed the thieves' tracks down-trail to a place on the Wenatchee River where it could be forded. Looking across the river, the men could see a band of horses grazing. When the civilian posse got within sight of the band of animals, they counted 10, just as described by the army scouts. A large pile of gear, including saddles, harnesses, packing, and camp items lay abandoned near the river's edge. The thieves had lightened their load, keeping their firearms and the sacks of concentrates. End of trail.

John Olden pointed out that, whichever way the murdering thieves went, food wasn't a problem because there was plenty of fish, berries, and game to be had. Their second opinion about the planned theft was that the heavy sacks of gold amalgam were dropped into the Wenatchee River with the idea of coming back and retrieving them later when the volume of water in the river dropped and cleared. Did they come back for their loot? We don't know.

The case went cold, but the fact remains that miners later taking placer gold from the river, downstream from the site of the abandoned horses and pile of other gear, also found gold-binding mercury amalgam in their pans.

TOM JOHNSON'S CLAIM JUMPED BY WILLIAM DONAHUE

By 1883, Tom Johnson was co-owner with Elmer Lockwood. They had a group of claims producing gold under the banner of the Shafer Gold and Silver Mining Company, which was known locally as the Lockwood-Johnson mine. Johnson bought the whole outfit in 1884, which included the original Culver mine 6 stamp mill. He continued to run it as the Shafer Gold and Silver Mining Company.

The claims were producing gold, and all went well for Johnson until 1887. This was the year William Donahue jumped Tom's Culver claim (it was a claim in Tom's group of mining properties). This happened because Johnson got sloppy about turning in his assessment paper work by the due date. Without Tom's knowledge, William recorded the claim on March 23, 1887. Why Johnson was so careless is a mystery he never explained because Tom's right-hand man, John Burmeister, who was working at Johnson's Bob Tail dig, warned him earlier about Donahue's intentions. Tom responded to the warning with the comment that he would kill Donahue if he attempted the jump.

January 1891 didn't start out well for Tom Johnson. At this point, William Donahue had bonded or entered into some type of sales contract and signed over the Culver claim to brothers William and Henry Bash. Donahue received the sum of $1,000 as down payment, was to be paid $2,000 on March 1, 1891, and would receive an additional $10,000 from the net profits.

Subsequent to the transfer of the Culver mine contract, the money set aside to pay off Donahue was redirected by William Bash to be held in account by the Culver Mining Company. Later this information was given in the lawsuit that William Donahue brought against the Culver Mining Company co-owner brothers Joseph and Edward Warner of Seattle and William and Henry Bash for the balance of the contracted money deal.

The Culver Mining Company owners immediately made arrangements to purchase 10 new stamps for their quartz mill and other mining equipment to improve on the percentage of gold ore being milled from the Culver mine. It appears that over 50 percent of the gold content was being lost because of gold-binding sulfides that were washed into the tailings.

SHAFER GOLD AND SILVER MINING COMPANY VS. WILLIAM DONAHUE

Tom Johnson made an appearance at Culver Gulch in May 1891, accompanied by Edward Blewett. They were there to look over the situation concerning Tom's jumped mining claims. Their decision was to bring suit against Donahue for possession of the Culver claim, even though an earlier judgment was in favor of William Donahue. This latest of Johnson's court actions came after several years of Donahue's uninterrupted possession and added mining development. Tom's stop-work injunction was meant to bind up mining activities so that very little work could be done until the claim title could be determined.

The US District Court at Seattle, Washington, was called upon to determine ownership of the properties in contention. The suit was brought by the Tom Johnson/Shafer Gold and Silver Mining Company against William Donahue, William Bash, his brother Henry Bash, and Joseph L. and Edward Warner. At this point, the Bash brothers and Warner brothers were involved on Donahue's behalf with a partnership buy-in. This was at a time when the Culver Mining Company was mining a 9 to 15-foot-wide ledge of ore containing gold-binding sulfides that ran $20 to $100 per ton.

Previous to their Blewett mining involvement, the Bash brothers of Port Townsend, Washington, sold their former mining interests in Okanogan County and brought their mining experience and money to Blewett. They invested the vast majority of money needed to bring the Culver property up to date and ordered new machinery. Should things go south, they would take the biggest financial loss. The Culver Mining Company associates combined $50,000, erected an extensive reduction plant, and extended the road to the Culver mine.

Tom Johnson alleged that the defendants trespassed onto the Culver claim property in March 1887 and took possession. Joseph Warner, with the firm of Warner Brothers of Seattle, stated that they bought the claim for which they were bringing suit to recover. A quick response from Tom Johnson, speaking for his Shafer Gold and Silver Mining Company, said he filed a *lis pendens* in the auditor's office at Ellensburg in order to protect unknowing investors interested in throwing their money in with the defendants at the Donahue Camp. (*Lis pendens* is a warning that there is a pending lawsuit against the title to the property in question.)

Tom Johnson's court case against William Donahue was dismissed due to procedural irregularities. This mistake compounded Johnson's Donahue-initiated misery.

TOM JOHNSON'S RETURN TO CULVER GULCH

Tom re-issued a warning statement about another impending lawsuit involving Shafer Gold and Silver Mining Company's Culver claim and continued to defend his belief that the Culver mine property was still his.

It didn't take Johnson long to saddle up and head for the town of Blewett when he heard that 10 wagons, loaded with stamp-mill parts and other mining machinery, was on its way to Donahue at the Warner brothers and Bash brothers' Culver Mining Company.

September 1891 marked a point where Donahue was directing a road-repair crew. They were getting the Blewett mine-to-market road into top shape all the way to Blewett Pass. This alerted Tom, and he decided to do more than depend on his past failed threats and pending court action. Johnson prepared to serve an injunction on the Culver Mining Company the moment they removed any ore from the Culver property during an impending filing for another work stoppage.

Donahue, not one to put up with the rattling of Tom's dull "word sword," filed a counter lawsuit against Johnson for several thousand dollars. This was an effort to regain some of the lost revenue that Tom's injunction would cause during any litigation proceedings. At this point, Johnson stepped aside and left his lawyers to carry on with the court decision.

During the distraction of the court proceedings, there were no reports of any of Tom's underground mining activities. It is known he was active processing Blewett-area mined ore at his six-stamp mill on a percentage bases. Tom's net gain from the contract milling reflected low returns for the heavy loads that were sent to the Tacoma smelter. The diminishing returns were due to transportation and penalty costs for difficulty in smelting complex sulfide ore that had to have expensive fluxing solutions.

JOHN A. JOHNSON (?-1891)

Note: John A. Johnson and John C. Johnson were both living in the Blewett area at this time. The two Johns will be delineated by their middle initials.

On the morning of St. Patrick's Day in 1891, Tom Johnson's younger brother, John A. Johnson, was found hanging at the end of a rope attached to a rafter in Nes Jensen's barn. The coroner was called upon to go through with the investigation. A minimum of effort was involved to close the case due to what was disclosed of the deceased. The cause of death was apparent, so the coroner called off the suicide inquest. The body was brought to the Cle Elum Cemetery for burial.

The incidentals leading up to John A. Johnson's death began in June of 1890. As the story goes, the 27-year-old Swede was in company with Bert Redman. Bert was a known ruffian, as opposed to locally well-known and likeable John. The setting was at a place named Green River Hot Springs, operating in southeast King County, Washington. Bert brutally murdered a man identified as Engineer Clark, and John A. was arrested as an accomplice. John A. turned state's evidence as the prosecutor's witness. Bert got sent to the penitentiary for 20 years, while John A. went free. John A.'s mind was tormented by the death of Clark, and he couldn't live with the guilt of being present at the snuffing out of Engineer Clark. Plus, John A.'s life had been threatened several times by Bert's friends because he had testified against Bert.

John A. was staying at the Nes Jensen farm as Jensen's farmhand on that fatal day. Jensen's family was aware that John A. got up at six in the morning and went out to the barn. When John A. was called for breakfast, he didn't respond. After a few more shouts to him, one of the family members went out to fetch John A. and discovered his hanged body.

WILLIAM DONAHUE (1851-1896)

William Donahue was twenty-something years old when he came to the Blewett/Culver Gulch area about 1880. His wife's name was Mary. According to known mineral claim records, she and William were active in some claims' sales and exchanges. When William was shot and killed in 1896, she remained in the Blewett area for several years. In 1903, Mary sold a Donahue-owned claim and then left town. From 1881 until his death in 1896, William had over 15 mineral claims that can be accounted for.

Mary Donahue died in 1928. William, Mary, and their son, William "Junior" are buried at the Holy Cross Cemetery in Ellensburg, Washington. Donahue's life is highlighted in the following pages.

TOM JOHNSON AND WILLIAM DONAHUE

WILLIAM DONAHUE'S MODUS OPERANDI, 1889

While at his early workings, Donahue seemed to be content as he worked developing one of his claims that had a shaft containing gold in a sulfide minerals deposit 3 feet wide. On May 23, 1889, it produced 16 ounces of free gold on the first ore milled. His energy was focused on his claim properties until August 1890, when William established a reputation for legally jumping claims. If a claim appeared to be inactive or had carelessly been neglected by lack of yearly assessment work or the ground was abandoned, Donahue would relocate the dig in his name.

There are two kinds of claim-jumping, legal and illegal. If the possessor-claim is not refiled by the annual due date, said claim can be jumped and relocated/recorded. On the other side is the illegal act of jumping and refiling over another miner's legally documented property. If the problem goes lawyer to lawyer in litigation, the property can be tied up for several years while the lawyers play tug of war with the facts and wallets of those involved.

Donahue would watch the claims around him for a miner's unguarded actions that would leave the claim vulnerable to a legal jump. He was mindful of avoiding a situation that included going into litigation that could lead to injunctions for a filed work stoppage. He was always looking for the easy pick, no strings attached.

WILLIAM DONAHUE TAKES A BREATHER IN SEATTLE, 1891

William's summer break went beyond the "breezing through town" kind of visit he'd planned. It started out with pleasant imbibing of adult beverages. But with William, memorable events can develop when primed with whiskey. Donahue's passion for life, when out on the town, espoused "two-fisted drinking and count the empties later" (with a two-fisted combat often being the end result).

Donahue arrived in Seattle about midnight and went to the Bijon Saloon on Commercial Street (today's First Avenue). While enjoying a self-salutatory cigar and drink, a stranger came over and invited him to buy into a draw-poker game. Oh yeah, cards! This night must have been arranged in debauchery paradise. How could he say no to several entertaining hands of cards to top off his grand entry into town?

A not-so-entertaining short time later, Donahue was down $65, about the same time that he detected one of the poker players, John Boyle, cheating by holding out cards. Pointing out the matter in no uncertain terms, William pulled his pistol and demanded his money back. The other three men at the table immediately pounced on Donahue, and in the engaged grabbing-biting-kicking battle, Donahue discharged his weapon twice, maybe thrice. Either way, it wasn't nice, as outcomes go.

Principal combatant Boyle stopped one of the bullets with his leg, but that hindered not the other three men who were beating the snot out of the floored remains of the increasingly less capable Donahue. Further monetary and physical hurt was being dealt to William by way of a pistol-whipping with his own gun, and the pickpocketing of his remaining $32, just as the police burst through the door to rescue his face from looking like raw hamburger.

Donahue and the three men were arrested, but John Boyle escaped the wound-inducing scrimmage and arresting situation. To top off the night's entertainment, William was billed $250 for his bail-bond and charged with deadly assault. He announced plans to prosecute his three assailants. He was talked into reconsidering, and no further news appeared on the topic.

It may seem strange that Donahue, a man possessing the knowledge of the world, would allow himself to fall in with such folks. But some friends of William knew he could lack common courtesies when under the influence of several spirited libations.

WILLIAM DONAHUE CELEBRATES—AGAIN!

Early in November 1891, William went searching for peace of mind on a winter break. The scene of Donahue's R & R was at Ben Richardson's residence in the mining camp, the site for the future town of Blewett (Ben had the Richardson claim somewhere near the Culver claim workings). Also in attendance was rancher Nels Peterson and miner J. D. Lindsey. The evening revolved around a poker game that involved food, whiskey, more whiskey, a little chit-chat, and later on, some meaningful combat including none other than Donahue. William's battle choice for the night was a short-lived fist fight with his friend Nels Peterson. Nels raised cows and bulls, but he wouldn't put up with any bull$*!! from Donahue. And so it went with William:

Bullish Will gave Nels his fill of BS words, plus more.
Nels's response was to pounce, knocking William to the floor.
It got rough and tumble as they tripped and stumbled out through the cabin's portal.
With slipping feet on the rain-wet street, the battle got near mortal.
Using Bill as a boat in a puddle-like moat, Nels christened him "*USS Admiral Bradley.*"
Then Ben interceded, and it really was needed for William was beaten up badly.
Beyond all the pondering and the moist floundering, Bill felt that he'd won the bout.
Said he, "No count to 10? I consider I win. After all, I'm still not knocked out."

While the court outcome regarding mining property challenges at Culver Gulch was on the back burner, William Donahue and a crew of 22 men were widening and improving the mine-to-market road for the transportation of the original Culver Mining Company's new 10-stamp milling equipment. In addition to the Donahue crew, all the miners in the Peshastin and Swauk Mining Districts agreed to contribute one week of labor, provisions, and necessary tools toward opening up the road on both sides of the Blewett Pass divide. This was to the advantage of both mining communities. Donahue was leading the construction on the Peshastin Creek side of the summit, down the road grade as far as Culver Gulch. His crews received wages from the Blewett area mining companies. The 10-stamp milling equipment shipped from the state of Colorado was at the train depot in Ellensburg waiting for the completion of the road, which was finally accomplished in mid-August 1892.

TOM JOHNSON SHOOTS AND KILLS WILLIAM DONAHUE, 1896

In 1896, after more lawsuits of various types against each other, Tom Johnson's bad feelings toward William Donahue ended in a fatal eruption of Johnson's unleashed anger upon Donahue.

Johnson and William, previous to their falling out as friends and compatible associates, had been mining partners. Johnson fully owned and controlled the mill and use of the Culver mine cable tramway built to the company stamp mill. Even after William jumped and took possession of the Culver claim, they were still bound by partnership in other mineral properties. Donahue's separately mined ore was still being run through Johnson's mill up to 1896 and under Johnson's control.

During the 1896 mining season Johnson gave orders that Donahue was not to enter Johnson's milling building as long as both their sacked ore concentrates were together inside. Donahue, on the other hand, was heard to say, "Hell or high water, I'm going to get my ore and haul it to the railroad station in Ellensburg." Donahue waited impatiently for the snow to melt off the road. With acute instinct for self-preservation and knowledge that he was going against Johnson's warning, Donahue strapped on his equalizing six-shooter. Donahue harnessed his team of four horses to a wagon on June 5, 1896. Then he drove to the mill and loaded up what he considered his ore concentrates.

Note: From here on through the account of the shooting, there will be a mix of how the story was reported in the newspaper and the differing and varied testimony at the court trial. Just as in any crime scene, witnesses' perceptions differ as to what they say they saw.

According to the newspaper account, as Donahue drove the loaded wagon along the roadside on the west bank of Peshastin Creek and crossed east over the Black Jack mine bridge, caution was abated by the onslaught of hunger pangs and accompanying growling stomach. What occurred next determined William Donahue's expiration date. As he crossed onto the main road, headed south toward Blewett Pass, Bill gave in to his gastronomic needs. He pulled up to O. B. Castle's hotel-saloon. Donahue secured his team and wagon to a hitching post and headed inside.

When the meal was done, 'twas time to run. But his team was toting a heavy wagon and could only plod along the uphill road. Time was on Johnson's side as Donahue started the slow climb up the road.

Heavy brush separated and hid the mill road across Peshastin Creek where Johnson was skulking on foot with a pistol in his belt and his rifle in hand, intercepting William's course of travel. Johnson stopped behind a tree and waited for Donahue to expose himself on open ground about 50 feet from Johnson (another person gauged the distance as 100 feet).

The story of the shooting differs again at this point. The testimonies in court generally state that Johnson shot Donahue with his pistol; although the pre-trial newspaper account said Johnson used his rifle. This is just one example of how news reporters took, and still do take, liberties as to how they interpret events to make them appear more interesting to read or interject their opinion. Perhaps due to vague memory or their illegible handwritten notes, they could get "grayzoned" with the facts. Donahue's horse team, at this point (according to court documents), had to stop and yield the right-of-way to another wagon hauling lumber. This was when Tom took the opportunity to put Donahue in his gun sight and fire three times.

The sequence of the bullet strikes is not known, but according to the newspaper report, Donahue was hit above the knee and another below, plus a fatal shot through the chest. His side arm was drawn when he rolled off the wagon and hit the ground mortally wounded.

Johnson's gunfire alerted the townsfolk of the deadly assault. Immediately after the lethal event, Johnson rode hard for Ellensburg and gave himself up to the sheriff. It was generally known among the Blewett residence about the ill feelings the two men held against each other. To add to the rumor factor, Donahue and Johnson each had his own friends and sympathizers.

Johnson's murder trial was held in Ellensburg. Judge James G. Boyle set a bond against Tom Johnson for the sum of $7,500 until he appeared before the superior court. He attained a struggling young attorney from Ellensburg to defend him through an offer that included half of Johnson's Culver Gulch gold claims. The lawyer accepted.

At the trial verdict sequester, a juror got sick (trial documents say that the replacement juror voted "not guilty." This forced a second trial that had to be put off for a few months. Witnesses for the defense were placed under a bond of $100 each; witnesses for the prosecution were bonded for $250 each (the news source gave no details for this decision).

John and Charley Anderson and Erick Albertson, witnesses for the prosecution, had to be boarded at Sheriff Stinson's hotel until their bonds were paid. The case finally resumed on March 3, 1897. There were about 50 witnesses examined during the trial. At the end of it, all but one of the jury returned a verdict of guilty in the first degree, so the lone dissenter allowed Tom Johnson to go free. The young attorney actually got Johnson out of a sure-fire necktie party. Johnson sold all his Culver Gulch claims for $33,000 and promptly gave half to the young lawyer.

Before Tom Johnson allegedly killed William Donahue, Johnson had a 10-stamp mill ready to go and a new heavy-duty ore scale on hand to weigh the custom ore he intended to buy and process. There were 50 tons of ore waiting to be processed at the time of the shooting that would have been run as soon as the new owners took the mill over. It was sold when Tom dissolved all of his Blewett holdings.

There were a lot of William Donahue's friends in Blewett, including his younger brother Charles, a potential for bad things to happen to Tom Johnson. Tom took the hint and his money and passion for mining over to the Swauk Mining District.

TOM JOHNSON'S SWAUK MINING DISTRICT EXPERIENCE, 1897

After Tom was cleared of the shooting death of William Donahue, he invested his money in a mine whose owner had also killed his former mining partner, in a drunken brawl. It was no surprise that the two alleged killers didn't trust each other. Each accused the other of high-grading gold from their mutual digs when one or the other man wasn't watching. After a steady run of fights and arguments over the issue, Tom's new partner settled the dilemma by bouncing a shovel off Tom's head. Tom got out of the mining partnership with the equally aggressive, hot-head mining partner.

Then before the year passed, after Tom's top-knot was scuffed up by the shovel, the other alleged killer in the dissolved Swauk mining partnership was found dangling from the end of a rope. Was self-help or outside help responsible for such an ending? We don't know; there were no follow-up details to the story.

CHARLES DONAHUE COMMITS SUICIDE, 1897

Within a year of the William Donahue murder trial, local obituaries heralded the death of his younger brother, Charles. He was a Blewett bachelor miner, born one year after William. Charles also liked his drinking sprees. After one lasting several days in August, he was under a major, mental depression.

On the morning of his gloomy mood, he put a revolver to his head and pulled the trigger. He was found lying in bed with his feet swung off to the side.

Another miner, named Joe Massey (brother of L. C. Massey, the general manager of the Warrior General Mining Company), was boarding with Charles and found him dead in their cabin. Charles left a letter indicating that certain folks owed him money and the IOUs should be used to pay for his burial. Coroner Edwards went to Blewett and held an inquest. The body was delivered by Joe Massey, Pete Anderson, and Mike McCarthy to Ellensburg for burial. Other Blewett miners in the group were Johnny Anderson, Albert Anderson, H. Desmond, John Aldee, and 61-year-old John Black. Shortly after the death of Charles Donahue, the Culver mine claim was sold for $50,000.

In November 1897, the five-stamp mill on the Donahue property was sold to Swain and Haight. They owned the Maud-O claim up in the northern slope, off Camp Creek in the Cle Elum Mining District.

ELEANOR MINING COMPANY, 1901

A recording was filed by Tom Johnson on October 21, 1901, as the Eleanor Mining Company (on the Pole Pick No.1 claim). This listing is the first indication that Johnson was back in Culver Gulch, or for that matter, that there was an Eleanor Mining Company active in Culver Gulch. Tom sold the Pole Pick No. 1 property to Chicago businessmen who obtained a patent on the claim in 1904. It was signed by President Theodore Roosevelt. The Eleanor Mining Company drove two southward-trending crosscuts to access the vein on the Pole Pick No. 1 property.

At this point, one tunnel (the Eleanor adit) was 200 feet long and had a raise run on the vein for 147 feet. At the 100-foot level of the raise was a westward drift 100 feet long. From this drift, there is a raise to the surface. A large amount of ore was stoped out of the 1- to 4-foot-wide vein that was mainly hard, milky-white quartz enclosed in serpentine. The gold-bearing rock was run through the Blewett Mining and Milling Company stamp mill. The ore assayed from $10 to $132 per ton in free gold.

TOM JOHNSON'S DEMISE, 1908

Johnson walked a rocky road through life, testing various professions. But by the spring of 1908, he met his final showdown. At this point, Swauk mine owner/businessman Frank Bryant's list of interesting careers included timber cruiser, game warden, and from time to time, prospector/miner and mine owner.

By following the storied details, it would appear Tom was still a candidate for anger management. Johnson was in his later years when Bryant entered Johnson's Cle Elum office at 6 A.M. with information that disputed a business account crafted between the two men. At the apex of the argument, Tom ordered Frank out of his office. To add emphasis to the command, Tom came at Frank with a riot club. Frank, being younger and a little quicker on his feet, maneuvered into the position of claiming the weapon under his own tight grip. The result was a lump on Tom's head, quite the opposite of the intent of the original possessor. Tom moved into Plan B, and in his club-emptied hand appeared … a .44-caliber pistol.

Frank made his countermove, gaining possession of the gun, in addition to the club, much to the dismay of twice out-maneuvered old Tom. But Frank was through with the fancy stuff, and he simply stepped back away from Tom and shot him in the side. The path of its trajectory after entering Tom's side went through the stomach, took a tour of the intestines, and made Tom's liver quiver before exiting above his right hip. Tom died within a few hours.

JOHN A. SHOUDY (DECEMBER 1841-MAY 1910)

John Shoudy and his wife, Mary Ellen, came to Kittitas Valley in 1871. He bought A. J. Splawn's Robbers Roost trading post. He established a new town called Ellensburg in this area and named it for his wife.

Shoudy first appeared in mining records at the Blewett area in May 1877, along with Harbin Cooper. The two men had a quartz claim (name

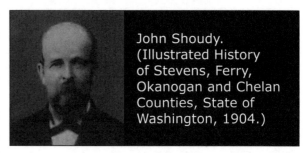

John Shoudy. (Illustrated History of Stevens, Ferry, Okanogan and Chelan Counties, State of Washington, 1904.)

not available) immediately north of where the historic stamp mill remains are located today (present-day names are used here for easy site reference). Shoudy had a long and successful career in the Blewett Mining District. His accomplishments will be presented throughout this book.

FRANCIS MARION STREAMER

Francis Streamer's occupations included preacher, justice of the peace, and historian. Although not known to have ever even prospected, he was a friend amongst the Blewett miners. In 1877, he passed through the mining district. He was alone and traversing his chosen stomping grounds, known as Washington Territory. This was the land he trekked to and through into the 1890s. Streamer was a welcomed guest of Blewett miners, such as John Ernest and James Lockwood at Ernest's cabin in the Culver Camp. Streamer was "just passin' through" in 1877 and a guest in the presence of his friends Jacob (Jake) Brusha, John Shafer, and Sylvester Culver. Streamer mentioned that the "old-time miners" were peculiar yet hospitable (that remark, in comparison to Streamer's eccentric personality and lifestyle, could be considered a compliment).

Francis noted there were three arrastras actively grinding gold from various quartz claims. One was showing better gold production than the other two. He made a tour of the early-known ore ledges in the gulch noting the various mineralized areas and what he thought was the geological activity that created them. Streamer made no mention of the mill robbery and death at the Johnson's mill.

MARSHALL BLINN

Some of the pre-turn-of-the-century gold- and silver-mine investors became interested in the mining industry after gaining success in other businesses, or they came from an old-money family base seeking to become self-made men. Others made their fortune by the old hands-on method.

Marshall Blinn's life indicates he wished to follow that self-made path. Hard-working, thrifty Blinn left Dresden, Maine, in 1827. He and his wife, Julie, headed for the Pacific Northwest. They made it to Hood Canal in Washington State. At the future site of Seabeck, Blinn established a lumber mill. After accumulating a fortune in the timber and ice business, Blinn looked for other ways to invest his money.

In 1876, he was made aware of the silver mines being opened by Okanogan Smith in the mining town of Nighthawk, Washington. Blinn invested in several mining partnerships with Okanogan Smith and others when silver ore was being discovered in profitable deposits and supported by inflated government silver purchases. This small, elite group of men was known as the Silver Kings. Blinn sold his mining interests and left the Okanogan area shortly after he heard that his mineral land investments were going to be part of the Moses Indian reservation. He decided to heed the announcement of new gold discoveries in Culver Gulch. From this point onward, Blinn's focus was on those much more accessible mineral deposits.

G. W. PARISH AND THOMAS PARISH

G. W. Parish was listed among the early (1874) miners who recorded mineral claims in Thompson (Culver) Gulch. The mining activities of G. W. and his son, Thomas, in the Blewett area are noted at other points in this book.

PARISH ORE-SHOOT

Thomas Parish (former King County assessor) is noted for the first time in 1900 when he took a lease on the Peshastin claim tunnel. He ran the adit an additional 85 feet and struck a massive ore deposit that developed into the Parish ore-shoot. It produced 2,000 tons of free-milling gold ore. The gold-bearing ore averaged $13 per ton, with assays as high as $10,000 per ton. His lease on the Key Note claim proved unsuccessful. The several-hundred-foot-long tunnel never produced any millable quantities of mineralized rock. During the year, Parish organized the La Rica Mining Company and quickly sold it.

In 1901, Thomas leased the Black Jack claim. His mining results were not noted. Four years later in 1905, he was placed in charge the La Rica Badger State properties. By the end of the year, he was noted as vice-president of the Washington Meteor Mining Company. The next year, Thomas organized the Alta Vista Mining Company. By 1907, Thomas was the company president, and his son Albert was the treasurer of Alta Vista. That same year, Thomas merged the Alta Vista Mining Company with the Washington Meteor Mining Company.

From 1907 until 1910, Thomas and Albert Parish faded from any reports involving Blewett mining activities. Thomas appeared at Blewett in 1910 when Charles Weaver is recorded thanking Thomas, John Olden, and John McCarthy for their assistance in locating and examining the old Blewett mine properties. Thomas Parish did not return on the Blewett scene after 1910.

MOSES BOLLMAN

Moses Bollman came from Ohio and started his early years mining in northern California, Montana, and Idaho. Having worked in several mining camps in the Northwest, Bollman chose to spend the remainder of his days in Chelan County, content with his mining activities in the Peshastin/Blewett mining camps.

Bollman started his 40-year Washington State residency in Yakima County as sheriff. His area of occupation was later apportioned off of Yakima County and became Kittitas County. During that time, Moses was 6 feet tall and weighed over 200 pounds, prime sheriff material. He scuffed up against the toughest types of frontiersmen and survived to prove he was worthy of the many accolades he received in his life.

He was well-to-do in his early days in the Blewett area and generous to the unfortunate folks needing a hand in rising up from their financial difficulties. He was an intelligent, self-made man and was always linked to soil and rock in one way or another. He gained much of what he possessed through the labor of his hands.

Bollman was 46 years old when he entered Blewett area as a miner/mine owner in 1880 and prospected various digs. He gave up mining for a while and took on the job of building a much-needed road to accommodate the various mine-related activities. As it turned out, Bollman was very good at road building. By 1882, he was back mining, and vice-president of the Tip Top mine, located on the west slope of Windmill Ridge.

During his involvements in Blewett area mining, he and his family lived in the town of Peshastin for a time. Later, miners took room and board at the Bollman's Blewett residence during his active participation in the Tip Top mine.

Information connected Bollman with small groups of Chinese, placer mining on Peshastin Creek. Bollman was on friendly terms with the Celestials, who were seen visiting the Bollman residence.

Other than in earlier placer mining up Negro Creek, the Chinese appear in no reference other than Peshastin Creek near Culver Gulch. Chinese placer miners were known to travel from the Swauk area placers northward over the divide and down Peshastin Creek on their way to richer placer digs. So it appears that they may have lingered along Peshastin Creek to test its potential for gold. Although, the reference could be about the time Moses and his kin were living in the town of Peshastin. At that time, the Chinese were known to be placer mining at the confluence of Peshastin Creek and Wenatchee River, on the Wenatchee River, and Columbia River. This would more correctly fit the facts about known Chinese placer mining on Peshastin Creek.

The last noteworthy piece of news regarding 74-year-old Moses Bollman and the removal of rock and dirt was his burial, July 11, 1908.

THADDEUS NEUBAUER AND ANTON NEUBAUER

Thaddeus Neubauer was born in Germany about 1858. He emigrated from Germany to the United States in 1882. There were many miners working mineral claims in the Peshastin Mining District upon Thaddeus's arrival into Blewett. Thaddeus had a long and productive gold mining career in the mining district. His accomplishments and mining activities are noted throughout this book.

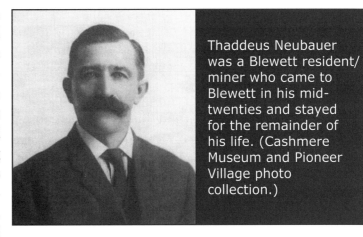

Thaddeus Neubauer was a Blewett resident/miner who came to Blewett in his mid-twenties and stayed for the remainder of his life. (Cashmere Museum and Pioneer Village photo collection.)

The Neubauer cabin was noted for its display of stuffed birds, antlers, big pictures, stuffed squirrels, and a big stuffed fish over the top of a door.

Anton Neubauer was born March 7, 1878, and was 26 years old and illiterate when he migrated from Germany and arrived at Blewett in 1904. He was 20 years younger than his uncle Thaddeus. Thanks to Blewett miner/mine owner Cliff Davenport, Anton was taught how to read and write.

Blewett resident/ miner Anton Neubauer, as a young man, stands cross-legged at the far right of the group of folks pictured on the porch of the Blewett hotel. (Photo courtesy of the Davenport and Barthol families, who were former Blewett residents.)

They became great friends and worked the mines together in the Peshastin (Blewett) Mining District for many years. Anton changed his surname after he arrived in the States. He exchanged his multi-syllable Polish name, Madibloski, to his uncle Thaddeus's surname, thereafter referred to as Anton Neubauer. After being a long-time resident/ miner in the Blewett Mining District, he died in 1965 at the age of 87.

Anton Neubauer was a Blewett resident/ miner who came to Blewett in his mid-twenties and stayed for the remainder of his life. (Cashmere Museum and Pioneer Village photo collection.)

ORIN B. CASTLE

Orin B. Castle was born in Illinois and went to California with his parents as part of one of the earlier Great Plains, frontier-crossing wagon trains. He grew up in Amador County. Orin held various jobs on his way to the Northwest.

Orin first started prospecting at the Swauk Mining District with mining partner J. F. Lyons. After several years in the Swauk area, he entered the town of Blewett in 1885, at 43 years of age. He lived there until he died 12 years later.

According to Orin's recorded mineral claims, he started mining in the leased fraction claim noted as the Blewett Tunnel, which was on the Culver claim. In 1896, he had the Lee and O. B. placer claims. During the same year, Orin acquired John McCarthy's old house and turned it into the Castle Hotel with an attending saloon.

ORIN B. CASTLE TAKES A FATAL TUMBLE, 1897

In the first week of August 1897, 55-year-old Orin Castle died in Ellensburg, Washington, shortly after being hauled to the town doctor. The cause of his fatal injuries was due to his wagon tipping over on a narrow mountain-pass road while heading for Blewett. Castle had various gold-producing mining claims in the Blewett area, plus hotels and saloons to his credit in his busy and prosperous Blewett lifestyle.

His common-law-wife, Ellen, and 10-year-old daughter Mandy were in California visiting relatives when the accident occurred. Mr. and Mrs. Alan McCullough, a childless couple, adopted Mandy after her father, Orin, passed on. Ellen moved to Spokane and lived with her other daughter.

JOHN FREIDERICH BURMEISTER, 1888

John Freiderich Burmeister and his wife, Anna, came to Blewett in 1888, one year after they got married. John was 33 years old, and Anna was 25.

In March 1902, miner/resident John Burmeister decided the threshold for a rite of passage had been reached by his 14-year-old son, Billy, and presented him with his first .22-caliber rifle. Billy promptly went outside, loaded the gun, and accidentally shot and slightly wounded his 17-year-old brother, Fred, "slightly" meaning he nailed him on the leg bone between the knee and ankle. Although it was an accident, shot is shot. Twenty-four hours later, a doctor arrived at Blewett to look at the wound and declared that it needed to be properly attended to in Leavenworth.

John spent the next several months working in the mines at Lake Chelan. He returned to Blewett in September 1905, only to vacate Blewett once more in October for a mining job in the extreme northeast corner of Chelan County's isolated back county at the Horseshoe Basin mines.

On his not-too-hasty second return following the "rite of passage" event, John worked for several weeks in the town of Peshastin before settling down for the winter in the town of Blewett. At this point, John's settling is relative to the hearth-and-home situation.

John and Anna lived in Blewett for 37 years, and John died at age 70 in 1925. Anna Augusta Burmeister moved to Spokane to live with a daughter (name not given) after John's death. John Hansel's son George Hansel married Margaret Burmeister, John Burmeister's other daughter.

John Burmeister was a prolific mine owner and miner. His top gold producers were the Black Jack, Golden Eagle, and IXL, followed by several mineral claims that equated to making a living but were not classified as rich producers of gold.

KING FAMILY

As a family unit, Edward King and his family first lived in the Swauk Mining District and recorded mining claims there in 1891 and 1892. In 1893, they all moved north over the divide to the area surrounding the confluence of Peshastin and King Creeks. The focal point for the clan was called

King Hill, which was located on turf encompassing the confluence of King Creek with Peshastin Creek. King Hill was the hub of the King family domain. From 1890 into the 1900s, Edward, Joel, and Tracy King and other family members were mining at their various King Creek placer and hard-rock mineral claims.

The King family was well known among the mining community around Blewett. Patriarch Edward was noted as being amongst one of the first groups in the early 1860s who placer mined near the confluence of Peshastin and Ingalls Creeks.

Edward King was tending to his placer and quartz claims during the early years when present-day Tronsen Creek and Scotty Creek were referred to as the upper forks of Peshastin Creek. This is the area where Mortimer Robertson and a few of his trusted friends panned for gold during their passing-through event in 1860.

PAT KING'S WAGON ACCIDENT, 1892

Nineteen-year-old teamster Pat King was transporting a wagon load of Blewett-bound freight along Scotty Creek road during the fall of 1892. At a location about one mile west from the creek's confluence with Peshastin Creek, a problem developed with one of the wagon wheels that required some roadside maintenance. While he was under the rig fitting a spare wheel on the axle, the heavily loaded wagon slipped off its axle stand and crushed him. Pat died, pinned to the ground under the vehicle. He was buried at the scene of the accident. His lone grave can be seen to this day alongside Scotty Creek road. There is a rectangular, 3-foot-high white picket fence surrounding the grave site. A carved white placard stands at the head of the grave stating in memorial "Pat King/ Killed September 23, 1892/Gone but not forgotten."

This is Pat King's grave site, as shown in 2013. Pat died in 1892 when his wagon slipped off its jack stand while he was removing a damaged wheel. (Photo by Vic Pisoni.)

KING RELATIVES AND MARRIAGES

Joel and Edward King were brothers. Joel, the older brother, moved from Blewett to the town of Lakeside on the south shore of Lake Chelan. Blewett miner, Edward King had a wife, Lena, and their oldest son was Edwin King. Edward was killed in a tunnel on the Black Jack claim June

The group at the left; from left to right: Joe Marko, Lena Marko, Lennie Griffin, and an unknown woman. On the porch: John A. Griffin and his son Jack in the dress, young Tracy King in the doorway, and Tracy's grandfather Joel King, pre-1907. (Clint Black photo collection.)

Left to right: Lena and Joe Marko, Lennie Griffin, unknown woman and boy, and young Tracy King in the doorway. Jack Griffin wears a hat. The woman and boy on the far right were not identified. (Clint Black photo collection.)

Lennie Griffin (profiled front left) at her Blewett cabin. She is with her family and friends. Young Tracy King is shown eating on the stool at center front. Elderly Joel King is far right. (Clint Black photo collection.)

10, 1896, when a large chunk of rock fell on him. After Edward King died, Lena married miner/mine owner John Griffin.

Late in Joel's life, he returned to Blewett from Lakeside and took up residence with his daughter-in-law, and Lena-King Griffin and his granddaughter Mrs. Joseph Marko.

Edward King's mining friends Torkel Tweet and Johnny Johnson entered the King family domain and, in 1905, recorded some cinnabar-mercury claims. They were located at the head of King Creek. The Griffin, King, and Marko folks were well known in the Blewett area. The above-mentioned families were well represented among mining-related jobs and miners who recorded mineral claims in the Peshastin Mining District.

KING CREEK AREA GEOLOGY

In the hillside just downstream from the mouth of King Creek, on either side of Peshastin Creek (no details were given), there were traces of gold that have been taken from the contact between granite and serpentine.

Also at these granite-serpentine contacts are some schistose deposits of a bright-green to dark-green color. Some serpentine is black and shiny to the point of being mistaken for obsidian. Within about 4 feet of some of these contacts, serpentine was found that had heavy stains of iron oxide and contained secondary silica in the form of opalized rock with very fine crystals of pyrite disseminated into them.

SHEEP MOUNTAIN/KING FAMILY MINERAL CLAIMS

Two of the King family claims were on Sheep Mountain. One was on a seasonal stream flowing west off the mountain slope and was often dry by the end of the summer season. A 200-foot-wide, W-shaped, reddish, rust-colored mineralized zone can be seen from the upper elevations of Five Mile Road. One placer claim was on Magnet Creek, and on the north slope of Sheep Mountain were two of the family's hard-rock digs.

An overall look at the King family claim recordings and that of their mining neighbors show proof of 29 mineral claims from 1860 to 1927. They dominated the King Creek area within ½ mile of the mouth of King Creek.

GEOLOGY OF THE KING FAMILY'S SHEEP MOUNTAIN CLAIMS AREA

Fossil-leaf collecting areas can be found near the ridges of Sheep Mountain and off the north-trending road cuts on the upper elevations connected to Five Mile Road. The leaf fossil areas are in the weathered banks and shoulders of the abandoned spur roads and on the open ground of ridge slopes.

A second point of interest is the many outcroppings of conglomerate rock formations in the slopes of Sheep Mountain. The rounded, abrasion-washed stones are cemented within the area's conglomerate rock structure. They are the remnants of the ancient ocean shoreline that was once the western edge of the landmass known today as North America. The tectonic movement of continent-size plates floating on the earth's inner magmatic mass (lava) came in contact with each other in a docking position under catastrophic pressure until one plate slid over and the other under. This action happened multiple times over millions of years and created the several mountain ranges in today's geology within Washington State. In the process, the conglomerate formations on Sheep Mountain were thrust upward to the elevated position where they are now located.

Gold has been found in certain conglomerate rock formations, but not in any of the crushed and panned samples that Northwest Underground Explorations processed from the westward slopes of Sheep Mountain. But this does not suggest there isn't gold there. As expert gold miner Bill Lancaster (now passed away) stated to the author in conversation, "You might not get color in the first attempts at prospecting the area. A bunch of samples might need to be done, but sometimes, *bang*, there she is, showin' up in yer pan."

JOHN (A.K.A. JACK) W. MCCARTHY

John McCarthy was born in Shakopee, Minnesota, where he fished and swam as a boy. He remained and worked in the area until 1870. His detailed journey westward, across to Washington Territory, began as a passenger on the first railroad train into the Red River area of the Dakota District. On the journey, John became ill with typhoid fever. The train engineer was Mike Douglas. Douglas helped John beat the fever with medicine out of a bottle, which leaves the details open to speculation.

The trip progressed to John hopping on a river raft and making a landing in Fort Gary, Canada. After a year at Fort Gary, his next move was to return on a new riverboat plying the Red River course, landing John at Dakota in the Black Hills Mining District.

In 1879, John traveled down along the Little Big Horn River in Montana with three friends to see the battlefield where General Custer and his men were massacred three years before. While gold mining in the Black Hills, John gained a

Seated at right front is John McCarthy. Sitting to John's right is his friend and fellow Blewett miner, Charley Striker. The two men in the second row are unknown (1927). (Photo courtesy of the Davenport and Barthol families, who were former Blewett residents.)

contract to build one of the first stamp mills in the region. He developed his own mining claim and proved it with high-grade assays. He sold it for $19,000, which was a very large sum of money at that time.

John's itchy feet had him leaving the Black Hills and arriving at Fort Keogh, Montana. A few years later, the fort was renamed Fort Miles in honor of General Nelson A. Miles. During John's stay at the fort, he was employed as a stagecoach driver between there and Bozeman, Montana. Butt-pounding on a hard bench seat couldn't hold John's imagination from following another Wild West image he wanted to pursue—buffalo hunting. Yep, John tried Buffalo Bill's profession. After a short run of de-crittering the wide-open spaces, it was time to move on. McCarthy recalled seeing (and evidently smelling) 2,000 hot, sweltering, odiferous buffalo hides stacked by a riverboat landing, ready for transportation downstream.

The newly finished end-of-the-railroad-line train terminal at Missoula, Montana, was omen enough for McCarthy to follow his ever-expanding vision to move farther west. He joined a party of folks headed for Seattle, Washington. When the group reached Ellensburg, Washington, John stayed and was employed to help build the first railroad roundhouse for the Northern Pacific Railway. He remained to build other Northern Pacific structures. John learned fast and did well, to the point where he went into his own business of buying buildings, building houses and offices, and making plans for building a lumber mill.

Unfortunately, on the Fourth of July 1889, Ellensburg caught fire, and his completed and partially built structures were destroyed. John stayed on after the fire to help rebuild the burned-out Northern Pacific Railway properties. During that time, John got married, but his wife died in 1890 while he was in the middle of his rebuilding work. In 1892, John and a man named Berg were in the blacksmith and buggy/wagon-building business at Ellensburg. McCarthy bought Berg's half of the company.

When the Peshastin Creek/Culver Gulch gold mining excitement of the 1890s became widely known, John responded to the call of the gold field with several visits down Peshastin Creek to Blewett. John decided in favor of heading north over Blewett Pass for a more permanent stay at the town of Blewett. There were saloons and several cabins on one side of Peshastin Creek and a hotel, several more saloons, and six cabins on the other side of the creek. John was soon employed by John Thompson to help work on Thompson's five-stamp mill.

In 1892, John was mining partner with Horace C. Henry (Horace later built the Henry Building in Seattle). They had a claim at the Summit Pockets area at the top of Culver Gulch that produced some very high-grade gold ore.

John McCarthy was among the earliest miners and a mainstay throughout the profitable and lean mining years in the Peshastin Mining District. His patience and steady efforts at seeking gold and other minerals paid off in the many personal mining successes in and around Culver Gulch. John was a typical image of a professional miner. As to his personal appearance, he was lean, had red hair, and jauntily perched his cap on the side of his head supporting a miner's lamp.

MIKE MCCARTHY COMMITS SUICIDE, 1898

Well-known Blewett miner/resident Mike McCarthy (38-year-old brother of John McCarthy) committed suicide on a Sunday morning in June 1898. The means was self-inflicted razor cuts. On that fatal day, Mike ate breakfast, went to the barn behind his brother's house, and slashed himself on a failed first attempt to end his life. At about that same moment, his sister-in-law surprised Mike when she came out to the barn. Mike jumped out a window and slashed at his throat again as he hurried away from the building toward Peshastin Creek. By then he was a dead man walking. About halfway between the barn and the creek, he thrust the blade a third time across his jugular vein and also severed the wind pipe. He crumpled to the ground before he could reach the water. His brother Henry and a few of Mike's friends took his body to undertakers Latimer & Scott in the town of Cle Elum. Mike was later buried at the Cle Elum Odd Fellows Cemetery. The talk around Blewett was that Mike's death was a result of unresolved personal problems and not related to heavy drinking, although it was said drinking the hard stuff was one of his passions.

CLIFF DAVENPORT (EARLY 1900s)

Cliff Davenport established an important and lasting presence in Blewett as a miner/mine owner. He was also the master of several other occupations that added greatly to the advancement of living conditions and mining activities during the Davenport family residency at Blewett. (Refer to the last chapter of the book, "Clifford Pennington Davenport Family Story.")

Cliff Davenport (Early 1900s) in his signature pose, and obviously not dressed for work. (Photo courtesy of the Davenport and Barthol families, who were former Blewett residents.)

One of the earlier water flumes that served the 20-stamp mill is under construction. In view is a surface tram that made transfer of supplies up the steep slope a much less labor intensive work environment. (Photo courtesy of the Davenport and Barthol families, who were former Blewett residents,)

Chapter Eight:
Early Culver Gulch Mines

CULVER MINE

1874

John Shafer was the first miner in Thompson (Culver) Gulch with the recording of his Culver claim in 1874. The Culver, at the beginning, was also referred to by local miners as the Shafer mine while John was present in the gulch and then for a time after, until about 1880. Understanding this helps clarify what could be confusing when reading Culver-Shafer related information. In 1880, Marshall Blinn officially recorded a Shafer claim, far separated from the Culver-Shafer

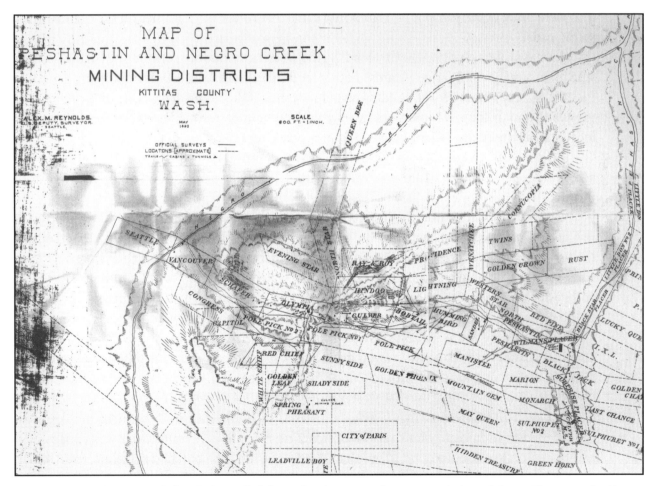

This is an early map of the Culver Gulch and other, nearby area mining claims. It presents the claim locations and names as they were arranged at that time. (Map by Alex M. Reynolds, US Deputy Surveyor, Seattle, Washington [1893]. Wesley C. Engstrom collection.)

area. It was on the south slope of the Negro Creek drainage. From this point onward, "Culver" correctly took prominence over the Shafer reference to the claim site, which was just one of the digs owned by the Shafer Gold and Silver Mining Company. During the 1880s until the early 1890s, the original Culver 10-stamp mill, south of Culver Springs Creek, was processing ore mined from the Culver claim.

1891

Holding true to earlier statements in January 1891, Henry Bash of the Culver Mining Company announced that teamster Bob Thomas arrived at the Warner Mining Camp with a four-horse team hauling a big load of machinery for the Culver mine's new cable tram system. At this time, the original Culver 10-stamp mill (located south of Culver Springs Creek) was running its own cable tram system. Information stating a tram crossed over gulches (rather than down Culver Gulch) indicates the mill processing the Culver mined ore was the original Culver mine stamp mill located about 150 feet south of Culver Springs Creek and within 50 feet of Peshastin Creek's west bank. This is the site where Northwest Underground Explorations member Terry Carlson discovered one of the 150-pound stamp mill cams that rotated to hammer on the ore-crushing stamp rods.

Thomas also transported the first load of gold-bearing sulfide ore concentrates to the Tacoma smelter for treatment. Warner promised other loads of sulfides to follow. The company had a two months' supply of lumber for building structures and all the necessary wood cut for scheduled tunneling and drifting. It came from Edward and William Blewett's Blewett Saw Mill Company, located near the confluence of Peshastin and Scotty Creeks.

The physical advantage of tram systems was its uninhibited route over deep gulches and across ridges. The ridges had tram stations with cable pulleys positioned on opposite ends of the cross-timbers, on which the bucket-carrying cables passed along.

Northwest Underground Explorations came upon a series of these collapsed tram stations in Culver Gulch. Our discovery of them indicated several different tram routes had, in the past, traversed down from the different mine-claim tunnel portals to some of the various historic stamp-mill sites and arrastra sites based along the waterpower sources of Culver Springs Creek and Peshastin Creek. Culver Springs Creek has a flow of water emanating from the porous rock in the ridge area forming a year-round feeder stream that flows eastward into Peshastin Creek.

One tram line route that Northwest Underground Explorations surveyed via hand-held compass ran above the North Star claim in a northwest-southeast direction to the original Culver mine 10-stamp mill located south of Culver Springs Creek. On one high-ridged rock outcrop, there was a notch cut out of the east-west trending ridge rock above the North Star mine between Culver Gulch and Culver Springs Creek. This was to accommodate the lengthy tram cable span as it dipped to its lowest point over the obstructing ridge line. A tram tower was constructed and bolted on a rock outcropping, less than 100 feet beyond the notched ridgeline, from which the cable continued down toward the original Culver 10-stamp mill.

By October 1891, the Warner brothers and Bash brothers were the controlling factors of the Culver Mining Company and showed their unfailing belief in the value of their Culver mine property with an estimated $50,000 in improvements. They had accumulated an impressive supply of ready-to-mill, gold-bearing sulfides.

Part of the new expenditures were invested in a system to reduce the sulfides at a cost of $3 per ton. It released the gold in sufficient concentration for the smelter to process. Every ton of high-grade ore from the mineral deposits in the Culver mine tunnels produced about 333 pounds of sulfides that needed a chemical process to free the gold from the rock. The gold value reduced from the sulfides into concentrates averaged $120 per ton. The quartz rock containing free-milling gold (gold needing only to be crushed free of its host rock and collected) netted a profit of $5 to $15 per ton.

A wagon road serving the mines was opened from Culver Gulch up to the divide (Blewett Pass) at the headwaters for both the Peshastin Creek side and Swauk Mining District. From the Swauk side, good road conditions continued through to the towns of Cle Elum and Ellensburg.

If all preparations went according to plan, the coming gold producing years in the Peshastin Mining District would reach bonanza proportions, according to the mining experts and mine-company stock promoters.

One of the Bash brothers was busy with a crew of 16 men. They worked three weeks repairing the winter-gripped road on the upper portion of the Swauk side of the Swauk-Peshastin divide and down to the Culver Gulch terminus. He had eight four-horse teams loaded with hay, which was used as part of the process to repair the damaged road. Some of the worst road conditions they encountered were at places that had 8-foot snowdrifts. The work crew was boarded at the ranch of prominent businessman and mining property investor August Sasse. His residence was located at the northern portion of the Swauk Mining District, south of the Blewett Pass divide.

At one of the bad spots in the road, "Jawbreaker" Eisendaker's horse took a tumble down a gulch. It was imbedded in a 20-foot snowdrift but was dug out by the road crew and suffered no ill effects.

One of the goals that the Culver Mining Company accomplished was to keep the roads open all winter so several horse teams could ship mined ore and return with supplies for the Blewett area camps. During the summer, the plan was to keep at least 20 of the horse-teamed wagons available, and busy, for hauling loads both ways. In 1891, there were 32 mineral claims recorded in the Blewett and Negro Creek area by a list of recognizable area miners.

Sad news was announced in December 1891; Mrs. Joseph Warner passed away while in residence and working for the Culver Mining Company. She was several months pregnant when she came from Seattle, Washington, to be with her husband. She died shortly after childbirth. Joseph was part owner and superintendent of the Culver mine at that time. This had a deep emotional effect on him.

1892

Joseph Warner was managing the Culver Mining Company in February 1892. Following the installation of a new tram cable, he had 10 stamps of the newly erected 20-stamp mill working steadily. It was crushing 20 tons of ore per day, with 10 more stamps soon to be installed and activated. The mill was run by shifts working around the clock.

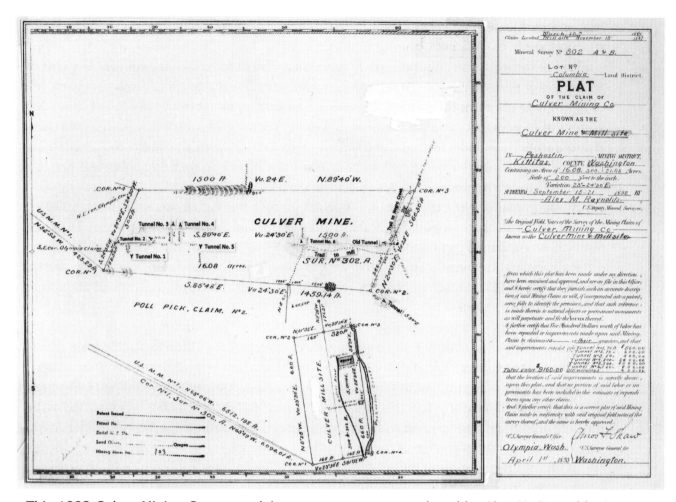

This 1892 Culver Mining Company claim survey map was produced by Alex M. Reynolds. It shows the tunnel sites and trail system as it then existed.

Man-handled sacks full of ore were hung on hooks attached to the tram cable. This system was used for a short time until the self-dumping tram buckets arrived and were installed. The cost of the old animal pack-train service was about three dollars per ton. The ore-bucket tram would transport the ore at 25 cents per ton. The other, lesser gold-producing mines in Culver Gulch were still using the ore-packing Cayuse trail system. Another advantage of the returning hooks, and later the ore buckets, was to use the returning containers for hauling mine timbers and other needed supplies up the gulch to the mine. The deep snow made the trails to the waiting shipments of ore inaccessible, but not so with the new, year-round, airborne tram system.

The "first in the state" bucket tram system had the unique status, at the time, as the longest free-spanning cable in the world, a distance of 2,197 feet from the Culver mine tram station at the mine and downslope to the first ridge. The following suspension of cable to the next tram station was 1,750 feet in length. The height of the ore buckets above the surface of the ground at times reached 500 feet.

Up until the Culver Mining Company initiated its bold tramline plan, the average span of ore-bucket cable from tram station to tram station was from 150 feet to 300 feet long. The weight of the new cable tram alone was about 6 tons. Then add from 4 to 5 tons of ore in transit, and it seems amazing from a layman's point of view that a system sustaining that much weight didn't collapse.

Within the same month, ore loaded on three wagons with four-horse teams each left the Culver mill. They hauled the sulfide-gold concentrates to Cle Elum for shipment by railroad to the Tacoma smelter. A gold production news-leak by Culver Mining Company part-owner Henry Bash gave forth a statement that he had also taken a 23-pound shipment of gold dust (gold was valued at $18.96 per ounce) from the Culver mill destined for Seattle, Washington. He boasted that there would be more like it before the summer was past. When it comes to gold, such statements are not something you air out so that outlaws in the area, who are waiting for a slip-of-the-tongue moment, can use the information according to their profession.

RICH GOLD STRIKE, 1892

In early April 1892, William Bash, Culver Mining Company superintendent, expressed in glowing terms the results of another high-grade gold strike. The very rich main ledge was averaging from $40 to $75 in gold per ton. The ore deposit the miners exposed was a pocket within the vein that was said to have produced large chunks of gold-studded quartz rock that were mucked out in pieces as large as a water bucket. Visible seams of gold the thickness of a lead pencil and large specks of gold were found throughout other portions of the quartz. The total production at the time of the report was 3,200 pounds of the high-grade rock.

With this report of the new gold discoveries in Culver Gulch, it didn't take long for moneyed mining men and investors to investigate what the Peshastin Mining District had to offer. Three men from Ellensburg, Washington, responded to the inspiring call. One of the men counted in the Ellensburg group was John G. Miller. He was a well-known and established businessman, based in the Wenatchee community. He was involved for several years in the pursuit of gold-bearing quartz properties in the Peshastin area. Back in August, John recorded three claims in the Culver Gulch/Warner Mining Camp area. A reference to a "Miller Ledge" said it was 20 to 25 feet wide where it outcropped at the surface, and it was a free-gold quartz proposition. Mining expert W. Frisbee, an experienced worker of quartz from the state of California, and Henry Weinman were his mining partners. The partnership report stated that they would finance and build an up-to-date mill that would add greatly to the daily ore tonnage processed—if the weather remained mild. In the meantime, the mining partners talked of making plans to build a 2,000-foot surface ore tramway down to the proposed mill. This indicated the loftiness of the claim site. Talk about the surface tramway was just that because nothing more has been found in any follow-up mining references about completion of the project.

FINANCIAL WOES

The Culver mine stamp mill was operating at full capacity that spring of 1892. They were processing recently found high-grade ore, but something was not right with the company's finances. By all appearances, the company should have been prospering, but they were short of cash and unable to meet the Culver Mining Company employees' $1,500 payroll. Some of the miners went on strike, refusing to continue working until paid the money due them. Four of those miners were identified as brothers Lee Seaton and George Seaton, John C. Doyle, and Charles Wright.

William Donahue (who earlier jumped Tom Johnson's Culver claim and, at this point, had control of mining its ore) noted that the company statistics and other profit-margin-related record books showed the company made a profit of about $3,000 on May 24, 1892. When Donahue asked for his cut as allowed by the contract that he and Bash entered into on January 15, 1891, his money was held back. And by the end of June, there was a company debt of $25,000 to $30,000 (no information was issued about the circumstances related to these suspicious activities).

Donahue accused the Bash-Warner consignors of unskilled and incompetent management. He also told the group he thought there was evidence indicating a large quantity of ore was sneakily shipped out. These actions, if true, prevented Donahue from determining the remainder of the company's value. Being a creditor to the company, he requested that a receiver be appointed to straighten out the financial mess that mysteriously emerged from what seemed to be a profitable operation.

Donahue tried to sue the Culver Mining Company for the money due him. Henry Bash counter-sued Donahue for part of the investment he made in the mining venture. Bash justified his dissatisfaction on the slow rate of incoming net profits.

The Culver Mining Company was forced to comply by the agreement (it would later be deemed non-binding) to the demands of those folks owed their pay. So the company promised to hold the readied gold bullion shipment at the mill until the employees got paid. The Culver Company managed to lull the anxious employees into a false sense of trust, and when the moment was right, the Bash and Warner group sent mine superintendent P. A. Deeny on a stealth mission to deliver the gold to Seattle.   Somehow the scheme was found out, and two miners caught-up with Deeny who was about to board the westbound train out of Teanaway Junction, which was located about 5 miles southeast of the town of Cle Elum. The ensuing confrontation ended with the two miners waving the train on to Seattle (minus Deeny), even though Deeny was in a superior defensive stance, pointing his pistol at them. After words were exchanged, it seems Deeny applied common sense to the situation because he and the gold returned to the mining camp in company with the miners. Meanwhile, whatever deceitful plans that were made in the back room of the Culver Mining Company office never got fixed.

CULVER MINE SOLD TO FOUR MINING COMPANY INVESTORS

Brothers William and Joseph Warner, J. M. Williams, and Horace C. Henry bought the Culver Mining Company lock, stock, and barrel. This amounted to paying off any litigation hanging over the property, paying the miners' overdue paychecks, settling other IOUs, et cetera. These settlements gained them a quit-claim title to the whole outfit for $50,000.

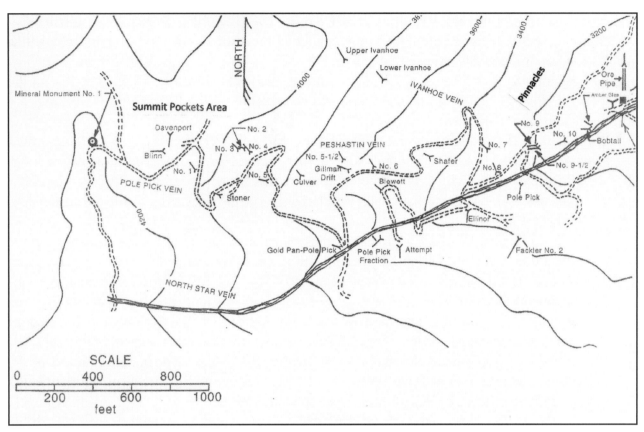

This map shows the Summit Pockets area in the upper elevations of Culver Gulch. Other gulch claims shown are positioned eastward and downslope as far as the Bob Tail digs. The Pinnacles rock formation is located northwest of the Bob Tail. Note: Bob Tail is shown as Bobtail on modern-day maps. (Map by Don Booth and Associates, Leavenworth, Washington [October 10, 1983].)

SUMMIT POCKETS AREA

The oldest and richest workings were discovered near the top of the ridge at the head of Culver Gulch. They are generally called the Summit Pockets. This area has no official mine-workings map that shows early Summit Pocket sites. The Blinn dig, Davenport Tunnel, and Tunnel No. 1 through Tunnel No. 4 were developed within the Summit Pockets system and heavily mined in the 1870s.

The gold-enriched rock was formed due to downward leaching from ancient gold-bearing ore-shoots, contained within lofty mountain ridges that have eroded away since their original formation. The Summit Pockets area is presently exposed at the ridge top.

The various underground workings of the early Summit Pockets ore deposits were developed and simply named Tunnel No. 1 through Tunnel No.4 on the west side of the massive basaltic dike formation. The dike intrusion ended the underground workings that originated on the east side of the basaltic dike, which is the Culver Gulch side. Other miners followed and recorded nearby mineral claims after Marshall Blinn picked up on the displaced veins east of the dike.

As the development in the Summit Pockets area continued, it was announced that the Tunnel No. 1 reached the 80-foot point, and Tunnel No. 2 was in 300 feet, with a 150-foot raise connecting the two adit levels. The raise followed a 3- to 4-foot-wide gold-bearing ledge that averaged $15 in gold per ton. It was estimated that there was 2,000 tons of ore in sight, which was worth about $30,000.

Tunnel Nos. 5, 5½, 6, 6½, 7, 8, 9, 9½, and 10 descend east of the basaltic outcrop on the slope, down the gulch numerically, and will be explained later as these tunnel workings are encountered in the text.

During the 1880s, the owners of the Shafer Gold and Silver Mining Company (who owned some of the ground on which Tunnel No. 1 through Tunnel No. 6 are located) ran a drift workings that traced the Peshastin ledge to the point where they became separated into several stringer veins. This is where the ancient basaltic dike has displaced the mineral leads into the ore deposits as they lie today.

In 1892, miner John McCarthy and Seattle businessman Horace C. Henry partnered to mine at the Summit Pockets area at the head of Culver Gulch. McCarthy was operating the mining end of the deal. An undocumented report states that they took $500,000 in gold from those digs. This statement cannot be verified. Perhaps the sum given was for the total gold mined from the Summit Pockets area. They may have done very well in their gold recovery, but the true amount is not known and questionable when considering the numbers that the report indicated. But, Henry doesn't show in any Blewett information after 1892, so when he did make his big profit, he knew when to "fold 'em" and left for Seattle. The Henry Building in downtown Seattle was financed with Horace C. Henry's money in September 1909.

Cliff Davenport managed a crew of miners who ran a tunnel on a white-quartz vein in the Summit Pockets area in 1931. He was contracted by the Gold Bond Mining Company. The effort struck gold-bearing white quartz. The Tacoma smelter paid a return of $35 to the ton. The old caved workings remained named the Davenport Tunnel on updated reference maps of the Summit Pockets area. Davenport remembered his conversations with the old-time Blewett miners. They recalled the early days when there were several hundred pounds of gold-infused, high-grade ore from the Summit Pockets that assayed at $65,000 per ton.

Karl Fackler was running a bulldozer through his leased ground on the ridge of the Summit Pockets area in 1940. He uncovered a shallow surface blanket lead that was 4 to 6 feet wide. The high-grade, gold-bearing white-quartz that he uncovered gained him a $3,000 paycheck from the Tacoma smelter.

BLINN PROPERTY, 1880

In 1878, a continuation of the gold-bearing ledge on the Culver Gulch side was traced to where it continued on the opposite side of the intruding diabase dike in Culver Gulch. It was exposed in the upper elevation mine workings of Culver Gulch. The diabase dike blocked and divided the east-west ore-veins system. The system was relocated on the west side of the ridge top and followed down the south slope drainage leading to Negro Creek.

Louis Queitsch, a predominant gold mining figure from the Swauk Mining District, was the original locator of the massive 6- to 7-foot-wide white-quartz outcrop on the Vancouver claim. It was exposed a few feet above the flood-level of Negro Creek. Louis discovered it before 1879, although John Ernest had possession of the Vancouver claim before Blinn took ownership.

Marshall Blinn made his first entry into the Peshastin area in 1880 to make test assays of the mineralized ore rock in the Culver Gulch area. He was in company with Professor Tuck and a group of men with practical mining experience.

In April 1880, the Blinn party went prospecting over the top of Culver Gulch ridge, west of the diabase dikes. Blinn followed a continuation of the vein passing through the Culver claim on the west side of the dike. The vein headed northwest, down the Negro Creek drainage to Negro Creek. Washington Territorial Auditor Tom Reed went with Blinn to his site of interest in August. After further review of the mineralized ground, Blinn made a commitment to buy and record the claims he observed. The first claims he recorded were the Shafer (the first official recording of a claim named "Shafer"), Olympic, Pole Pick No. 3, Seattle, and Vancouver. The claims extended from the head of Culver Gulch, downslope from US Mineral Monument No. 1 and across Negro Creek. The Vancouver claim, up until that time, had the largest exposed, white-quartz vein deposit in the state.

An early type of this Joshua Hendy two-stamp mill would have been the setup to accompany the Huntington mill during the beginning stages of Blinn's mining development on the Vancouver claim. (Cashmere Museum and Pioneer Village.)

During 1880, Blinn had a two-stamp mill and a Huntington mill shipped from The Dalles, Oregon, and up the Columbia River by riverboat. The mill was then transported overland to where it was assembled 2 miles up Negro Creek on the Vancouver claim. The function of the water-powered stamp mill was to process free gold from the quartz, but the mill was not equipped with concentrating tables.

Blinn's two-stamp mill and the Huntington mill reduced 50 tons of ore over a two-month period in 1880 and were shut down. The ore was assayed at $10 to $70 per ton in gold (at $18.94 an ounce), but only $4.50 in gold per ton in fine gold could be saved due to the high sulfide content. A small percentage of copper was also lost.

L. A. Wheeler was managing the property in 1882. Wheeler tried to improve gold recovery from the ore but gave up after a year. John Ernest relocated the Vancouver claim on September

6, 1883. After Ernest quit the Vancouver claim, Blinn sold the five-claim group to the Cascade Mining Company, which had them patented. Cascade Mining Company ran the mill in an effort to make it pay, but they also abandoned the effort within two years. No further reports indicate that the Blinn mill was restarted by anybody after Cascade Mining Company shut it down. Shortly after the sale to the Cascade Mining Company, Marshall Blinn and his family moved to Portland, Oregon, where he passed away in 1885.

The group of five claims was bonded from the Cascade Mining Company to Edward Blewett in 1889. Blewett ran a 200-foot crosscut tunnel on the Olympic claim in an attempt to cut the vein in the Culver ledge; plus he ran a number of open cuts that showed free gold in the rock. After Edward's interest in the properties faded, the group of claims went back to the Cascade Mining Company.

By 1910, the workings on the old Blinn claims consisted of a long tunnel, driven southeastward from the south bank of Negro Creek on the Vancouver claim, and other tunnels distributed among the five claims for a total of about 1,000 feet. The direction of the veins is a western continuation of the Peshastin vein, which runs within these five properties. The drift tunnel on Blinn's Shafer claim, located on the Negro Creek drainage, was an effort to trace the ledge into the Peshastin vein. The ledge, in turn, separated into several veins that are part of the Summit Pockets system near Mineral Monument No. 1.

SHAFER GOLD AND SILVER MINING COMPANY

Ira Canaday bought the Culver claim from original owner John Shafer and recorded it May 20, 1880. He then sold it to James Lockwood and Harbin M. Cooper in June 1880. During this transfer of ownership, the Culver mine was commonly called the Culver-Shafer mine by the local Blewettites.

Early reports about the Culver mining tunnel were included in the Shafer Gold and Silver Mining Company group of claims, up to the point when William Donahue jumped the Culver claim and muddled up the question of the property ownership.

Wagons would pull up to the mill's ore-storage building to load the sacked ore for shipment to the Tacoma smelter. But the yearly problem following each winter was the disruption of wagon travel to the "outside" until road damage could be repaired.

Before the heavy snowstorms hit in October, new Shafer Gold and Silver Mining Company owners James Lockwood and Harbin M. Cooper were doing quite well. The company mines reported a production of over 8 tons of gold ore and processed it with the arrastra that was bought along with the claims. It netted them $630 when gold was about $18 per ounce. They stayed late in the season, operating the water-powered arrastra until the water froze.

It was at this point that there were an accumulation of seven claims representing the company and a name change to Shafer Gold and Silver Mining Company of Nevada. They were the Culver mine, which included the Shafer Tunnel, the Little Culver, the Hummingbird, the Pole Pick; the Bob Tail (Wye Tunnel), the Fraction claim, and the Sandel (at this point, Elmer Sandel was gone from Culver Gulch).

Three of the main veins in the gulch run through the various Lockwood-Cooper claims. The veins run between walls of serpentine and porphyry rock. The vein in the Culver claim workings widened from 2 to 10 feet as the tunnels progressed. At one point, the vein swelled to 16 feet in width. The ledge that the ore was mined from was reddish-gray quartz with occasional zones of transparent light-green talc, which was infused with white crystals throughout its structure. In this type of rock, a magnifying glass would reveal plainly seen free gold in flake form.

Twenty one tons of ore were crushed in November to close out the 1880 mining season. It netted $69.77 per ton in gold, for a total sum of $1,465. This is an example of how highly profitable the early Culver Gulch gold-mining developments were.

As in almost all the areas of new mineral discoveries, the easy profits on the surface came first. The clever, business-minded, early miners knew when the gold was getting harder to find in their digs, and with gold fever in the air, it wasn't difficult to sell a diminishing-profits claim to some eagerly waiting newcomer. In some cases, the claim was leased with royalties payable to the owner of the property. If the leasing party found more high-grade ore, the mine owner profited well. If it went beyond what the owner thought was in the claim, he could take over the dig when the lease was up and receive full value for the remaining gold.

Beginning in May 1882, Lockwood and Cooper continued to crush ore and extracted $250 in gold amalgam from each 5 tons of rock. It appears that they were cashing in on other miners' manual labor when the two men signed a contract with Moses Bollman to crush 100 tons of Moses's high-grade ore from the Tip Top mine in their Shafer Mining Company mill.

In July, James Lockwood was seen in several of the region's towns showing high-grade samples of the quartz ledge belonging to the Shafer Gold and Silver Mining Company of Nevada. He also made arrangements to have his claims surveyed. By the end of September, Peshastin Creek was running so low that it was threatening operation of the miners' arrastras, although two mills were still working for the Culver mine, and two for the Tip Top property.

October was a month of continued mining activity for the Culver mine when John A. Johnson (Tom Johnson's brother) was contracted to continue work on the Shafer workings through the winter months. Other miners who were known to work at their mines at one time or another were Dan Shaser, Bill Elliott, Tom Flood, Jim Watson, and Harry Savage. Harry was killed by a cave-in while working in the Culver mine. A large amount of supplies was shipped to the camp for John's use. Good fortune continued for the Shafer Gold and Silver Mining Company of Nevada when an ore vein in one of the developing tunnels widened to 22½ inches and continued its high-grade content. The mine reported a production total of 109 ounces of gold for the season.

1883

By February 1883, Harbin M. Cooper was absent from any further reports concerning the Shafer mine. He left to take up residency in the town of Goldendale, Washington. Miners James Lockwood, son Elmer A. Lockwood, and Tom Johnson appeared to be the new co-owners of the Shafer Gold and Silver Mining Company of Nevada, although the locals called it the Lockwood-Johnson mine. James's brother Elmer W. Lockwood was directing the winter tunneling on the original ore deposit of the Shafer ledge. The workings reached the 200-foot point, and the depth under the slope was at 50 feet. It was the richest mine workings in the whole camp that winter, with a large stack of ore ready for processing. The progress the miners made on the vein indicated there would be increased production during the year.

In May, the Shafer Tunnel (on the Culver claim) reached a depth of 375 feet. The workings was said to pierce through one high-grade ore deposit 100-feet long and one 30 feet in length without knowing, at this time, to what extent the ore would continue above and below the adit level.

The mining camp at the base of the gulch had a boarding house, which was little more than a large cabin in size, and other businesses that were very basic at meeting the needs of the miners.

By early June 1883, James Lockwood's son Elmer A. was the Shafer Gold and Silver Mining Company of Nevada president. An experienced old Comstock miner and mill man from the state of Nevada named Charles Whitman became supervisor. Lockwood's new mining company partner, Tom Johnson, personally bought the Pole Pick mine, which was originally worked by Ezra Brusha for several years. Before Johnson purchased the Pole Pick, Brusha had left the claim idle for a time before selling it to John G. Miller and David Freer, who sold the Pole Pick for an unknown price to Tom Johnson. Johnson also received Miller and Freer's three water-powered arrastras.

Soon Culver mine supervisor Charles Whitman had the three arrastras engaged in crushing gold-containing quartz along with the company's five-stamp mill. Even with all the milling equipment going wide open, there was a need for more of the same to keep up with the demand to process full ore bins. Then mid-summer, low water levels and the resulting insufficient water power diminished the milling capacity.

A 21-day run of Lockwood-Johnson/Shafer mining company ore was completed, and the result was a yield of $1,800 in free gold. The concentrator had produced 4 tons of reduced sulfides containing gold that was estimated to be worth about $300 or more per ton. Tom Johnson was ahead of the curve because he had ordered a steam-powered six-stamp mill that was just about to arrive and help solve the desperate need for more ore-milling capabilities.

The next news heralded was that Tom Johnson's new San Francisco-manufactured, steam-powered, six-stamp mill with two batteries of three stamps each was stomping away on high-grade Culver ore. The ore was from the Shafer ledge at the face of the tunnel where the vein held productively strong. There were 20 tons of rich ore on the dump that assayed at $30 to $50 per ton in gold at the market rate of $18.94 per ounce in free gold; that was independent of the gold values saved from the sulfide content of the ore.

1884

By July 1884, the Shafer Gold and Silver Mining Company of Nevada decided to lease the company claims to Howard Walters with an option to buy. The deal included use of the stamp mill, two arrastras, a boardinghouse, blacksmith shop, saw mill, and the company's trail and wagon road privileges. The agreement was terminated when Tom Johnson bought the whole outfit for himself, and James Lockwood exited from any further mining activities in the gulch.

One hundred twenty tons of rock was in ore bins down at Tom Johnson's Shafer Gold and Silver Mining Company mill, ready to be crushed. Shafer Gold and Silver properties were having another banner year, with a total of 112 ounces of free gold mined. Aside from the 4 tons of high-grade sulfide material that the concentrator saved, the concentrates contained more gold per ton than the free-gold-bearing quartz. From 1877 to June 30, 1883, the company properties yielded a total of $36,000 in gold.

BLEWETT TUNNEL

It is interesting to note that there was no Blewett claim recorded. The Blewett Tunnel is located on the Culver claim. The Shafer Tunnel is about 200 feet northeast of the Blewett Tunnel at the same elevation. The Shafer Tunnel is also on the Culver claim. Blewett Gold Mining Company was established in 1891, which could indicate the year the Blewett Tunnel began its underground development. The Blewett Tunnel was reported to have extensive underground mining development by 1893.

Northwest Underground Explorations members Todd Carlson and Jef Miller geared up in 2011 and rappelled 80 feet down a 300-foot shaft to the Blewett Tunnel level, into which the Shafer Tunnel is said to connect with the Blewett workings. They found the Blewett Tunnel and Shafer Tunnel portals caved in and blocked by several tons of rock. Farther into the workings, rock-fall debris blocked complete examination of the Blewett Tunnel.

POLE PICK CLAIM, POLE PICK NO. 1, NO. 2, AND NO. 3 CLAIMS

Even with the three different maps—1893 Reynolds map, 1910 Weaver map, and 1934 Gold Bond Mining Company map—progression of the various Pole Pick claims remains somewhat uncertain because of missing data. Assertions about claim positioning and ownership likewise rest on shaky ground.

The Pole Pick No.1 was originally recorded in 1874 as the Johnson-Davidson property by John Johnson and S. C. Davidson. A 1901 claims-survey document shows the Johnson-Davidson claim as part of the Pole Pick No.1, owned by the Eleanor Mining Company. This mining company/claim name switcheroo is another example of how Culver Gulch mining data can become confusing without documentation to help and occasionally sort out these discrepancies. For example, the earliest map (1893 Reynolds map) shows that the Pole Pick No. 2 was joined to the south claim line of the Olympic claim. On Weaver's 1910 map, the Pole Pick No. 1 claim is shown as Pole Pick No. 3. Gold Bond's 1934 map named it Pole Pick Extension No. 2.

Further information about the development and production of the Pole Pick claims will be explained in this book in historic progression with verbatim data where available.

GOLDEN PHOENIX (NORTH STAR)

It is important at this time to interject the activities of William Donahue. Donahue recorded the Golden Phoenix claim October 1, 1882 (later it became the North Star). Donahue and family members D. T. Cross and John F. Dore ran their first crosscut tunnel on the Golden Phoenix (North Star) for 125 feet into a 5-foot-wide, brown-oxidized quartz vein. Then they ran three adits 100 feet long at different elevations in the direction of Culver Springs Creek. One thousand tons of ore was stoped and processed at the Blewett mill. It returned $20 in gold per ton.

J. E. Reynolds and his mining associates were noted recording the North Star (old Golden Phoenix) claim on August 18, 1891. Reynolds was followed as owner by Peter Anderson. Patrick Henry had the North Star in 1904. John Burmeister did Henry's assessment work for him that year. During 1907-1908, John McCarthy drove two more adits on the North Star vein. In 1907, a combined total of 100 tons of North Star and Golden Eagle ore were run through the Golden Eagle mill. It yielded $5 in gold per ton.

In 1910, several assays taken from various places on the vein showed $1 to $15 in gold per ton. The Golden Eagle Mining Company owned the North Star from 1911 to 1915.

IVANHOE

John Shoudy and Howard Walters originally recorded the Ivanhoe claim on August 11, 1890. The Hindoo name replaced the Ivanhoe banner upon relocation. It was recorded March 31, 1891, by J. D. Lindsey and W. E. Miller. James Wilder preferred the name White Elephant under his ownership, and the name Hindoo was discontinued. The Ivanhoe workings and various other names are encountered later in data about this mine.

BOB TAIL (WYE TUNNEL)

1874
James Lockwood originally recorded the Bob Tail claim.

1880
The Shafer Gold and Silver Mining Company of Nevada owned the Bob Tail claim.

1882
Wilmer Cooper was the owner of the Bob Tail claim.

1894
Blewett Gold Mining Company was the owner. The company contracted the Bob Tail to lease miners who produced 300 tons of gold-bearing ore.

1897
The Warrior General Mining Company bought the Blewett Gold Mining Company. They became the new owners of the Bob Tail claim. Al Lundberg and mining associates leased the Bob Tail claim.

1903-1910
Washington Meteor Mining Company was the owner. Several individual owners have had possession of this claim since 1910, and it is presently under active ownership

This dig was run on the vein for a depth of 50 feet. The minerals assayed at $30 to $40 per ton in gold. At this time, the Bob Tail claim was the terminus for the original Culver Gulch narrow-width wagon road. The remainder of the gulch was accessed by pack trail up to Mineral Monument No. 1, located on the ridge top.

LOWER CULVER GULCH MINES

HUMMINGBIRD

1874
Samuel Culver originally recorded the Hummingbird.

1880
The Hummingbird was one of several claims owned by the Shafer Gold and Silver Mining Company of Nevada.

1882
George Henton was in possession of the Hummingbird in July 13, 1882, but by August 23, 1882, E. W. and James Lockwood were the owners.

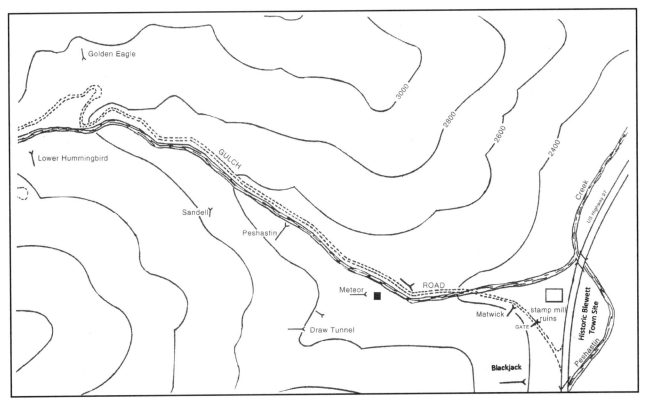

Several top-gold producing gold mines are represented on this mapped section of the lower elevation mines at Culver Gulch. (Map by Don Booth and Associates, Leavenworth, Washington [1983].)

1887
J. P. Cumminsky relocated the Hummingbird, naming it the Exchange claim.

1896
The Warrior General was in control of the Hummingbird.

1903 through 1910
Washington Meteor Mining Company held ownership of the Hummingbird.

Present
The present workings in the Hummingbird consist of a 150-foot crosscut adit to the east-west vein structure, which was 2 to 4 feet wide. There is a total of 500 feet of workings.

SANDEL

The Sandel workings are a crosscut tunnel that was driven 300 feet from the portal to intersect the Peshastin vein. From that point, series of drifts were run east and west for over 1,000 feet. As the ore bodies opened up, there were stopes developed both above and below the tunnel level. Even though the McCarthy and Parish ore-shoots were massive in size, the Sandel workings did not access them.

Searching for written details about the Sandel did not reveal much. After several explorations into the Sandel workings by Northwest Underground Explorations, it was obvious that there were far more rock and ore deposits mined than we could find data to explain.

1874
John Olden and Peter Wilder originally staked and recorded the Sandel claim.

1880
The Sandel became one of several claims owned by the Shafer Gold and Silver Mining Company of Nevada.

1896
The Warrior General Mining Company owned the Sandel.

1903
The Sandel became Washington Meteor Mining Company's property.

1910
Washington Meteor was still in possession of the Sandel.

PESHASTIN

By 1903, the focus on the Peshastin claim was mainly through the Washington Meteor Mining Company's Meteor Tunnel. But, up until the Washington Meteor Mining Company took over physically mining their company ore, there was a period of lease miner activity. Underground development went through several progressive stages under these different lease owners. The following information presents some of those known mining activities leading up to 1903. The problem herein is very few of these activities survive in accessible record form. There are dates and names missing for the discovery of some of the ore strikes, and locations are generalized.

1894 to 1903

From about 1890 to 1894, William Donahue and family members John Dore and D. T. Cross spent a few years running a crosscut to the Peshastin claim vein. Then they stoped out ore from the vein. In 1894, the three men bonded the Peshastin claim to miner George W. Martin of Minnesota. Martin also took a lease on the Blewett Gold Mining Company mill. George ran 100 tons of ore from the Peshastin claim adit portal, down a surface ore chute to the stamp mill. The ore he mined was not producing a profit, so George's lease was cancelled.

Dexter Shoudy picked up a lease after Martin's failed attempt. He continued the tunnel westward and took out about 80 tons of ore. The milled ore was valued at $21 per ton in gold. Eight tons of Shoudy's concentrates paid $100 per ton.

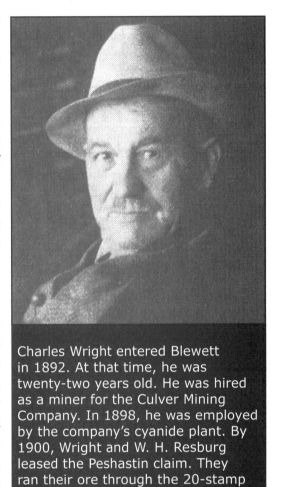

Charles Wright entered Blewett in 1892. At that time, he was twenty-two years old. He was hired as a miner for the Culver Mining Company. In 1898, he was employed by the company's cyanide plant. By 1900, Wright and W. H. Resburg leased the Peshastin claim. They ran their ore through the 20-stamp mill and cyanide plant. (Photo by the *Wenatchee World* newspaper [1950].)

1896

Mike McCarthy and Henry Rosenberg struck very high-grade ore with their lease on the Peshastin claim. The gold-bearing ore pocket filled three ore cars yielding them $5,000. Two heaping handfuls of decomposed ore paid a value of $30 in gold. Tom Johnson's newly purchased 10-stamp mill was processing the ore.

Somewhere in the mix of the leases that were contracted, John McCarthy is credited with making another very rich and large ore deposit discovery that assayed at $3,000 per ton in gold. This discovery became known as the McCarthy ore-shoot.

1898

T. John Vinton leased the Peshastin claim and was mining gold from a 5-foot-wide white-quartz vein (no other details available). For a short time, Judge James G. Boyle had a lease on the Peshastin.

1900

In January, the Peshastin claim was leased to W. H. Resburg and Charles Wright. The lease also allowed them to operate a cyanide plant to process their ore. Unofficially they called themselves "The Peshastin Mining Company" in June 1900. Within the year, these lease-miners struck their objective, a mineral lead at the end of a 200-foot crosscut tunnel at a depth of about 300 feet under the ridge slope. Free gold was plainly visible in the ore.

Thomas Parish took his turn after the Peshastin Mining Company left the scene. He ran a tunnel another 85 feet in a pre-existing working and struck very high-grade ore. This massive ore deposit developed into the Parish ore-shoot. It produced 2,000 tons of free-milling gold ore that ran $13 per ton and several tons of gold-bearing sulfide concentrates.

1903

The Washington Meteor Mining Company began developing a tunnel westward to tap the Peshastin claim ore-shoots and vein deposits at a lower level. By this point in its development, there was over 700 feet of tunnel leading to either the McCarthy or Parish ore-shoot (there was no way to identify which it was). But a few hundred feet beyond the ore-shoot in a westward trending working was one of the man-ways connecting the Peshastin claim's Meteor Tunnel with the Peshastin workings.

DRAW TUNNEL

The date on which the Draw Tunnel workings were begun is not known. It is about 120 feet above the Meteor portal and located in Draw Gulch. The purpose of this westward driven adit was to follow the ore vein and, by raises and winzes, to connect with the Washington Meteor workings and the Peshastin vein's underground development. These three levels accessed some very large and rich gold-producing ore deposits.

GOLDEN EAGLE

John Burmeister recorded the Golden Eagle claim on December 20, 1895. D. W. Locke followed by refiling and recorded the Golden Eagle on April 26, 1899. Lucy Wilder, James's wife, and D. W. Locke refiled and recorded the Golden Eagle on February 26, 1900. On April 23, 1900, James Wilder recorded the Golden Eagle as sole owner, minus D. W. Locke.

Without the full overview of the claim's records and with the disjointed mining activities reported by the local newspaper, John McCarthy was incorrectly named as discovering the Golden Eagle in 1902. McCarthy is correctly credited for the 1902 discovery of gold in the Golden Eagle upper tunnel that he developed, most likely on a lease contract. But McCarthy did not discover

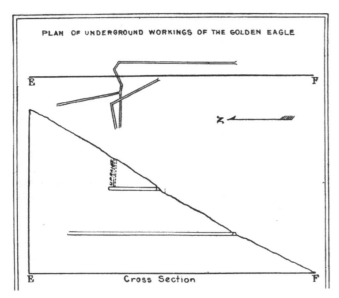

PLAN OF UNDERGROUND WORKINGS OF THE GOLDEN EAGLE

Cross Section

This diagram of the Golden Eagle mine tunnels is from Bulletin No. 6 by Charles E. Weaver [1910].)

the original lower workings. His discovery of the upper tunnel was on the same ore vein, located 200 feet directly above the original, lower adit.

John McCarthy ran the upper Golden Eagle crosscut tunnel northwest for 110 feet to the vein. It was composed of quartz, calcite, and talc that were disseminated throughout with iron pyrite. Two assays were taken across the vein near a raise. It showed $3.75 to $4.10 in gold per ton when gold was valued at $18.97 an ounce. Then a drift tunnel was run to the west on the vein for 65 feet. As the vein extended to the west, it narrowed to stringer veins. Beyond the face of the drift, the vein entered into the Hawkins breccia rock formation and continued through the ridge into the Golden Guinea claim, located on the south drainage slope of Negro Creek.

The raise in the upper Golden Eagle adit once opened at the surface on the slope. It is now filled in. The location of the raise in the upper drift tunnel to the surface is 4 feet from the intersection of the crosscut and drift. The lower crosscut tunnel runs due north for 650 feet and has short drift tunnels branching off it.

During the early years when Wilder first engaged in his Golden Eagle activities, he and his family took up residence in the town of Cashmere. James spent the milder weather days of the mining season at his White Elephant (Ivanhoe) mine and other mining digs. The 40-foot tunnel on the Kennelworth dig, located on the south slope of the Negro Creek drainage, was an attempt to cut into the vein on the Ivanhoe property.

The White Elephant was relocated by name change back to the Ivanhoe banner in 1902 for reasons known only to Wilder, possibly because he had mining partners involved to defer costs and labor that were included in the reorganization and name change. In 1907, he moved back to Blewett. At this time, documentation picks up the fact that he did have mining partners who were part of the Ivanhoe mine activities and other claims involving mining partnerships. Due to Wilder's lasting presence, folks around Blewett began referring to him as an "old-time miner."

Golden Eagle Six-Stamp Mill, 1907

M. F. Peak and son were the owners of the Golden Eagle claim at this time and are credited with erecting the Golden Eagle Mining and Milling Company six-stamp mill with amalgamating plates. The mill was run by a 25-hp Fairbanks-Morse engine. A combined total of 1,000 tons of ore were reduced by the mill from both the North Star mine and the Golden Eagle digs under the Peaks' ownership. Ore values varied from $5 to $20 in gold per ton.

In 1908, M. F. Peak and his son sold controlling interest in the Golden Eagle claim to W. W. Block, a superior court judge from Everett, Washington. John McCarthy was made general manager. The six-stamp, Golden Eagle mill was run by steam power at the time of this owner-ship change. Later it was converted to electricity.

Golden Eagle Mine and Wilder Group (Three Claims), 1910-1915
James Wilder's group of claims in 1910 was the Ivanhoe, Amber Glee, and Kennelworth. The Kennelworth had a 40-foot tunnel and was joined along the north line of the Ivanhoe. The Ivan-hoe was the most promising of the three claims. The width of the vein was 2 to 6 feet, ran east to west, and was almost at a vertical pitch/strike. The ore carried gold and silver.

An assayer named Bogardus indicated that the gold ran from a trace to $72 per ton of ore. The rich deposits were spotty. One hundred fifty tons of ore was mined. There are presently four adits on the property; one is completely caved, and its exact portal location is not known.

James Wilder family, *left to right:* sons Ray, Byron, and Roy; James and his wife, Lucile, and daughters, Mildred and Hazel. Lucile baked the wedding cake for Blewett residents Cliff and Annie Davenport. (Photo courtesy of the Davenport and Barthol families, who were former Blewett residents.)

From 1910 to 1915, there is a lack of mining information or reports of activities on these Wilder claim holdings, other than another report that stated James had a group of six claims.

Wilder's mine-related projects picked up in 1915. Twelve recorded mining claims appeared, including a relocation of the Roy and Ray and new claim additions, the Laurel, Gold Sand placer, Crystal placer, Nubia, Opal, Zara, Rowena, Maggie, and a location recorded as the Ivanhoe mill site.

Ivanhoe Stamp Mill, Today
Presently, the Ivanhoe stamp mill site down by Negro Creek is a barely recognizable patch of ground where little vegetation grows. Only ashes, a few fire-bricks, and 4-foot-long bolts exposed in heavy, rotting timbers remain at the mill site.

Members of Northwest Underground Explorations have often followed information from newspaper articles written by Kate Bailey. Kate was a childhood resident of Blewett and later became a reporter with the *Wenatchee World* newspaper. She knew many of the last remaining old-time Blewett miners. As a result of those impressive times, Kate wrote of local news and also historical reminiscences of her childhood and teenage years as a Blewett resident. She was a prolific Blewett-mining-area history advocate who helped preserve its colorful town and mine-related stories.

Thanks to Kate, Northwest Underground Explorations located James Wilder's Ivanhoe mine-ore bunker. It was moldering into the ground and barely recognizable just off the north edge of the saddle area of the ridge known by the name "Pinnacles" for the two prominent ridge-top rock outcrops separating Culver Gulch from Negro Creek. A 1-inch cable was secured to one of the pinnacle rock formations and attached to the old ore bin to help stabilize and hold the ore bin in place.

Upon further exploration, we found a half-buried, 4-foot-diameter bull wheel that was intact. It had friction brakes. A lever connected to a steel belt loop was attached to an iron cam block once used to stop the rotating wheel and movement of the two 1-inch-thick cables. They carried the ore buckets between the ore bin and stamp mill and back up to the ridge. No data was found to indicate how many stamps were used in the mill, but by the small amount of remaining mill-site evidence, it was probably no more than a four-stamp operation.

The two tram cables headed in a line-of-sight northeasterly direction from the ridge-top ore bin for about 2,000 feet in an elevation drop of 1,000 feet to the mill site. When Terry Carlson and I were on one of our NWUE bushwhacking and historic mining-site searches, we followed the cables down a brush-tangled and tree-fallen slope. While descending through the thick brush, the tram cables were discovered. They were not connected to the bull wheel at the time of the discovery. It was determined from the remains of old timber debris lying on the slope that James Wilder had used a Bleichert type of construction for the aerial tram system.

There is a multi-corner switchback trail still in evidence that travels below and along the downed cable line that terminates at the mill. We didn't see the trail on our first excursion following the cable down to the mill on Negro Creek, but we found that our route of travel passed within sight of the War Eagle claim tunnels on its way to the creek bottomland where it ended at the stamp mill.

The narrow switchback trail was found on a later trip into the Negro Creek drainage by NWUE members Todd Carlson and Jef Miller as they returned after a long day of searching for known digs located on the north slope of Negro Creek in Section 35 (T23N-R17E). The home stretch on their return was a scrambling, 1,000-foot, bushwhacking ascent straight up the south slope of Negro Creek. At that time, they cut across onto the switchback trail, established the route, and followed it up to the Ivanhoe ore-bin area at the Pinnacles area on the ridge.

The Wilder/Ivanhoe stamp mill is about 1 mile from the mouth of Negro Creek on the south side of the creek and 300 to 400 feet west of the presently unrecognizable, old Cedar Grove campsite. The mill site is 300 feet south of Negro Creek, hidden by a thick growth of underbrush.

James Wilder's tunnel-site claim, as reported in his filed claim report, is noted to be located about 500 feet south and upslope from the Ivanhoe mill.

GOLDEN EAGLE MINE/CONSOLIDATED GOLD MINES AND REFINING CO., 1912

Frank S. Ernest, son of old-time Blewett miner John Ernest (who died in 1894), and Frank's Spokane-based mining associates organized the Consolidated Gold Mines and Refining Company in 1912. Included in the deal was control of the Golden Eagle Mining and Milling Company. It was capitalized at $800,000 and sold shares for $1 each. Ernest was in possession of all but 6,000 shares of the Golden Eagle stock. Frank and his mining partners also had a five-year lease and a bond for all rights, title, and interest to the Blewett Mining and Leasing Company. The Blewett Mining and Leasing Company held a lease on the old Washington Meteor Mining Company property, and it was subleased to that company's manager, Frank Ernest.

The man standing on the beam at the top of the Golden Eagle mill picture was not identified. *Left to right:* Thaddeus Neubauer (both hands on hips), Cliff Davenport, and Walter Suckling (holding the bucket). (Photo courtesy of the Davenport and Barthol families, who were former Blewett residents.)

Frank's company did extensive development work and blocked out $200,000 worth of ore. The six stamps were still in place on the Golden Eagle digs, but because the ore was not free-milling as first supposed, cyanide tanks were installed on the Golden Eagle property. The mill capacity was 50 tons of ore per day. There were three shifts working around the clock, with eight men on each shift.

In 1917, John McCarthy and F. Leroy Thurmond took a lease contract on the Golden Eagle and five other unnamed Culver Gulch mine claims. Thurmond was designated as superintendent in the partnership. This was five years after Frank S. Ernest was owner of the Golden Eagle mill. Some of the machinery and equipment used by McCarthy and Thurmond included crushing rollers and a cyanide plant powered by a 25-hp gasoline engine. This later milling system appears to be less efficient than that of Ernest's 1912 setup because the 1917 plant processed 100 tons of ore per week. This may have been due to less ore being mined and sent to the mill. An aerial tram 1,800 feet long ran from an unnamed mining claim to the Golden Eagle mill. There were several hundred feet of workings within the leased claims. They were mining white-quartz veins

Walter Suckling, mining associate at the Golden Eagle mine, is driving a customized Culver Gulch vehicle. (Photo courtesy of the Davenport and Barthol families, who were former Blewett residents.)

enclosed in serpentine. The mill averaged $10 in gold per ton and, on occasion, reached $500 in gold profits during a month.

After a long absence of news about the Golden Eagle properties, Walter Suckling and his wife were known for their "Suckling mill" activity on the Golden Eagle mill site in the 1940s. They were also involved in other mining activities while living on the claim in the old assay office cabin. Mrs. Suckling was from England and was known to be an exquisite baker and an avid knitter of stockings. In 1947, Walter was working for Karl Fackler at the Pole Pick No. 1 claim, which was leased from Gold Bond Mining Company.

BLACK JACK

1874
The Black Jack was originally discovered and recorded by John Somers. The gap between 1874 and 1890 was not explained.

1890
John Ernest had possession of the Black Jack in August. Then the mineral claims records show John A. Shoudy relocated the claim under his name in December.

1892
The same ownership turnaround occurred again when Ernest had the Black Jack for six months, and then Shoudy took over during the winter months (again, without explanation).

1896
Dexter Shoudy assembled a crew of miners who took ore from a ledge of blue quartz that ran 2 to 5 feet wide. They tunneled 200 feet along the ledge and also did some stoping. Then they went 200 feet above the lower adit and ran a crosscut tunnel into a rock outcrop. It showed free gold in a red porphyry dike with cinnabar dispersed throughout. Two hundred sixty tons of badly sorted ore was milled in Tom Johnson's 10-stamp mill. It managed to yield $8 per ton in gold

This lowest Black Jack tunnel is located on the west bank of Peshastin Creek, a few feet above water-level. (Chris Bell photo collection.)

when gold was valued at $18.98 an ounce. During this time, while working in the Black Jack mine, Edward King was killed when a 3-foot chunk of ceiling rock fell on him. Dexter Shoudy and business partner Frank McCandless paid Mrs. Edward King $1,000 on an insurance policy held by her husband Edward.

1899

E. A. Grunden was actively mining on the Black Jack claim. He was taking high-grade ore from the Peshastin vein.

1901

A report stated that Thomas Parish had a turn owning the Black Jack. These odd changes in ownership throughout a single year had a reason; yet it was not made available to the public.

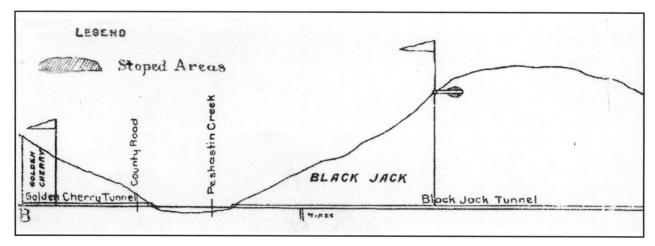

The Golden Cherry mine is on the east side of Peshastin Creek, across from the Black Jack claim. Both of their underground workings are on the Peshastin vein system. (Charles E. Weaver map, Bulletin No. 6 [1910].)

1903

The Washington Meteor Mining Company was in possession of the Black Jack claim. The company is also noted as having control of the Black Jack mill.

1907–08

The Badger State Mining Company is credited with ownership of the Black Jack mine.

1910

Washington Meteor Mining Company declared singular ownership of the Black Jack.

1918–21

John Burmeister was owner of the Black Jack and Golden Eagle mines, along with several other claims.

1921

Amalgamated Gold Mines Company, as owner, brought the Black Jack back into its full control upon striking free gold in the creek-level tunnel. The mine manager was present when the 12-inch vein was struck. The vein held strong as it was stoped. Two hundred pounds of ore averaged an assay of $400 per ton. The gold extracted from the amalgam was valued at $700, and the sulfide concentrates ran as high as $192 in gold per ton.

1927

E. L. Ballinger took a turn at working on the Black Jack under his relocated (leased?) name as the Phoenix No. 1 claim.

1931

George Watson went through the same change pattern. He changed the name of the Black Jack to the Watson No. 6.

1935

Cliff Davenport, his son Herman, Raymond Barthol, and Anton Neubauer began clearing out the caved-in portals on abandoned mine claims during the depression years. By 1939, they discovered new deposits of gold on the Black Jack claim. The owner was notified, and after an agreement was made, they all made a good chunk of money.

MINES EAST OF PESHASTIN CREEK

GOLDEN CHERRY (GOLDEN CHARIOT, EUREKA)

The main tunnel for this mine's underground development is irretrievably buried below US 97 at about the water level for Peshastin Creek.

Jacob Somers recorded the Golden Chariot in 1880. A newspaper notice was printed in 1886 regarding Somers's Golden Chariot. It was in either a lease or ownership situation with the claim name changed to Hunter. The owner or lessee was not named. Then after lapses of information and goings-on at the mine, John A. Shoudy appeared with a filed recording on the Golden Cherry mill site on June 23, 1891.

The data from this point is laced with statements of the mine's name change. This was possibly due to lease contracts to Eureka starting on October 13, 1891, at which time; John Kendle recorded the Eureka as a relocation of the Golden Chariot. Next to record the Eureka claim was Pat Hurley on June 11, 1892, followed by Mose Splawn on September 24, 1892. Louise Herman intervenes with a claim name-change recording back to the Golden Chariot claim. By 1894, owner Dexter Shoudy recorded the name back to Eureka. In 1902, Dexter was at the helm of the Phoenix Mining and Milling Company. The Eureka mine was one of the company's properties. Dexter was president and general manager, E. A. Grunden was vice-president, and John Shoudy Jr. was secretary treasurer. The company capital stock was valued at $150,000.

In May 1905, a rich, free-gold quartz vein, said to be several feet wide, was struck in a Eureka adit, but which one, upper or lower, was not identified. Gold in the ore could be seen with the naked eye. John Griffin was a company officer in 1905 and relayed the good news. The Golden Cherry (note the name change) underground workings totaled 970 feet by 1910, and assessment work done by the current owner, the Tip Top Consolidated Mining Company, was mainly done on the Golden Cherry claim.

TIP TOP, 1880-1910

Jacob Somers recorded the Tip Top mine in 1880. The ore vein was located high up the west slope of Windmill Point, above the vein structure of the Golden Chariot. It was an eastward extension of the Black Jack (Peshastin) ore vein. After Somers located the Tip Top claim, he sank a shaft on its main ledge for a distance of 75 feet, followed by two lower crosscut tunnels that struck the ore vein. One adit was 400 feet long, and the other was 80 feet in length. The sulfide ore was removed via a stope to the surface, hauled downslope by pack animals, and then run through an arrastra located on Peshastin Creek. The vein averaged about 2½ feet in width with an east-to-west strike. The rock encountered in the workings was part serpentine and part breccia related to the Hawkins Formation.

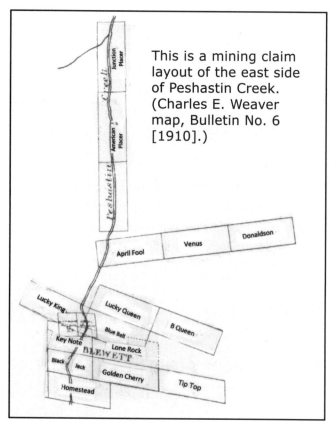

This is a mining claim layout of the east side of Peshastin Creek. (Charles E. Weaver map, Bulletin No. 6 [1910].)

Young Tracy King stands under the manmade, debris-containment roof at the opening to the upper Tip Top mine workings (Windmill Point). The heading above him, written in white, states "Taken out here $21,000." (Grace Browitt Elkins photo collection.)

A reference to an assay indicated an average of $40 per ton in gold at that time.

For T. John Vinton, miner/owner of the Tip Top mine, the dry spring-summer season of 1882 got even hotter in June, around ten in the morning. His house burned to the ground along with $500 worth of clothing, bedding, and other provisions. The flames started in the nearby camp of Tip Top miners Ed Halter and Bill Kirk. It spread over the dry ground and, in turn, ignited Vinton's building. All that was left were ashes before anybody could do anything to extinguish the flames. Ed and Bill also lost everything they had at their camp, which valued $200.

Seven men worked through the winter at the Tip Top mine. They were tunneling and sinking a shaft in order to pile high-grade ore near the mine portal. When the next season started, they would send ore-loaded pack animals down to their Peshastin Creek arrastra.

The Tip Top annual meeting was called in March 1883. Elected company officers were, John A. Shoudy as president, Moses Bollman as vice-president and superintendent, and A. Lawrence as secretary. Company directors were John A. Shoudy, Willis Thorp, Dick Price, A. Lawrence, and Moses Bollman. Stock shares were listed at one cent each.

Tip Top miners ran 102 feet of tunnel at a cost of $15 per foot. Three shifts of men developed the workings; Dick Price, William Donahue, and Bill Lodge were among the miners. A report from the *Kittitas Wau-Wau* newspaper stated that the result of that development effort paid $1,521 in five hours. Among the rich deposit were two gold nuggets worth $472. In June 1883, rich ore was struck at the bottom of the Tip Top shaft. It was a well-defined vein, 15 inches wide. The Tip Top arrastra processed the ore.

Shortly thereafter, the mine gained attention once again when it made $1,800 from a 30-day clean-up of free-gold ore during the same month.

1894

In April, William Kirk and Blewett's constable, E. M. Baldwin, leased the Tip Top claim. They ran the ore through their leased Tip Top arrastra. Vinton got $1 for every ton of ore they processed. Baldwin and Kirk were getting $20 to $40 in gold per ton of ore. Meanwhile Vinton was busy at his Vinton and Sulphuret No. 1 gold claims.

1895

In January, Tip Top owners John Shoudy and T. John Vinton mined and stockpiled very rich Tip Top ore during the winter.

By June, Tip Top ore was being run through two arrastras, operated by miners James Kirk, Edward King, and William Donahue.

1896

In January, even with heavy snow piled up on the higher elevations of the Tip Top property, the miners worked throughout the winter and stockpiled rich gold ore.

During June, Vinton was showing folks in the nearby towns his gold-bearing bromide ore that assayed $100 to $200 per ton. It was noted that there was 100 tons of ore ready for milling.

The next month, the Tip Top Mining Company ore was being treated at Tom Johnson's 10-stamp mill. The mill was busy processing 50 tons of good-paying gold ore. By December, the Tip Top mine had another 50 tons of ore on the dump.

In November, Vinton's Tip Top mine was busy milling 50 tons of good-paying ore that was stacked on his ore dump. That was the best news of the month, because right after the announcement, all the bridges on the Peshastin side of Blewett Pass were washed out by a surge of flood water.

1897

In May, the Tip Top Mining Company filed for articles of incorporation. Those involved were T. John Vinton, Charles S. Bolger, Judge James G. Boyle, and mayor of Ellensburg, Austin Mires. Trustees elected were T. John Vinton, James G. Boyle, Dr. B. S. Scott, and E. G. Fleming. Company capital stock was placed at $250,000, and shares at $1 each. About 30,000 shares of treasury stock was placed on the public market at 10 cents a share. The Tip Top mine arrastra was actively grinding out 12 tons of ore at $30 to $40 per ton in gold. They also got $314 worth of gold from crevicing the calcite/quartz stringers on the roof of the tunnel.

TIP TOP MINING AND MILLING COMPANY (FORMERLY THE TIP TOP MINING COMPANY)

1897

In November, new officers of the reorganized Tip Top Mining and Milling Company were President T. John Vinton, Vice-president E. G. Fleming, Secretary James G. Boyle, and Treasurer J. C. Hubbell. The trustees were T. John Vinton, C. H. Stewart, E. G. Fleming, C. J. Hubbell, and Judge James G. Boyle.

1898

T. John Vinton let it be known around town that the Pole Pick mine he was leasing and working had 2,000 tons of paying ore in sight. In Vinton's other leased Peshastin claim mine, he had a 5-foot-wide ledge carrying gold in the quartz. Vinton's company leased the Tip Top mine to James Kirk.

1899

In June, T. John Vinton and his business partners in the Tip Top mine had a list of winter accomplishments and development updates to publicize. The company reported, the uppermost, east-trending, Tunnel No. 1 was 141 feet in length with a stope from that level to the surface. The Tunnel No. 2 level workings were below No. 1, and a winze went from No. 1 level for 40 feet down to the Tunnel No. 3 level. At 190 feet from the portal of No. 1 was a 15-foot-deep winze area. The workings continued for 150 feet from the winze to the face of the tunnel. The workings accessed a ledge 18 inches wide that ran assays from $45 to $1,500 per ton in gold. There was water in the winze of the No. 3 level that hindered getting to the ore deposit. On the Tunnel No. 4 level, a crosscut was scheduled to run under the winze where a raise would connect to the ore and also drain the flooded winze. The raise was expanded into a stope 60 feet in length on an 18-inch vein that cut into the ore-shoot, which was between well-defined walls.

The Tip Top ledge ran east-west into the west slope of Windmill Point ridge. Vinton gave a description of the tunnel workings. No. 3 level was a crosscut 138 feet to the ledge, then 138 feet east on a stringer vein. No. 4 level was a crosscut northward for 288 feet. The length of the tunnel from where they struck the first ledge was 90 feet. Here the ledge was 3 to 4 feet wide containing sulfide ore. The distance from the first ledge to the second ledge in the tunnel was 150 feet. The ledge was 14 inches wide and carried good sulfide ore.

The Tip Top arrastra was 1,800 feet downslope on Peshastin Creek. Northwest Underground Explorations discovered and noted a very early Tip Top stamp foot-base-plate artifact for a single- or two-stamp mill near the caved portal of a long lower tunnel working. The length of time the stamp mill could have been used depended on the depth of the snowpack and how long the melting process lasted. After the run-off water stopped, the stamp mill was idle for the rest of the mining season, and the ore was packed down to the company's arrastra.

1900

In January, a vague reference, with no location provided, indicated that the Tip Top Mining and Milling Company had the use of a leased, 20-stamp mill. This description indicates they may have been leasing the Warrior General Mining Company mill—the old Blewett mill.

An obituary in November 1900, noted the death of T. John Vinton, part owner of the Tip Top Mining and Milling Company.

TIP TOP CONSOLIDATED MINING COMPANY 1904 (FORMERLY THE TIP TOP MINING AND MILLING COMPANY)

John Griffin was at Blewett as a resident mine owner. He entered into active control of the Tip Top mine. In mid-January 1905, he and Con Bell were actively developing the mine workings. At this point, Griffin had discontinued his physical involvement in any underground development due to a nagging hip infection.

In September, the Tip Top Consolidated Mining Company was newly organized. F. D. Schnebly was president, F. L. Smith was vice-president, and John Griffin was secretary/treasurer. H. W. Hale was the company lawyer (Hale was Mrs. John Griffin's brother).

1904

John Griffin passed away. The cause of his death was from the lingering illness of his hip infection.

1905

By May, John Shoudy was president and manager of the Tip Top Consolidated Mining Company. D. C. Burchum and W. T. Burchum were newly involved, heavy investors and members of the board.

TIP TOP CONSOLIDATED GOLD MINING COMPANY

1910

The company had changed its name again, and Tip Top Consolidated Gold Mining Company had possession of the Golden Cherry mine. Miners Con Bell, Joe Mead, and Bill Tuttle worked underground throughout the winter, driving a tunnel on the vein structure. Eventually, they struck ore containing gold visible to the naked eye. The workings reached 970 feet during the 1910 mining season.

LUCKY QUEEN

A copy of the official mineral claims book, page 51, in the DNR Library at Olympia, Washington, shows the Lucky Queen claim was recorded August 8, 1892, by Gus Nilson and John Ernest. And as further verification of the Lucky Queen mine referred to herein, the 1893 Reynolds mineral-claims map shows proof of the Lucky Queen's existence before 1894.

The ground on which the Lucky Queen was located (before the claim belonged to Thaddeus Neubauer as the Lucky Queen) had no previous name other than Lucky Queen that could be verified by any available data. It can even be suggested that either Ernest or Nilson could have had singular ownership of that dig before the men formed their partnership connection to the Lucky Queen. This point is presented because John Ernest and Gus Nilson had a friendship and mining connection back in 1882–83. At that time, Ernest had the Vancouver claim up Negro Creek, and Nilson had the adjoining claim to John's dig. Ernest was also in a mining partnership with Gus Nilson on the Nilson and Ernest claim, recorded April 10, 1886. It was located near the Summit Pockets mining area at the top end of Culver Gulch.

Gus "Bull" Nilson was part owner of the Lucky Queen mine. (Wesley C. Engstrom collection.)

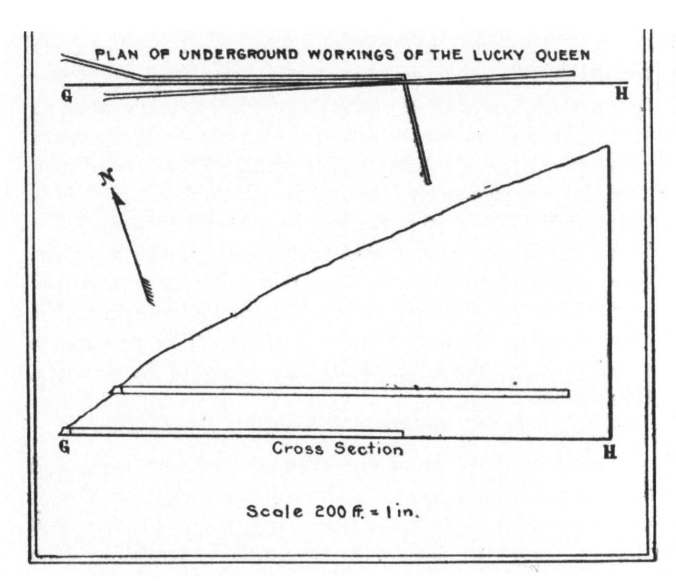

The Lucky Queen mine workings is shown in this diagram. (Charles E. Weaver, Bulletin No. 6 [1910].)

POKER GAME

Unusual circumstances revolved around a five card stud poker game. They occurred in early 1894 at a card game in which Nilson was playing with Thaddeus Neubauer and several other miners. As the popular story goes, Thaddeus Neubauer and Gus Nilson were the men holding the two remaining hands betting on the card game's impressive pot of poker chips, money, gold, or whatever the currency happened to be. Nilson was in a position to fold or come up with something to bet, thus calling on Neubauer's poker hand (at this point John Ernest's connection to the Lucky Queen mine has not been determined). Nilson bet the Lucky Queen mine, and Thaddeus Neubauer coincidentally drew the lucky queen card to fill an inside straight and win the whole deal. These are the hard facts according to record. The Lucky Queen was the Lucky Queen before Neubauer took possession of his lucky queen.

The popular, other Lucky Queen short story comes off equally entertaining but fails the facts test. This isolated version has John Ernest losing the claim to Neubauer, possibly because Ernest and Nilson were both present at the card table.

The claims records show that Neubauer had possession of the Lucky Queen mining claim from 1894 to 1897. In 1894, John Ernest got involved in the Lucky Queen ownership again through a mining partnership deal with Neubauer and Peter Anderson. John was required to do his one-third part of the yearly assessment work and was responsible for filing his own work report. No written record shows the progression of how or when John Ernest did his part of the assessment work.

Ernest died in August 1894 when he fell into the grinding pit of his arrastra and received a fatal dose of ore grinding trauma. John's untimely death left a loophole that his estate attorney/executor John Shoudy decided to use to gain possession of the Lucky Queen as property for the Ernest estate.

It is evident that there was enough of a gray legal area that the whole mess eventually went to court. Why it took four years before the case was brought to trial and judgment made was left unanswered. And during this time, why were Neubauer and Anderson allowed to continue mining the Lucky Queen if litigation was underway? Maybe they cut a deal with the Ernest estate, via Shoudy, by sharing the gold taken from the mine during the four-year period.

LITIGATION, 1898

In early April 1898, a legal battle over ownership of the Lucky Queen was brought before Superior Court Judge Davidson. The case involved Thaddeus Neubauer and Peter Anderson as plaintiffs and John A. Shoudy, defendant. Judge Graves appeared for the plaintiffs and H. J. Snively for the defendant.

Neubauer and Anderson stated that they were the rightful owners of the Lucky Queen mine along with John Ernest. Thaddeus and Peter proved that they did their proper yearly amount of required assessment work, but there was no available paperwork for John Ernest's yearly part. Therein lay the problem and the loophole that Shoudy used as the Ernest estate administrator to legally jump (by proof of non-filed assessment work) the Lucky Queen mine claim and gain possession for the Ernest estate.

John Ernest had not kept a known written record of his yearly assessment work before his death. The court then declared the Lucky Queen claim as open for relocation and recording through the Ernest estate, which was controlled by John Shoudy. The Lucky Queen ownership dilemma was settled before the end of 1898 when John Shoudy, through the Ernest estate, sold Neubauer and Anderson the Lucky Queen.

LOWER TUNNEL TRAVERSE

In 1938, geologist Ward Carithers of the Washington State Department of Geology did a traverse of the Lucky Queen that gave some insight to the tunnel's structure, mineralization,

Ward Carithers, right, with an unidentified associate. Ward was an agency field geologist for Washington State in the 1940s. (Vic Pisoni photo collection.)

and other pertinent data. At the time of the traverse, the claim was owned by old-time miner Thaddeus Neubauer.

The tunnel was driven on a shear zone in serpentine rock that averaged about 3 feet in width, with a 6-inch gouge seam on the north wall. Gold values taken over the years were from talc seams, calcite stringers, isolated pockets, and lenses in contact with the main shear zone. Samples taken by Carithers showed free gold in the talc of the gouge seam in the raise. Throughout the main tunnel were crosscut snub tunnels. The underground workings, including the raise, crosscuts, drift, and main tunnel totaled about 600 feet.

Charles E. Weaver's Bulletin No. 6 report of 1910 varies from Carithers's in that it included an upper tunnel located 40 feet higher. The 412-foot-long upper tunnel was cut on the same vein to the face of the workings. From there, a drift was run right for 120 feet. Rich pockets of free-gold ore were taken from quartz, calcite, and talc in the vein.

Thaddeus Neubaeur deeded the Lucky Queen to his nephew Anton Neubaeur in July 30, 1941.

Horse-mounted tribal folks passing through Blewett in the 1890s. (Cashmere Museum and Pioneer Village photo collection.)

Chapter Nine:
Blewett Gold Mining Company

This 1899 photo shows the flume that transferred water from Culver Springs Gulch to the Blewett Gold Mining Company's 20-stamp mill. W. C. McKean stands, holding a rifle on his shoulder. (Cashmere Museum and Pioneer Village photo collection.)

1891

A 10-stamp mill was built by the Culver Mining Company. It was located on the west side of Peshastin Creek, south from the mouth of Culver Springs Creek (see the Reynolds map). The mill had four Woodbury concentrators that helped process the ore from the upper Culver Gulch claims. The ore was brought to the mill by a cable tram.

It was sold the next year to Edward and William Blewett, owners of the Blewett Gold Mining Company. Up until this time, the Blewett brothers' occupation in the Blewett area was the ownership and operation of a lumber mill at an area near the confluence of Peshastin and Scotty Creeks.

1892

The Blewett Gold Mining Company built a new 40-stamp-capacity mill and installed only 20 units in the mill building. It was located at the foot of Culver Gulch in the vicinity of today's old historic mill remnants (remains of the historic mill on site now [2013] is not the original Blewett brothers' stamp mill). Destruction, by fire, of one 20-stamp mill, and removal and replacement of the final, historic 20-stamp mill as it is located today, will be explained later in the book.

Later, the 10-stamp mill on Peshastin Creek south of Culver Springs Creek was sold to Thomas Johnson. His newly purchased mill treated ore from the Pole Pick, Peshastin, Black Jack, Tip Top, and ore from mines located on the ridge between Culver Gulch and Culver Springs Creek.

Records show 160 men doing various jobs in their assigned capacities for the Blewett Gold Mining Company and their saw mill. This count may include a combined total of mine owners William and Henry Bash and Blewett brothers' employees. On the dumps of the tunnels that were being worked, there was a total of 2,000 tons of ore. When their mill began operating after a slight delay, there would be 50 men needed to mine and to run the milling system.

But an undisclosed, shared ownership agreement between the Bash and Blewett brothers was not working out for the Blewett brothers. Edward and William had to sue the Bash boys for $40,000 to recover their loan investment.

It was also noted that the Blewett Gold Mining Company and associated, private investors paid out a total of $200,000 in the Blewett Camp, which included their store and saw mill. At that time, J. M. Williamson was secretary, and H. J. Evens was noted as supply buyer for the company.

It's not hard to imagine that the economic depression had something to do with what was transpiring. Plus, court litigation was ongoing with the powers-that-be from the Culver Mining

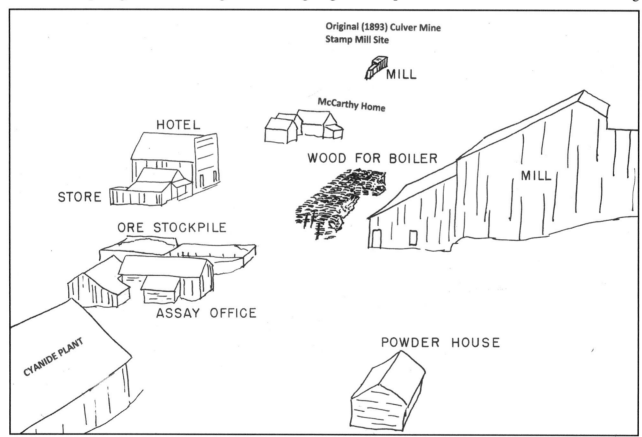

Kate Bailey sketched this remembrance from her days as a youngster at Blewett. Some of the unnamed buildings were identified by Blewett childhood resident Phyllis Barthol-Cramer. Phyllis also gave the location of the schoolhouse. It is out of sight to the right (west) of the McCarthy home. The author provided the location of the original (1890s) Culver mine stamp mill building site in the far background. (Cashmere Museum and Pioneer Village photo collection.)

Town view of Blewett (about 1900). (From Silver Occurrences of Washington by Wayne S. Moen, Bulletin No. 68, Washington Dept. of Natural Resources [1976].)

Company. This was the precursor of the Culver Gold Mining Company, which included some of the same individuals that were tied in with the court-litigated Culver Mining Company. Surprising is the fact that somebody in the courtroom didn't shout, "Get a rope." All the men in the partnership had outside business interests to deal with, and who knows what kind of financial beating they were taking in relation to those capitol ventures.

With the Blewett Gold Mining Company now in complete control of their assets, it was capitalized at $3,000,000 and issued 300,000 shares at $10 per share. The mill was ready to operate with its 20-stamp capacity. An ore concentrating plant was built that did away with having to haul unreduced ore to the Tacoma smelter. The new company officers stated their intention to add another 10-stamp unit to increase the milling capacity to 30 stamps. Additional expenditures to develop the tunnel workings and machinery were $10,000 to $15,000. It was felt that these completed and paid additions would make the mining camp attractive to potential purchasers of Culver Mining Company stock, The persuasion factor involved here was that the mining business-wise investors, seeing those projects already built and paid for, would be confident that their mining company shares would go into producing gold and would not be invested in getting to the point of milling immediate dividends. They saw their place in the timing of things as on the profit end of the Culver Mining Company schedule.

The Blewett Gold Mining Company was also in the process of having another stamp mill erected on Negro Creek. It was on or near the old original Vancouver claim stamp mill, a claim they recently picked up from the Cascade Mining Company. (In 2010, the author was on a hike along Negro Creek with Dan Carlson. At that time, Dan found evidence of the mills' past existence on the high-bank area of the south side of Negro Creek.)

The Blewett brothers may have realized they were monetarily overly involved and were trying to reel in some of their invested money. At about this same time, Edward Blewett was vice-president for the Wilman, Pearsall, and Blake Companies related to the mining activities in the Monte Cristo Mining District.

The Blewett Mining campsite had five stores, three restaurants, two boarding houses, a number of small open-air eateries, and several residential structures.

1893

The boasted total of 50 stamps operating, which included the collective stamp mills in the Blewett area by March, and many men mining wasn't working out for the Blewett area stamp mills. The extended freeze and late accumulations of snow put a damper on stamp-mill activities. Only 10 stamps of the 20-stamp battery were crushing ore at the Blewett mill. The idle 40 stamps among the other stamp mills in the camp were projected to start as soon as the machinery was in working condition.

By July, the Blewett stamp mill had crews working three eight-hour shifts a day with $300 to $400 in mineral values out of every 40 tons of rock processed. There were 62 men employed by the Blewett Gold Mining Company, with a monthly payroll of $6,400 per month.

In the month of September 1893, it was noted that the Blewett Gold Mining Company quartz mill was the only one in Kittitas and Chelan counties that was in operation. And the last correspondence of the year (December) noted that the Blewett Gold Mining Company stamp mill was still pounding away on free-gold quartz, and 60 men were on the payroll.

Blewett mining camp became the legally established town of Blewett, Washington.

1894

The Blewett stamp mill was silent for three months, and the economy of the town was negatively impacted due the fact that the $6,400 in payroll was no longer feeding the local area coffers.

In May, William Donahue leased the Blewett Gold Mining Company 20-stamp mill for 30 days to process free-milling, high-grade gold ore from his Culver claim.

Resident/miner Peter Kuchen was given a contract during the mining season to build the ore-bucket tramway from the upper workings belonging to the Blewett Gold Mining Company down a different route to the company's new mill. After completion, the first run lasted eight days and transported 545 tram buckets of ore. The previous tram line was said to be a failure. Kuchen had lumber delivered by the Blewett Saw Mill Company that amounted to 90,000 board feet. This lumber was used at the Blewett Gold Mining Company stamp mill.

Later, George Martin took a lease on the Blewett Gold Mining Company stamp mill. He ran 100 tons of ore from his leased Peshastin claim, down a surface ore chute to the mill. The ore was too low in value to be cost effective, so George's lease was cancelled.

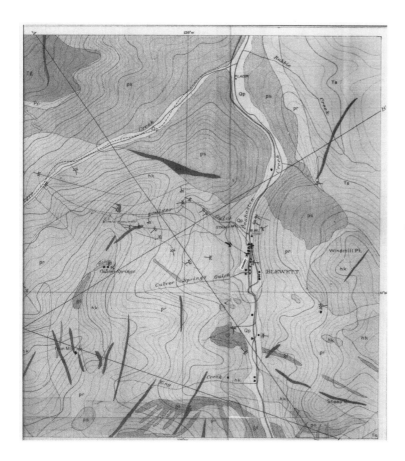

Geological map of Blewett. (Charles E. Weaver, Bulletin No. 6, [1910].)

In September 1894, the Blewett Gold Mining Company was contracted to crush ore from Tom Johnson's Pole Pick mine. There was also ore coming down from the Culver claim and from some adjacent mineral digs. Excellent wages were made during this time.

When the mill finished running the ore, mill foreman E. C. Sterling leased the facilities for five months and ran high-grade ore from the Blewett mine on a share basis. Sixteen mineral claims were recorded in 1894.

1895

By March, the Blewett Gold Mining Company leased several of their claims to independent miners. There was 1,000 tons of ore, all totaled, in those various leased claim ore bunkers and mine dumps.

The Blewett Gold Mining Company mill was running with full crews in May. Ten men were hired, five on a night shift and five on the day shift. They were processing the accumulated ore from the combined Blewett Gold Mining Company leased claims. It took three weeks to run all the ore through the stamp mill, and then it shut down after the lease-miners' ore was finished.

The result was a gold brick weighting 121 ounces, for a total of $2,290.53. The gold brick was shipped off to Seattle. It was the product of 252 tons of ore that also yielded 14 tons of sulfides.

As demonstrated in this scene; large mules were capable of carrying very heavy loads. Here two of these animals are packing an iron "Bull" wheel to a mill site. (*The Engineering and Mining Journal* [1895].)

Gold output for that year, beginning in April, was more than it had been for several years past. That was due to the old ore leads being worked more thoroughly and systematically, thanks to the miners leasing gold-rich claims from the Blewett and Culver mining companies.

During the beginning of August, the Blewett Gold Mining Company stamp mill was once again processing ore. O. B. Castle had enough ore from his leased Blewett tunnel workings to keep the stamp mill running for about 30 days, and there was ore coming in from other mines to keep it going until October. The last three months of the mining season when the Blewett Gold Mining Company mill operated, it netted only $4,000 at $3 per ton from 1,333 tons of raw ore that it processed. But the general question was, "Why wasn't the Blewett mill making better pay from the ore?" The answer: A large part of the gold, due to the presence of arsenic, was not caught on the amalgamating plates; it was passed off with the residual waste material. By the end of July, the Blewett Gold Mining Company was running their concentrates through a new style concentrator at the rate of 1-ton-per-day for a net gain of $175.

In the meantime, the old mill (Blewett Gold Mining Company stamp-mill) completed a 17-day-run of Culver mined ore that processed 40 to 50 pounds of mercury-gold amalgam worth $144 to the pound; not including unprocessed sulfide concentrates. Plus, there were still 300 tons of ore to run from the Bob Tail mine, and afterward the mill was shut down. This was noted as the most successful gold mining season the Culver Gulch mines had experienced at this point in their existence.

Chapter Ten:
1892 Mining Activity

CULVER MINING COMPANY BECOMES CULVER GOLD MINING COMPANY

In 1892, there was a change of name from Culver Mining Company to Culver Gold Mining Company. This occurred when Joseph Warner began purchasing supplies and hiring men. It was a way to identify and represent the responsible parties for which he was acting as manager in certain side activities, separate from the incorporated Culver Mining Company.

The ploy was that no corporate act was preformed, and the public was led to believe the Culver Gold Mining Company was paying the bills. When it was time for outgoing payments due, it was accomplished through the individuals that Warner was representing. These individuals were in no way bound to the Culver Mining Company. In this way, these partners were not held to the responsibilities of paying old Culver Mining Company debts. They were in a holding pattern until all pending court litigations were clear. At this point, the former Culver Mining Company was thereafter called Culver Gold Mining Company.

CULVER GOLD MINING COMPANY

In 1892, there was renewed interest in the Warner Mining Camp when the Blewett brothers purchased the Culver Gold Mining Company. New log cabins were being built by incoming prospectors and merchants. Among that miner influx were John C. Johnson and P. F. Peterson, who were new joint owners in a dry goods store. About this same time, the Culver Gold Mining Company tool house and cook/dining house burned down. That put activities at the stamp mill on hold for a few days, but ore production coming from the mines was not impeded.

CULVER GOLD MINING COMPANY SEASON OPENS

In March 1892, the Blewett Gold Mining Company was not incorporated yet. The Culver Gold Mining Company ran the new stamp-mill building (with 20 stamps installed) at the foot of Culver Gulch. There were also 10 stamps added (for a total of 20-stamps) to the old Culver mine stamp mill located on Peshastin Creek, south of the confluence of Culver Springs Creek. The winter-mined stack of $20 per ton free-gold ore would soon be processed by a proposed total of 50 stamps at the various stamp mills. But all was not well in the mind of company manager

Edward Blewett. He was being monetarily stiffed by the Warner brothers and Bash brothers. They continued to avoid making any payments to the Blewett brothers of the four-man partnership in the revived Culver Mining Company. It also involved the newly established, unincorporated Blewett Gold Mining Company. Edward sued to get back the $40,000 advance he had made on behalf of the participating partnership and won. A total of 400 claims were recorded in the district at this point.

BLEWETT MINING COMPANY BUYS THE ORIGINAL BLINN CLAIMS

The Blewett Gold Mining Company, Major Ezra W. Clark, and another group bought the old Blinn properties. The Cascade Mining Company received an undisclosed amount of money for the claims. They were the Olympic, Shafer, Seattle, Vancouver, and Pole Pick No. 3. Joseph Warner was named the manager of the Olympic claim under Edward Blewett, who owned one-third of the company.

GOLDEN CROWN CLAIM

W. R. Rust recorded the Golden Crown claim April 28, 1892, and then patented it on May 25, 1892. It was on the upper elevation of the south slope of Culver Gulch and joined to the east property line of what would become the Golden Eagle claim in 1895. The dig had a 125-foot adit that went in about 75 feet, headed northward, and then the workings took a 60-degree turn to the northwest for the remaining 50 feet. When members of Northwest Underground Explorations last visited the claim site in 2012, the portal was open, but a dirt berm backed up water that was shin-deep.

WENATCHEE-PESHASTIN TOLL ROAD

The prevailing conversation in the region in February 1892 concerned transportation by way of a toll road. The route discussed was between Wenatchee and up Peshastin Creek to the mine-to-market road connection with the Culver Gulch mines. The mining companies and small claims miners offered a volunteer work party system. Their self-interests were focused on the north-to-south approach to the mining camps at Ingalls Creek, Negro Creek, and Culver Gulch.

The Cle Elum, Leavenworth, and Wenatchee merchants, farmers, and ranchers also realized the benefits of the connection with the Peshastin mine-to-market road. The resulting through-road would be an incalculable benefit to the towns at both sides of the Wenatchee Mountain Range.

Meanwhile, there was an unfulfilled need existing within the finished southbound-northbound road system in the Peshastin and Swauk Mining Districts. Roads without creek-crossing bridges also needed to be addressed. But the Swauk-Peshastin road/bridge construction remained in the talking stage.

Yearly road building and repair was a very demanding activity in the 1880s through 1900s in the Peshastin Mining District. (Cashmere Museum and Pioneer Village photo collection.)

ROAD CONDITIONS BETWEEN PESHASTIN AND SWAUK CREEKS

By October 1892, the road between the Peshastin and Swauk areas was in bad shape. Some stretches were so eroded away that only pack animals could get through. It got to the point that some miners volunteered to start road repairs. William and Edward Blewett had 15 of their mining company men to help with the repair work under the supervision of August Sasse. As usual, the men did an excellent job.

ARRASTRAS, STAMP MILLS, LUMBER MILLS, AND OTHER MINING EQUIPMENT

Most of Peshastin Mining District history focuses on the large-company, gold-producing mills that showed high gold output. However, there were always several non-company stamp mills

This (crude) variation of a one-stamp mill has parts missing, although it does represent the general idea of its construction. (Photo by Vic Pisoni photo.)

The miner uses this single-unit rocker equipment, first shoveled gold bearing sand and gravel into the top of the box. Then water was poured over the material while rocking the device from side to side. This reduced, separated, and caught the gold along its lower-placed riffle system. The lighter, valueless tailings were washed onto the ground. (Vic Pisoni photo collection.)

actively pounding ore and arrastras grinding free gold from the quartz rock. Some were one-stamp mills; others were from individual two-, three-, four-, or five-stamp units. In addition to the larger mill types, there were gold-producing rockers that separated the gold from the creek's placer materials. Unfortunately, at this time, the exact locations and owners of most of these old mill sites are not known.

In April 1892, the depths of snow in the Blewett area insured an abundance of water to run the mills. It was encouragement enough that miners Gillespie and Hayes built a 10-stamp mill in order to make capital gain off the anticipated ore output for the coming season. The Culver, a Warner-Donahue controlled and owned mine and 10-stamp mill, expected 25 to 30 men to work the mine and mill. The new Culver Mining Company mill would have the latest in amalgamating plates, all built by Hendricks and Selthoff Machinery Company of Denver, Colorado.

In the meantime, the Warner brothers constructed and operated their own company sawmill. The mill was turning out about 3,000 board feet of lumber per day. The location of this sawmill was not explained.

MERCURY (QUICKSILVER) AMALGAMATION/USING A POTATO RETORT

This one-man sluice box is being used to process gold-bearing material. (Vic Pisoni photo collection.)

One of the free-gold extracting techniques making the rounds at the mining camps required the use of a potato. After the gold was freed from the quartz rock or black sand and crushed to a fine powder, it was amalgamated (absorbed into the shinning ball of mercury). Then one end of the potato was cut off, the inner pulp was removed, and the amalgam of gold-absorbing mercury was placed inside the potato. Next, a shovel or flat sheet of metal was placed over a fire, and the potato with the amalgam was placed with the cut end on the hot metal. (There were variations of how to contain the amalgam in the potato once placed onto the heated source.) As the amalgam got hot, the mercury turned to vapors, was absorbed and captured into the surrounding potato, and was unable to get out. The gold was now free of the mercury and in the form of a button on the shovel, or whatever metal used. The piece of gold could be picked up after cooling, and the mercury could be saved for future use by submerging the spud in cold water and the pulp pulled apart. In this manner, the quicksilver would sink to the bottom of the container and could be recovered.

This is an example of a homemade mercury retort—not recommended. (Vic Pisoni photo collection.)

BLEWETT'S HISTORIC SOMBRERO-SHAPED STONE ARRASTRA

The solid, one-piece, historical-site arrastra was made from an outcropping of ground-level rock. It is on the east side of Peshastin Creek just above creek water level. It was added to the National Register of Historic Places in 1974.

US 97 is very dangerous to cross. Safely park your vehicle on the west side of the highway. Work your way upstream about 300 feet from the culvert that routes the creek under US 97. The culvert is located near the beginning of the road traversing Culver Gulch. From there, decide your course along Peshastin Creek to the stone arrastra. The safest way to enjoy the site is to view the stone arrastra photo.

There are several speculative stories about the origin and machinations of this very old ore-grinding mill. It was noted by the old-time miners that the mill was active during the short leadership of US President James Abram Garfield (1881).

Historian and author Wesley Engstrom interviewed a man in 1971 that lived in the active mining town of Blewett as a young boy. The old-timer stated that the arrastra was referred to as "ancient" by the local residents. Also, there was a set of collar yokes that would have been on the ends of an axle indicating that it was powered by one or two horses harnessed to the device. The axle is speculated, since it is no longer there.

Successful Swauk Mining District gold miner Ollie Jordin told of what he once observed, indicating the arrastra was powered by animals. It did not require the use of waterpower and all the attending gears, shafts, etc.

Being knowledgeable of such antiquated, historic mining and milling devices, Engstrom also suggested that the grooved track path in the arrastra resembles more the impression made by the wheels of a Chilean mill. It is similar to the drag-stone method, only the Chilean ore-crushing action is done by either two or three heavy stone or steel wheels. They roll over the ore in a crushing manner, as opposed to the grinding action of the drag-stones. He also noted that the drag-stone method would require a hole in the dome of rock at the center of the stone arrastra, which is not present on this particular milling device.

The author is sitting at the edge of Blewett's historic, sombrero-shaped arrastra that is permanently worn into surrounding rock by the ore grinding action of drag stones. Peshastin Creek flows by in the background. This stone arrastra is located west of Blewett's historical town site monument. (Photo by Vic Pisoni.)

Chapter Eleven:
1893—Economic Depression and Other Depressing News

Economic depression began in January 1893 and lasted until June 1894. But it never fully recovered, and a second economic slump hit again in 1897. The gold-mining digs in the Blewett/ Peshastin, Cle Elum, and Swauk Mining Districts were an asset during the economic fall. Town-based businesses, barely making it, failed to provide jobs. Small-scale gold miners accounted for a labor force of folks who made a living.

Some gold-placer miners lived a hand-to-mouth existence. Others were at a higher standard of living, but the activity gave each miner a sense of independence and self-reliance by avoiding a breadline kind of survival.

The mines and miners needed supplies, thus they brought monetary help to the nearby towns with their purchases. Even the farmers and ranchers realized taking their produce to the mining camps was a good source of assured revenue.

But in June, another nail was driven into the economic coffin that affected counties encompassing the town of Ellensburg. The Ben Snipes and Company Bank of Ellensburg closed its doors and suspended further business.

BLEWETT MINING CAMP SOCIAL SCENE

In good times and in bad, saloons played their part in the affairs of the Blewett Mining Camp social scene. They extended their services helping to dull folks' awareness of the depressing effects of the bad times that had set in. The Blewett Camp was known for its low-key character, as opposed to rowdy Roslyn, a coal town to the southwest of Blewett, on the south side of the Wenatchee Mountain Range. There was always drinking and gambling and a shady lady or three here and there amongst mining camps in the north-central Cascade Mountains. But Blewett was not noted for any commercial activities of the red-light kind (except a vague mining news reference in 1896 by miner Mike McCarthy of Blewett that included, "There is somebody who keeps a well beaten path to the Red House").

The Swauk Mining District had only one mention of that sort of activity. A short blurb in an 1893 newspaper told of the Liberty miners bemoaning the fact that, "Since the Goddess of Liberty left town for a more steady and dependable source of income, the boys had to go to Ellensburg, Cle Elum, or Roslyn to find a woman to show them a good time."

The Blewett population was not noted as disruptive by nature. Yet they could not be nominated as halo candidates either; likewise for their mining brethren in the Swauk district.

These miners appear to be anticipating a social event. (Linda McCune photo collection.)

That brings attention to a deeper based source of good morals in the Blewett Camp—the resident families. Families associated with mining and mining camp activities tended to stay in place longer than those in mankind's debauched faction, including gambler, thief, murderer, and any other realm of lawlessness imaginable. Plus the late 1890s saw a maturing of sorts in the mining districts of the north-central Cascade Mountains areas, especially in the Peshastin and Swauk Mining Districts. The presence of wives and children in large numbers seems to have had a calming effect on the mining-camp population.

When the family-oriented women got organized, they improved or brought in many of Blewett's needs for the benefit their families and the community. Undoubtedly, by using more genteel mannerisms, the women extracted good results, including for their children's education. It wasn't long before the Blewett Mining Camp organized its first school district and hired a teacher for the summer months.

VIGILANTISM AND MINER'S COURT

Some circumstances arose where vigilante committees were formed to control lawlessness where no lawful authority was established. In the town of Blewett, there were a few crimes committed. For the most part, the Blewett-based offenders had an awareness of their guilt. On occasion, the lawbreaker would go to Cle Elum or one of the other towns and turn himself in to the sheriff.

Blewett was a town that had a somewhat decent moral compass. Acts of vigilantism were not needed according to Blewett's lesser degree of disruptive or unlawful level of activities. Civic committees were formed when a situation called for such actions. In one instance, a Blewettite was acting up, and a civic committee settled the problem. The alleged offender was told in no uncertain terms what his options were—end of story. The miners as a group formed mining districts with specific mining laws to govern their own members. If a miner had a beef with somebody about a mining-related problem, a court of miners would listen to the facts. Then by a vote of yea or nay, a decision would be made to settle the matter. These actions in themselves provided a degree of law and order. Reactions to serious, felonious situations have been reported about other mining camps that were considered as out of control if a swarm of vigilantes resorted to having a hanging party courtesy of Judge Lynch's court.

PESHASTIN AREA SPRING FLOOD

In early May, along came an added burden to the depressed area—the sudden melt of deep-layered snow on the slopes of the upper elevations. It came scouring its way down the roads in a fast and furious manner. The high water from the spring melt took out most of the bridges on both Swauk Creek and Peshastin Creek. The Peshastin Creek side was in serious trouble. Folks there were caught with no way to replenish food supplies and were soon nearing the point of starving.

The manager of the boarding house where the company miners were staying impressed upon the mine company owners the lack of food. He stated that if company folks expected their employees to work, they had to be fed. The mining companies decided that it was in everybody's interest to open the company food supplies. It was three weeks before the snow melted enough to get the first string of pack-train animals loaded with food into the mining camp at Blewett. It was the worst spring that the oldest resident miner in camp could remember. The stranded mining population was also held back from sending ore shipments. To help stave off starvation, John Hansel made the challenging trip to Blewett with a horse drawn sled, loaded with food, from his ranch at the mouth of Ingalls Creek. In June, the provisions shortage continued.

Miners George and Dick Madden had several claims they were eager to get to, particularly their snowbound, very rich, leased quartz claim, the Olympia. But, they too had to wait for the snow to clear and the arrival of wagon loads of supplies.

However, John Thompson wasn't much on waiting. He wanted to get back into camp ahead of the crowd, and it almost cost him his whole outfit. Heading down a very narrow place on the Peshastin Creek trail, John could only watch as his two pack animals did a slipping-critter kind of tap dance off the treacherous trail that evolved into a bouncing, leapfrog roll together down the steep slope. When the cyclonic blur of twisting horses and packing assemblage came to an abrupt stop … wonder of wonders, there was indication of life in the wreckage. In fact, what appeared to be an outstanding tribute to a well-anchored diamond-hitch packing job saved the day. The pack animals and contents survived with no apparent psychological or physical side-effects.

One death in a Culver Gulch mine occurred in October. It was a miner named Johnson (not Tom or John A. or John C. but another surnamed Johnson). He was killed in a Culver claim tunnel when a large chunk of rock fell on him.

This 1890s view shows the old Blewett Pass road as it enters northward past the homes in the foreground and toward the center of the scene where the 20-stamp mill roof and south side of the building is located to the far left, mid-frame. (Chris Bell photo collection.)

BLEWETT

SILVER PANIC OF 1893

The Sherman Silver Act went into effect on July 14, 1890. It increased the amount of silver the US government was required to purchase each month. Mining companies glutted the silver market, which drove the price down to where it could not be mined profitably. This required the United States to purchase even more silver. The plan backfired. People turned in their silver notes for gold, which depleted the US gold reserve. In response, the act was repealed August 8, 1893. Banker J. P. Morgan helped with a massive gold loan (for a commission), and it helped save the nation from bankruptcy.

In the early 1890s, the silver mine owners had shot themselves in their financial foot with the bullet of greed. The US government finished them off by shooting them in the other foot when it repealed the silver act. The result was a crippled silver mining industry. Almost all silver mine production came to a standstill because it was no longer profitable to mine silver at the lower rate of exchange. This would explain a lot of the cutthroat activity involving the disappearance of mining company funds and the lawsuits that followed. As it turned out, once again, gold was king, and there was renewed interest in gold mine production.

Chapter Twelve:
1894—Peshastin Mining District Is Formed and Other Happenings

The Peshastin Mining District was formed May 1, 1894, and C. E. Freeman was the first claims recorder. Using a Metsker's map of Chelan County, the boundaries for the Peshastin Mining District may be followed as explained. East of the Swauk/Blewett Pass area, locate Mt. Lillian in Chelan County (R19E-T21N, Section7). From Mt. Lillian, go directly north to the Wenatchee River. Follow the Wenatchee River westward to the town of Dryden. From Dryden draw a line to the mouth of Ingalls Creek. From the mouth of Ingalls Creek, go directly west to Ingalls Peak. From Ingalls Peak, follow the Chelan-Kittitas county line back to the starting point, Mt. Lillian. The town of Blewett is somewhat centered within the Peshastin Mining District.

BLEWETT'S GOVERNING OFFICIALS

One of the first items of business after the establishment of Blewett as a town was to put in place a basic form of government. C. E. Freeman was the first justice of the peace for the Culver Precinct, E. M. Baldwin was constable, William Donahue was the supervisor, E. C. Sterling was postmaster, and Culver School District No. 42 was formed with Mrs. Edward King as clerk. It was decided a 24x36-foot, double-use town hall/school building was needed. Residents, who were able, would donate all the building materials, and 30 men volunteered three days labor each to help erect the structure.

The bearers of the petitions for the aforementioned Blewett officials were Louis Speaker, a Blewett merchant, and W. F. Patterson. The county commission approved all that the Blewett residents requested.

MINE CLAIM LEASING POLICY BEGINS

In 1894, a common practice began. Certain sections of mine claims were leased on a royalty basis of ore output, as well as based on the milling costs. This led to lease miners working harder and being more meticulous when sorting (high-grading) their own ore. The result was highly cost-effective mining, compared to when they were working for company wages. They opened up and stoped out the rich sulfide ore deposits located in the upper portions of Culver Gulch. About 60 men worked in the mines and mill when both were in full operation. In turn, the Blewett Gold Mining Company also started leasing sections of their mine claims to a small association of miners. This move increased incoming company revenue. The leasing system lasted for several years with good results.

The Blewett resident population swelled with the addition of want-to-be miners and their families. They were fleeing from the economically depressed towns, and Blewett got its share of folks that migrated to the gold-bearing ground of the Peshastin Mining District. Fifteen prospectors and their strings of pack animals were the last arrivals of the month at the beginning of the 1895 mining season. This was the year that the district hit its population peak of about 500 folks. Soon after, it started to lose folks that didn't have the know-how or resolve to stay with the labor-intensive demands related to gold mining. By 1911, there were permanent Blewett residents hanging onto the small or individual mine claims. This was similar to the mineral-claim owner-tradition of past low-gold production years. They stuck with Blewett and made a living by taking gold out of Culver Gulch and nearby areas.

AN UNSOLVED MURDER, 1894

The subject of an unsolved murder from 18 months past was discussed around the saloons and elsewhere in Blewett. The skeletal remains of a man's body were discovered in the Wenatchee Mountain Range with two bullet holes through two shirts, a vest, and two coats. A group of jurists went up to the body site to view the scene of the crime. They declared it a homicide, buried the remains on the spot, and headed back. Unless somebody confessed to the murder, it would remain a mystery.

BLEWETT CEMETERY

The date for the establishment of the Blewett Cemetery is uncertain. The fact that John Ernest was its first customer in 1894 credits that date as close enough. A physical "search and locate" field trip of the old Blewett Cemetery site by Northwest Underground Explorations in 2006 indicated that none of the cemetery grounds or old artifacts and site indicators remain. The bridge that once spanned Peshastin Creek is gone. The road from the old bridge landing on the west bank leading up to the cemetery area is still in evidence. The standing landmark cedar tree has fallen and is moldering into the ground. The gate is gone, and so is the cable that hung there. Northwest Underground Explorations noted some depressions in the ground, but it was inconclusive if they were natural or manmade. The only item recognizable on the "find list" was the old road leading from Peshastin Creek to the cemetery site area.

The graves, in order of death, were:

1894, August, Friday the 13th—John D. Ernest (father of Frank Ernest). John was crushed to death in his arrastra.

1897—Reginald Wilder. Two-months-old Reginald was the son of Mr. and Mrs. James Wilder,

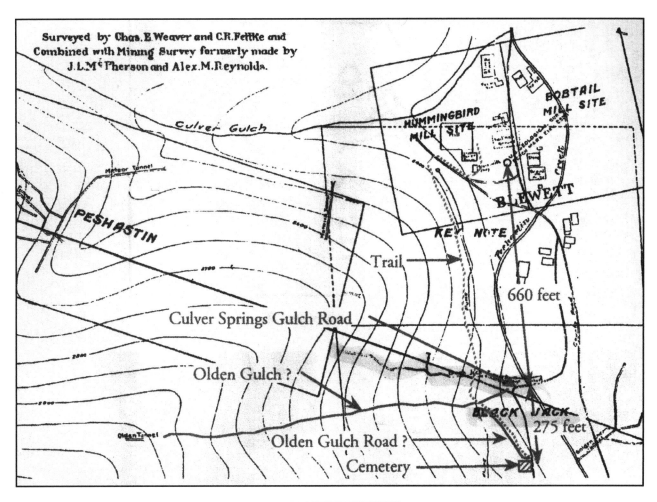

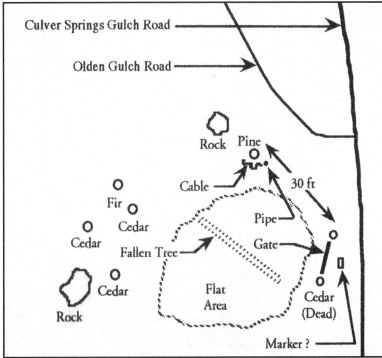

Above, Wesley C. Engstrom's Blewett cemetery landmark diagram is overlaid on a map from Charles E. Weaver's Bulletin No. 6 (1910).

Left, Sketch of Blewett cemetery (not to scale) by Wesley C. Engstrom.

and brother to twin brothers Roy and Ray Wilder.

1905—Thomas D. Hall. He died from a stroke.

1905, March 18—Thomas B. Douglas. Born in Perth, Scotland, Tom was first in line for his father's earldom but declined in favor of his commoner true love. He arrived solo at Blewett during the 1890s. He died of a stroke.

1906, November—Thomas Hill. Born in Sweden, 48-year-old Thomas died when a 5-gallon kerosene can he and John Olden were using as a powder magazine that was packed with dynamite exploded while they were drying the dynamite over a fire. They were working at the headwaters of Negro Creek in the Mountain Lion mine at the time of the accident. Olden escaped serious injury. He stayed with Hill until he died. Later, Olden and a group of men hauled Hill's body several miles back to Blewett and buried him.

1910—John Olden. Born in Sweden, Olden arrived in Blewett in 1874, living and mining there for the remainder of his life. John died at 80 years old.

1910, January 20—Joseph (Joey) Thomas Hill. Eight-year-old son of Mr. and Mrs. Jim Hill, Joey died of diphtheria.

CHELAN MINING DISTRICT FORMED

When the Chelan Mining District was established in October 1894, it mainly overlaid the existing Peshastin Mining District area, although it did extend farther east to cover the Mission Creek, Mission Ridge, and Devil's Canyon areas as an extension of the outer (eastern) boundaries of the Peshastin Mining District. Mainly, it fulfilled a need for a mining district to cover mines starting just about 10 miles west of the town of Wenatchee, newly incorporated in 1893.

At this time, the Blewett mines were attracting attention as the hoped-for new gold-mining bonanza of the region. Culver Gulch was the rising star of the Peshastin Mining District.

The Wenatchee area miners were quick to respond with the organization of the Mission Creek Mining District. The boundaries of the Chelan Mining District was then dropped from use and ceased to exist. Why the Chelan Mining District area was allowed to overlay the Peshastin Mining District was not explained.

BLEWETT VOTER/ELECTION PRECINCT IS ESTABLISHED

The first official Blewett township business for November 1894 was to set up an election precinct. Thus, the Culver Precinct was established for the residents in Blewett and the surrounding cabin population.

Chapter Thirteen: Hydraulic Mining

Clarence Jennings and mining partner J. T. Medhurst were operating a hydraulic mining operation on Jennings's placer during the second week in October 1894. The Jennings's placer was located on the east side of Peshastin Creek. The placer claim crossed the mouth of Ruby Creek and headed northward across Jennings Creek (an unnamed drainage creek on modern maps), just north of Ruby Creek. From there, it crossed Riley Creek (named after Tom Riley, who mined there, but the stream does not appear identified on any map because it is a seasonal run-off gulch).

Clarence Jennings created a ripple of excitement when he displayed what was found in the clean-up from the riffles of their long tom sluice box. Clarence aroused the mining folks' curiosity with a show of large amounts of very coarse gold and some nuggets. The gold was pressure-washed from a very small displacement of ground. The nuggets were valued at fifty cents to $2. The total amount of gold discovered was not given. Jennings said that nearly an ounce of gold per day per man was mined. How many days and the head count went unanswered. He boasted that about 400 men could eventually have employment on the claims in the next gold-mining season (1895).

Clarence's biased story mostly indicates an attempt to promote the claim with estimations based on hoped-for pockets of gold. This is somewhat similar (only with less physical foundation of hoped-for continued gold recovery) to hard-rock miners' attitude towards their chances of finding gold in place within a quartz-vein structure.

This is an example of hydraulic mining activity using a 10- or 11-inch monitor nozzle. (Vic Pisoni photo collection.)

ORTING GROUP HYDRAULIC MINING COMPANY, 1894

E. C. Wilcox recorded this group of claims on November 8, 1894. They were located ½ mile north of the town of Blewett.

CASCADE HYDRAULIC MINING COMPANY FATALITY, 1896

A mining-related death took place on August 27, 1896. Captain Jack F. Crawford from the small community called Boise located near Buckley, Washington, and his two mining partners, E. C. Wilcox and Frank Holly, were on their Cascade Hydraulic Mining Company dig preparing their hydraulic mining equipment. It was located about 1 mile below the mouth of Negro Creek, on the west bank of the creek. When they first started joining their claims together under one title, they registered as the Crawford-Wilcox-Holly Hydraulic Mine. Cascade Hydraulic Mining Company was chosen shortly after as its recorded name.

Starting up Negro Creek, the company built a 2,000-foot ditch that included a connected flume routed down Peshastin Creek to the hydraulic mining area. The water pressure at the hydraulic nozzle was built up by the water dropping along a downward gradient of 130 feet as it coursed along the 2,000-foot-long ditch and down to their placer site.

Everything was set up and in working order as they made a final inspection at an elevated, ancient creek-bed level. The elevated (30 feet above the present level of Peshastin Creek) gravel-and-dirt "bench placer" was the ground they were going to wash into their long tom sluice boxes.

Crawford was a large-framed man, 45 years old, quite strong and agile, and was adept and familiar at negotiating the terrain of his chosen profession. He went on a final tour of the hydraulic piping system, and started up the loose footing of a steep- sloped, 30-foot-high bank. As he reached the halfway mark, the ground gave way, and on his uncontrolled descent, a large, dislodged boulder came pounding down and slammed into Crawford's chest. The force of the blow knocked him through the air for 12 feet, and he struck the back of his head against a stationary boulder with enough force to snap his vertebrae. It killed him instantly. His body was taken to Coroner Stafford in the town of Cle Elum and then transferred for burial in Buckley, Washington.

It came out in his obituary that he had served in the US Navy and Army. He served under General Custer as one of his most trusted scouts, and during that time, he became known as the "poet scout." Several bullet wounds on his body were witness to the fact that he had faced life-threatening danger many times. Odd and sad was the fact that Crawford's last wound was mortal and showed only scuffed skin on the back of his neck.

After the death of Captain Jack F. Crawford, W. A. Crawford appeared on the scene in September (relationship unknown) and was taken into the partnership. The three men hydraulically mined down to the old channel-level bedrock. Gold nuggets and "pickers" up to $7 were taken.

They did not bother with saving the fine gold mainly because the men were using only wood riffles and didn't incorporate mercerized plates in their gold-saving system.

PESHASTIN PLACER MINING COMPANY, 1897

During 1897, Allen C. Mason and mining partner John Snyder were the main stockholders of the Peshastin Placer Mining Company. The two men were in the process of setting up a hydraulic operation using a giant monitor (pressure nozzle) and a series of sluice boxes at their claims located north of Blewett on Peshastin Creek.

However, they had to wait for the heavy spring snow melt in order to run the hydraulic nozzle at full power. In the meantime, they were getting small gold nuggets off the bedrock by using a two-man sluice box. Part of the hydraulic system was a 3x3-foot flume that was 4,000 feet long, which ended in projecting a highly pressurized, earth- eroding stream of water from the end of a 10-inch hydraulic nozzle opening. The flume that delivered the water down to the mining site was installed by a man named Hurd. He also did the flume work for the Cascade Mining Company's entire statewide claim holdings.

MOHAWK (HYDRAULIC) MINING COMPANY, 1897

The Mohawk (hydraulic) Mining Company grabbed everybody's attention in November 1897. News of developing preparations for 10 placer claims to be hydraulically mined in the spring of 1898 was discussed. They had a crew of men building a flume and fitting 16-inch diameter pipe that would reach a combined total of 6,000 feet in length when completed to the hydraulic mining site.

The Mohawk company claims extended down Peshastin Creek 13,000 feet. The claims were expected to average about $1 in gold per cubic yard of material washed at the cost of five to six cents a yard. Three men would wash 600 cubic yards a day. The optimistic (promotional) view of the company was that there was enough gold-bearing material there to keep the company busy for 20 years.

Then an over-the-top statement from the Mohawk Mining Company came out. The company followed their previous announcement by declaring that there would be three giant hydraulic monitors washing down several million cubic yards of auriferous material off the elevated, ancient gold-bearing benches, from bedrock up to the grass roots. A statement with a promotional flare to Mohawk's advantage was made about several hundred thousand dollars in gold that was recently recovered from the nearby Culver Gulch claims. A reference was also made about 42 gold ore ledges within 1 mile of the Mohawk company placers. (Once more, here is a mining company masking the fact that there was not enough information for the company to make an in-depth statement. This is due to most of those alleged gold locations being in a state of uncertain, future development or having uncertain yields of gold.)

RUBY (HYDRAULIC) PLACER, 1897

In May, the placer claim that got a lot of attention was the Ruby placer, owned by Sherman Donaldson and W. S. Bloom. They made public notice that they intended to power-wash with a hydraulic monitor on an ancient high-bench placer. It was located near the confluence of an unnamed feeder stream flowing westward off Windmill Point into Peshastin Creek. No results from these hydraulic activities were given.

RUBY GROUP (HYDRAULIC) PLACER, 1897

In June, Riley Eisenhower, John and James Lynch, and J. T. Medhurst were owners of six placer claims that began at the mouth of Ruby Creek and were headed in-line upstream. They used a hydraulic system to work the gold-bearing creek material. Here again, no activity report was available. When a group from Northwest Underground Explorations examined the area of lower Ruby Creek, there was an elevated area that appeared to be old hydraulic wash-tailings. The area is heavily overgrown with brush and small trees, making the tailings area difficult to discern.

Chapter Fourteen:
1895 and 1896

BLEWETT MINING AND MILLING COMPANY

Somewhere in the time frame of the leasing activity, the Blewett Gold Mining Company became the Blewett Mining and Milling Company. The head amalgamator in 1895 was William Elliott.

The 20-stamp mill system was not a cost-effective operation because of the passed-off, gold-bearing, arsenic-containing sulfide tailings worth several dollars a ton. This floured the mercury on the plates and prevented the plates from catching all the gold, even though the gold values recorded still appear to be impressive.

Dams were made to contain the passed-off, gold-enriched sludge into ponds. These would be treated by a more sophisticated process for recapturing the mineral values that were being lost. The lost gold in the ponds was processed in the summer of 1896 when a group of men formed a business for the purpose of cyanide-leaching the gold-sulfide tailings.

The mill completed running Orin Castle's ore from a leased fraction of an unidentified claim and started on ore from Dexter Shoudy's newly acquired fraction claim lease. Often, fraction claims, such as these, are leased (in part) from full-size claims with recorded names. This leaves the other part of the claim open for lease, or it is left to the owner/owners to mine. In some instances, only a tunnel on a claim was leased. This caused confusion for some observers of Blewett area mining activities. For example, news reporters and other folks erroneously called the Blewett Tunnel and Shafer Tunnel "claims" or "mines" when, in truth, they were mining developments within the Culver claim.

The ore was mined from a tunnel that Shoudy developed at the west end of a fractioned property that was not identified. He removed a labor-intensive 700 tons of ore in two months. It yielded a $222 gold brick from free-milling rock and $60 to $100 per ton from 40 tons of concentrates.

James Wilder was next to run his ore through the mill. Wilder's claim names were absent from the initial base data. Claims records revealed at that time James owned the Capitol property located west of the Culver claim and was joined to his Pole Pick No. 2 (named Alta Vista in 1874). Also on Wilder's holdings list was the Wilder claim located 1,000 feet east of the Culver claim and joined to the Hindoo (Ivanhoe) dig. The Blewett Mining and Milling Company ran on James Wilder's ore for about 30 days and then became idle. The amount of ore processed was not noted, other than being called an average cleanup (whatever "average" was in general terms was not told).

Part of the mine names and location vagaries are due to the on-again, off-again system of leasing portions of mine claims and not verifying the production details in an orderly fashion. The same goes for the various cyanide operations that seemed to flourish in the proximity of

Blewett in 1895–99. Related information is veiled in unclear or undeclared ownership/lease arrangements, misinformation, or simply the lack of data.

The mill reduced 2,469 tons of ore from the Culver claim. The ore assayed at $12.62 per ton in gold at market rate of $18.98 an ounce. Plus there were 473 tons of custom sulfide ore, making a total production in gold bullion of $60,000.

SOLID GOLD BAR WEIGHING 38½ POUNDS, 1895

The Blewett Mining and Milling Company was at the forefront of the news with a report about a solid bar of gold weighing 38½ pounds. Gold was valued at $18.93 an ounce making the gold bar worth about $11,660. The gold was accumulated from the various, miner-leased Blewett Milling and Mining Company mines, but no information identified what portion individual leased digs contributed. The gold bar was sent to Ellensburg via some means or other of stealth or extremely heavily guarded transportation (the travel details were not available). It was shipped outbound by the Northern Pacific Railway.

The amount of bullion processed at the Blewett mill and shipped in 1895 amounted to about $50,000, according to mill superintendent E. C. Sterling. This was a tribute to how well the lease miners on the Blewett and Culver Gulch properties were doing.

FIRE AT THE NEW BLEWETT MINING AND MILLING CYANIDE PLANT, 1895

The finished Blewett Mining and Milling Company gold-recovering cyanide plant was reported to be the second built in the state. It was leased out to Mr. Dolan and John C. Johnson in November. Just as the final coating of hot liquid asphalt was being painted on the cyanide holding tanks, an explosion occurred. The resulting fire spread and destroyed the nearby concentrating works that were close to the mill. The north side of the cyanide plant, the cyanide electric plant, and the north part of the stamp-mill building were burnt to ruins. However, the machinery was not damaged in the stamp mill due to the employees' heroic actions.

The Blewett Mining and Milling Company owners lost $1,000 due to the fire. Dolan and Johnson didn't have the cash in hand to help with the rebuilding project without financial help. They were left unable to process 12 tons of sulfide ore concentrates stored at the mill site. The untreated ore represented a $1,500 loss for the two men, which may, in part, have been turned over to the company for Dolan and Johnson's share of the repairs.

CALIFORNIA MILLING AND MINING COMPANY, 1895

The new company, California Milling and Mining Company, was owned by a San Francisco man named Butterbaugh and two Blewett miners, John Dennett and Tom Johnson. The two Blewett miners operated a small four-stamp mill that had 250-pound stamps and a side jigger or concentrator. Some of the Golden Phoenix (North Star) ore was treated at the mill. As it turned out, the ore-milling results were not a cost-effective proposition for the company or miner/owner Butterbaugh from California, who had possession of controlling company stock. So, two months later, the mill was shut down, and Butterbaugh was seen California-bound.

On the heels of the California Mining and Milling Company closure was an up-dated sulfide-ore processing mill and cyanide plant that was ready as a lease operation. This was courtesy of Mr. Dolan and John C. Johnson with newly obtained capital backing. The mention of another new cyanide plant coming to Blewett was becoming a reality. A foundation was being graded off, and the mill parts were on site for final construction. A chlorination crew was busy putting together some cyanide tanks for the treatment of sulfide ore.

After an expedited job of structure replacement and associated repairs caused by the cyanide plant fire, the Blewett Milling and Mining Company mill was almost ready to restart. The new building was not joined to the repaired older stamp mill building, a decision made after the experience of the accidental fire.

PACK TRAIL WASHED OUT, 1896

In January, the snow on the Peshastin-Swauk divide was 6 feet deep, and snow was at a depth of 3½ feet in the town of Blewett. Yet, that didn't stop John Burmeister and several other miners from recording claims in the dead of winter.

Francis Streamer was a former justice of the peace who evolved into a much talked-about eccentric personality. He roamed the far reaches of the tribal villages and pioneer settlements and towns. He was often in residence with his tribal friends, whom he was known to defend with great oratorical vigor. Streamer walked into the town of Blewett in April 1896 with the news that the trail coming up Peshastin Creek, below Blewett, was washed out and even difficult for pedestrian travel. Washed out roads and trails were a yearly occurrence and responded to as these situations arose. The trail was in such bad shape that sure-footed horses had problems, and it certainly was not suited for wagon travel. He surmised that it would be quite a while before wagons could get through to Blewett and the Culver mines.

That was bad news, and the scarcity of food at Blewett became an issue. This was followed by reports that wind-downed trees blocked the road, and fast snowmelt had scoured out additional sections of the trail.

Some relief was given to the stranded Blewettites in the form of extra food that was stored at John Hansel's ranch and brought to Blewett. Orin Castle and two unidentified mining partners started the mining season early and continued to produce good ore from their leased fraction claim. Castle stacked the ore and had it ready for the Blewett Mining and Milling Company to process as the year's first run of ore.

The miners who stayed in camp for the winter were spared the problems that would delay the new season of incoming miners due to the terrible road conditions. The problem they did face was one of an insufficient food supply. The Blewettites were hoping for an early snowmelt to improve all the various drawbacks poor access had caused. The Blewett mining population was getting concerned about their situation.

Then news of the Alaska gold-field strikes hit town, and the seemingly endless waiting for something to happen was over. Blewett lost a considerable number of miners to the stampede north to the Yukon and Alaskan lure of gold riches that weren't being met satisfactorily in Peshastin Mining District claims. For some of the miners within the mining district, it was a year of intermittent inconveniences, either related to the Blewett mines and owners or as independent miners dealing with similar problems to a lesser degree. Some folks could see the possibility of Blewett becoming a solid and enduring mining company town if things ever got to the point where there was a continuous flow of ore being produced and milled throughout the year. So far the town's history as a dependable source of rich ore was not the continuous gold bonanza hoped for, but more of an on-again, off-again situation.

Tom Johnson bought the old 10-stamp mill from the Blewett Mining and Milling Company, He added canvas tables, had men do repairs, and added a cyanide plant to the milling system. Most of the ore that Tom's mill processed was coming from the Pole Pick claim.

Johnson started processed ore for other Blewett mineral claims. He accepted ore from the Tip Top, Black Jack, and Peshastin claims and from digs located on the ridge between Culver Gulch and Culver Springs Creek. He was also in the process of opening a store in Blewett.

The leased mines and non-leased portions of the company mines were going full throttle. They were taking out enough ore to keep mills pounding, reducing and leaching gold out of Culver Gulch rock for quite a long run.

For the men who resisted the temptation to head north to Alaska, there would be no idle hands for anybody seeking work. Miner Mike McCarthy joined the growing ranks of the miner/businessman mind-set by opening a store in Blewett and was noted to be doing a profitable amount of business.

CYANIDE TREATMENT PLANT, 1896

During 1896, while the other cyanide plants were focusing on the ore coming directly from the mines, Mike McCarthy and F. G. Rosenberg recalled some gold sulfides not caught by previous milling systems. They remembered when the Pole Pick, Hummingbird, and other active mines had been worked the old way 12 to 14 years before. The gold was washed off onto the tailing piles due to poor mill reduction and processing by the earlier mining companies.

With this thought in mind, they built a small, crude two-tank cyanide treatment plant with a capacity to run 2 tons of sulfide material per day. Under a share-profit agreement with the stamp mill, it was purposely erected near the mill to also reprocess its passed-off values.

McCarthy and Rosenberg built dams to catch the slime that held the passed-off gold. This was caused by the old gold-collecting nemesis, arsenic, which prevented the mercury from catching all the gold. Six hundred tons of tailings averaging from $3 to $30 a ton in gold were extracted by their cyanide process. The two men recovered a considerable amount of gold for themselves.

With the Blewett folks busy at the mines and associated mining commerce, the atmosphere in town was that of a nice, respectable mining community. There was no out-of-control drunkenness, no fights (that maimed or led to death), and nothing that would normally catch the constable's attention.

E. C. Sterling was still the postmaster at Blewett and superintendent of the Blewett Mining and Milling Company. Superintendent Sterling estimated that the company mill would start about the first of May on 1,000 tons of stacked ore and would be running ore from Blewett mines for the remainder of the summer.

A lot of processed ore needed to be moved out and transported on the roads as soon as possible, but the eroded road surface was stable only for pack animals at this time. As bad as the road was during the winter, George, the mail carrier, completed every delivery. The one claim recorded in April was Edward King's Iowa Belle placer.

There was much attention given to the fact that the road between the Swauk area and the town of Blewett was open to wagon travel early in May. It was emphasized by the news that William A. Hale was running an express wagon from Ellensburg to Blewett once a week, filled with fresh meat, eggs, butter, and vegetables. It was the first team of horses in over six weeks to make it to Blewett.

Edward King took over as road supervisor for the district. He repaired the road to the north of Blewett, making it passable for wagons. Peter Wold had no trouble herding five milk cows from Ellensburg to Blewett. A new school teacher, Miss Barnett, was in town for the season, opened classes for 30 students, and organized a Sunday school schedule. John Shoudy was one of the Sunday school teachers.

FOREST FIRES, 1896

Forest fires were the talk of the month of July. They affected everybody's life. They caused breathing difficulties for some and irritated eyes for everyone. The haze was so thick that the sun could be viewed without using a darkened viewing glass. The smoke permeated throughout the whole north-central Cascades Mountain area. It was allowed to burn itself out because there was a lack of men to fight it.

LEASE MINERS EARN BIG BUCKS, 1896

James Muldoon and John Burk had a lease on a portion of the Culver mine. They cleaned up about $4,000 on a short run of ore processed at the 20-stamp Blewett mill. A crew of miners, led by Joseph Love and Martin Lewis, had the other fraction of the Culver claim. The total take in gold for these lease miners was $8,000 from 532 tons of ore over a 12-day run at the mill.

The Blewett Mining and Milling Company 20-stamp mill finished running 80 tons of ore in August 1896. The ore came from the Peshastin claim. It was leased by F. G. Rosenberg and Mike McCarthy but owned by Dexter Shoudy and James Boyle. It put $1,800 in Mike McCarthy's and F. G. Rosenberg's pockets. Superintendent of the mill, E. C. Sterling, and amalgamator-in-chief, William Elliott, were about to run one more load of ore through the mill to end the season.

At this juncture in the activities of the Blewett Mining and Milling Company, their mill switched over to reprocessing the gold-bearing sulfides that were rejected by the quartz-gold milling system. The sulfide-gold was washed out and impounded in the mill's holding pond. The escaped gold in the sulfides, held by the tailings pond, was separated through the cyanide plant system. The result was $10 in gold per ton.

MERCURY/GOLD AMALGAM WORTH $400 IS UNEARTHED, 1896

In October 1896, someone was in the right place at the right time. A series of vague comments fueled a story of mysterious circumstances—a chunk of mercury/gold amalgam worth $400 was unearthed at a dig on one of the old claims. Nobody offered a clue to its origin. Local sentiment regarding the facts called it "good fortune" and needed no further explanation. There was one recorded claim in October.

WINTER CHALLENGES, 1896

In November 1896, another washout alert reached Blewett. All the bridges on the roads leading to the Swauk and Peshastin areas were carried away by high water. This caused another shortage of grub and other provisions. The town of Blewett took inventory and came up with an estimate that there was six weeks' supply of food on hand. If the bridges didn't get repaired quickly so the wagons could get through to the anxious Blewettites, then everything would come to a standstill. All activities in Blewett slowed down considerably. There was no newsworthy information of any kind related to mining coming out of the Peshastin Mining District.

The leased claims and some of the larger individually owned mines and claims were known to continue working during the winter. This may have been due to the fact that the big mining companies leasing the digs and processing lease ore had enough food in their company store to keep the company turning a profit.

The Blewett Mining and Milling Company mill water pipes froze in December 1896. Superintendent Sterling stated that the mill probably wouldn't start again until May 1897. The company had leases out on the Culver claim assigned to John McCarthy and the now-deceased Charles Donahue. From this point onward, McCarthy maintained the lease as a solo proposition. The Bob Tail and Hummingbird claims were leased to Al Lundberg and associates, and a fraction claim to O. B. Castle. These mines were worked during the winter. Ore was extracted and stockpiled until the mill opened in May 1897.

Other claims being worked in 1896 were T. John Vinton's Tip Top; it had another 50 tons of ore on the dump. Vinton's claim assessment work was being completed and work on his Sulphuret No. 2 claim reached ore at the face of the tunnel. The Tip Top, Vinton, and Sulphuret No. 2 claims were owned by Vinton and Damman. The Lucky Queen claim, owned by Thad Neubauer and Pete Anderson, was actively mining ore, as was the Sun Set claim, owned by Henry Weinman and John Kendle. E. A. Grunden was doing assessment work on the Pole Pick, and the cyanide plant owned by Mike McCarthy was keeping busy turning out bullion.

WARRIOR GENERAL MINING COMPANY BUYS THE BLEWETT MINING AND MILLING COMPANY, 1896

There was a noticeable decline of mining activity late in 1896 after Edward and William Blewett sold their company to the Warrior General Mining Company, a group of Seattle and Boston businessmen. Without having specific documentation with factored-in dates, the available data showed that in 1896 the Seattle-based group paid the Blewett Mining and Milling Company $36,000 for its property. This included claims and related mining tools and equipment. The claims in control of the Warrior General Company were the Culver, Sandel, Bob Tail, and Hummingbird. The company president was G. W. Bragdon, vice-president was R. S. Nichols, John Compton was secretary, L. C. Massey was general manager, and I. C. Gilman held an unknown position. E. C. Sterling was still superintendent of the 20-stamp mill. Gilman went to San Francisco to purchase new mill concentrators.

On the property were large bunkhouses and the 20-stamp mill building with new Wilfley tables. The ore being mined was assayed from $12 to $41 a ton in free gold. The free gold ore uncharacteristically increased in richness with depth. Usually the gold found at depth in the gulch digs was locked into sulfide ore.

The 20-stamp mill was handling full capacity production at times. The Warrior General Mining Company said it would eventually have 60 stamps pounding on ore. This meant the inclusion of additional stamp mills at Blewett as soon as several of the tunnels they were depending on for gold ore could be developed.

The plan was to prepare the underground workings of these claims for further development. Although the money was exchanged and formal paperwork took place, it was recognized that the practice of leasing portions of those claims to small groups of miners would continue. Operating the old Blewett Mining and Milling Company 20-stamp mill (now owned by the

This crew of miners is in front of the lower portal of the Golden Cherry mine. They are working a Long Tom sluice box alongside Peshastin Creek. (Cashmere Museum and Pioneer Village photo collection.)

Warrior General Mining Company) was also continued on a royalty basis. At this time, reorganization, or more correctly, a sublease contract spin-off was transferred from the Warrior General's control to the Chelan Mining and Milling Company. It continued leasing some of the Warrior General Mining Company properties. No doubt it raised legality concerns in the minds of observers and company-involved stock holders. As for the miners, they were noted to reference the old Blewett Mining Company claims as being under the indirect control of the Warrior General Mining Company.

Then the milling royalty arrangement came to a standstill because the profitable oxidized quartz ore that contained free-milling gold diminished in value. The mill was not set up to process the gold-bearing sulfide ore that the miners encountered.

Chapter Fifteen:
1897, 1898, and 1899

FOOD SHORTAGE IN BLEWETT AGAIN, 1897

In January 1897, word got out that the camp ran out of meat. The folks in Blewett also bemoaned that the roads were still in deplorable condition. However, the mail came through at irregular intervals by a ski equipped mail carrier (the pioneer description of skis at the time, was to call them snowshoes).

Nothing noteworthy was written about mining in January, although it was common knowledge that there was underground mining activity going on. Six mineral claims were recorded during the month.

Blewett miner/resident Cliff Davenport and his wife, Annie, out for a snow walk. The building in the background is the Blewett general store/post office. (Photo courtesy of the Davenport and Barthol families, who were former Blewett residents.)

FEBRUARY 1897 SNOW REPORT

An early snow report told of a stagecoach driver returning from an uncompleted trip to Blewett. The route was blocked due to 9 feet of snow on the pass separating the Swauk and Peshastin Mining Districts. The heavy snowpack also had a positive side: The hydraulic miners would have plenty of water in the spring to run their nozzle heads.

1897 MINING ACTIVITIES BEGIN

Thaddeus Neubauer and Peter Anderson were extending the tunnel on their Lucky Queen claim during May. They blasted into a rich pocket of gold. The Lucky Queen put out a clean-up of $10 in gold per pound; total amount of pounds was not stated. The Warrior General (old Blewett mill) 20-stamp operation finally thawed out and was able to run 600 tons of ore. A new sawmill was being constructed downstream from Blewett.

Several smaller mining operations survived the Warrior General Mining Company mill shut down. The small mine owners did it with the help of two arrastras that were in operation, but there was still a need for an improved cyanide plant.

Then Tom Johnson bought bought a 4-stamp mill north of his Culver Springs Creek area mill. It was located by the west bank of Peshastin Creek, about 300 feet northeast of the 20-stamp mill. He changed this mill into a cyanide plant. The building was later used as a horse stable, although in present-day thinking, it would be deemed unhealthy to house any living critter. Twelve mineral claims were recorded in June.

Tom Johnson leased his refurbished cyanide plant to Mike McCarthy and Henry Rosenberg in July. For a second time, the two men had a cyanide plant, which they kept working day and night. They processed the backlog of sulfide ore that was heaped in waiting burlap sacks. Mike and Henry produced a $1,000 gold brick that was sent to the government assay office at Helena, Montana. Johnson received $10 per ton as lease payment for the cyanide plant.

BLEWETT GOLD VERSUS KLONDIKE GOLD

A statement floating around Blewett questioned the wisdom of local miners going so far north to the Klondike when nearby gold deposits existed in their own territory. One of the reasonable responses was that the rich gold-producing ground was all taken in the Blewett and Swauk Mining Districts. But the miners who did stay in the Peshastin, Swauk, and Cle Elum Mining Districts figured that even if a miner could get $100,000 in three years in the Yukon, compared to $50,000 in Washington State for the same length of time, Washington was their preference. This was because the hardships in the mountains of Washington did not challenge the body and strength of will to the extremes that they did in the frozen wilderness of gold fields in the Yukon-Alaska territories.

Two Kittitas miners who transplanted to the richer gold-bearing grounds in Alaska had their gold-mining results printed in a local newspaper. One, Charles Pond, wrote a letter from the Yukon to the *Ellensburg Dawn* newspaper that stated his hometown friend Edward Thorp was heading south out of the Alaska with 40 pounds of gold dust. Thorp was going to resupply and head back north to Alaska.

Most of the mining news in September 1897 was dominated by the Swauk Mining District. The Warrior General Mining Company itself was shut down related to any mining or ore production. Superintendent E. C. Sterling was still in charge of the 20-stamp mill in October and was pushing through tons of Culver Gulch ore that was mostly coming out of the leased claims in control of the Blewett Mining and Milling Company. The Warrior General Mining Company processed that ore for a fee as they worked to complete the set-up for eventually mining and milling their own company ore.

INVENTIONS

Miner John Kendle invented an instrument for locating minerals. He claimed the machine could find a gold coin or a silver coin put in separate boxes at a distance of 25 feet, plus it could distinguish between gold and silver.

Still tinkering, John Kendle used the winter mining slowdown in December 1897 to start manufacturing his battery-operated mineral detector. The mineral locater was made of heavy copper wire, and affixed to the end of the apparatus was a light bulb made of his concocted secret elements. It was supposedly able to locate minerals 100 feet below the surface, tell the pitch of the vein, and locate rich deposits of ore. According to Kendle, it could also detect minerals up to 150 feet on either side. John was pushing to have the mineral detectors ready for spring sales if all things worked out according to plan.

One of the last reports for the year was about W. A. Hageman, the new owner of the Flodin mine located in the Swauk Mining District. He purchased Tom Johnson's old five-stamp mill.

1898 WINTER MINING IN THE BLEWETT AREA MINES AND OTHER ACTIVITIES

Only the old-timers at Blewett could remember snowstorms as bad as the one that dumped deep, damp snow in January 1898. It was made doubly heavy by a hard rain that resulted in considerable damage to buildings. In this case, a section of the mill housing the concentrators collapsed under the weight of the snow and caused $2,000 to $2,500 in damage. Superintendent Sterling of the Warrior General had a crew of men immediately cleaning the wreckage, repairing, and rebuilding. The roof of the cyanide plant was also crushed. The owners of that property were in Seattle and rushed back to repair their damages. The horse stable of the Golden Phoenix mine was flattened to the ground. Fortunately, no animals were in the stable at the time.

In addition to the heavy, wet snow, the weather was unusually cold in January and the following months. The leasing miners' main concern was focused on tearing at the innards of the earth and hacking away at rock with the intent of locating new mineral deposits. The non-lease miners, including more than a few of the prominent older miners, chose to challenge the weather with the filing of 15 recorded mineral claims in January.

The Golden Phoenix Mining Company had a crew of miners doing a great deal of work on their leased Black Jack mine. They ran a 300-foot crosscut tunnel that reached a ledge of ore 3 feet wide, showing gold in some of the rock.

The McCarthy brothers, John and Mike, were working their leased Culver claim and struck a 5-foot-wide, white-quartz vein of pay ore. The ore that the leasing miners were getting was of good quality. However, John Shoudy pointed out that a better or different system of milling needed to be inaugurated because only 25 to 35 percent of the assay value was being saved.

Early in February, a Chinook (warm) wind blew through the Swauk-Peshastin area. Its arrival may have warmed the cockles of some folks' hearts, but it was short lived. The eroded road conditions made wagon travel almost impassable due to the road-scouring effect of the fast snowmelt.

The new road connecting the towns along the Wenatchee River to the Great Northern Railway stations became a bone of contention to the towns of Ellensburg and Cle Elum. Due to improved access, the towns north of Blewett began to receive some of the mining business that was once held in an exclusive monopoly by Ellensburg and Cle Elum. Some of Kittitas County's lost revenue went northbound and was being handled by stores on the Wenatchee River side of Blewett Pass. Eventually, the trade problems began to balance out. More commerce was shared between the distant but connected towns of central Kittitas County and northern Kittitas County, soon to become Chelan County.

Blewett people and others nearby spent the month of February 1898 active in storm-damage repair. Due to the unexpected road damage, things mining-related and otherwise seemed not to be newsworthy. There were no additional recorded claims emanating from Blewett.

ROAD CONDITIONS AND NEW ROADS

A commission of interested folks gathered to discuss options for a road to serve the people living between Leavenworth, Peshastin, and Blewett. Cash and labor were offered during the meeting for the much-needed year-long-use road between the towns of Blewett and Peshastin. But an additional $800 to $1,000 would be needed through the county commissioner's office. The pleading went on and on, but no action was decided upon—for a second time. Still, 1898 would be a year of road building.

The more immediate concerns of the Blewett folks were the facts that no road existed between Blewett and Negro Creek or between Ingalls Creek and Negro Creek. Horses in single file were the means of hauling supplies between those destinations. It started with about two miles of primitive wagon road between Blewett and Negro Creek. This connection gave Blewett access to several miles of landlocked road routed up Negro Creek as a means of access to mine sites and to supply miners.

Previously, all the drill steel, blasting powder, and other mining supplies were brought to Negro Creek from the north on a wagon road. It started at the mouth of Peshastin Creek to its transfer point at Ingalls Creek. Then everything was transported over a pack trail from Ingalls Creek to and up Negro Creek. There was also the yearly problem of road repair between Ingalls Creek and the town of Peshastin.

In the meantime, the road up Culver Gulch was being extended up to Tunnel No. 9. Pack-trains would then have to negotiate the steep trail between Tunnel No. 9, passing alongside the gigantic basaltic dike intrusion. The pack trail ended west of Tunnel No. 1, at Mineral Monument No. 1 on the top of the ridge.

Above Tunnel No. 9, the gulch road split, going westward up to Mineral Monument No. 1 and another road heads ¼ mile northward to the rock outcrop called the Pinnacles. The Pinnacles are in the area where the trail ended on the ridge saddle separating Culver Gulch from the Negro Creek side.

GOLD AMALGAM STOLEN FROM BLEWETT MILL

Hard times seemed to generate hard crimes, at least in Blewett, as indicated by $600 worth of gold-amalgam material that went missing (stolen) from a mill building. In June 1898, the amalgam stockpile was noted as being shorted from the original total amount. In fact, it was realized that almost half the amalgam was missing at weigh-in time (the weight/volume was not reported). The less-than-detailed, odd description for the theft said it showed a loss of about "$500 to the ton." The theft was attributed to a young miner.

OTHER HAPPENINGS

Miner Joe Mead recorded and worked his placer claim on Peshastin Creek. He was also known around town for his talent as an Italian guitar player and romantic ballad-singing troubadour. Shortly after he filed on the dig, he uncovered an isolated deposit of placer gold that paid him $2,500. Joe evidently knew when to hold 'em and when to fold 'em because he folded and left Blewett shortly thereafter.

In 1898, Charles Wright started as an employee at the cyanide plant in Blewett. When the plant closed down, he and his family moved north of Blewett where he worked at his father's sawmill. Wright was back in the Blewett area again in 1935 during the Great Depression. He was panning for gold on Peshastin Creek to eke out a living on a placer dig he had abandoned several years before.

GOVERNMENT ACTIVITY

With all the gold production going on in the Cle Elum, Peshastin, and Swauk Mining Districts, a new government assay office was established in Ellensburg, Washington, in July 1898. This eliminated the long trip to the government assay office in Seattle.

James Wilder became Blewett's postmaster. Bill Patterson, merchant and miner of Blewett, was a candidate for the office of sheriff in September.

BLEWETT MINING LULL

News of events mine-related took a dive into production limbo in 1898. The leased mines in Culver Gulch and a few non-gulch mining companies were working to produce large piles of ore for milling. Few new prospects were being developed, and from the point of view of the non-company miners or lease-miners, the Peshastin Mining District didn't look promising. Although rich ore was found in the company-owned mines, no large bodies of ore were located elsewhere in the Peshastin Mining District. The large-scale mine operators invested a lot of money, only to find that most of the high-grade gold deposits were comparatively smaller than first estimated. The new normal became only a few gold-discovery hot spots with long stretches of barren rock in between. The small-mine owners were making a living, which was sufficient for them and their families under the conditions of a nationally depressed economy.

PEG LEG TANDY

In 1898, a miner named Tandy was in residence at Blewett, but under what capacity as a miner is in question. Tandy was a Civil War veteran who wore a wood peg leg to replace the one lost in battle. Added to his diminished physical abilities was poor eye sight, which didn't help in his choice of employment—or other activities.

A Civil War vet named Tandy had a wood peg leg, a dandy,
And his roomy, a Labrador retriever, except in fact 'twas a beaver.
Tandy should have used caution, which he didn't do often.
So when he took off his wood, it got chewed on real good.
After a year, come one fall, Tandy had to lean on the wall
'Cause his wood leg was noticeably short.
Repair was a steel rod, attached to the leg log.
Of his companion, he would make sport.
Then one day …
A storm was a-brewin' as the beaver starts chewin'
The stump leg as it leaned on the porch.
Then lightning did strike at the beaver's last bite.
Result … a critter mortally scorched.
Tandy made a new crutch; as for looks, wasn't much
But shaped like a mine tool, it was.
So…
Whether he used it at home, or when mining alone,
It did whatever it does.

JOHN KENDLE'S PROBLEM WITH *IT*, 1899

John Kendle's oddities finally caught up with him in January 1899. Or perhaps he stood too close and too long near the contained secret ingredients used in his new minerals detector. Either way or both, John's behavior was startling enough to urge the folks in Blewett to contact Sheriff Brown of Cle Elum to look into the current situation at the Kendle family cabin. Resident-miner Kendle was experiencing a warp in the continuity of his five senses relating to the realities of life.

So there they were—he and the children blockaded in their cabin, minus his wife, Sara, who was in the hospital at the time. He made a gun port on each of the four cabin walls. He armed his sons and daughters and told them to watch and shoot at whatever it was that had spooked John. No identifying details were offered to explain what *it* was.

What happened to set up a lawful response to the problem started when Kendle wrote to Governor John Rogers to send a company of US troops to help defend him from the presence of … whatever *it* was that he thought was a threat to him and his family. Well, evidentially *it* was real to John no matter how *it* appeared to the outside observer. What mattered to him was to have the resources to repel *it*. Bottom line, *it* made sense to John.

Governor Rogers saw at once what to do about *it*, the right thing for *it* to end peaceably for John Kendle. Kendle, according to Governor John Rogers, needed a little R & R within the padded walls of a room at the Medical Lake Mental Hospital to accommodate the renewal of Kendle's future peace of mind.

Sheriff Brown headed for Blewett to facilitate Governor Roger's request to check out the situation. However, he was stopped on the Swauk side of Blewett Pass by a horrific snowstorm of historic proportions and had to turn back. The situation was cause enough to discontinue his investigative trip to Blewett. The accumulation of deep winter snow put the Kendle matter on the back burner. It left John Kendle and his kids to remain by themselves until the spring snow melted enough for Sheriff Brown to get to Blewett on horseback.

All the residents in and around Blewett were snowed-in and insulated from contact with the outside. But the mine workers could get up Culver Gulch and continue driving tunnels and extracting ore. Even with the unusually deep snow, somehow there were 15 Blewett area claims recorded at the county assessor's office in January.

CHELAN COUNTY IS ESTABLISHED, 1899

Originally, the portion of today's Chelan County south of the Wenatchee River was formed by the Washington Territorial Legislature in 1863 as Ferguson County but did not get organized. Finally, March 13, 1899, Chelan County was formed through the backing of two powerful businessmen, attorney Frank Reeves and Arthur Gunn, organizer of the Wenatchee Power Company. With the event of newly created Chelan County, the mines of Blewett were no longer physically or economically a part of Kittitas County.

April 1899 was another dud as far as news about mining activity coming out of the Culver Gulch and Blewett area mines. A few insignificant claims were recorded. Other than that, the

These two men are putting the finishing touches on John Olden's wood-framed arrastra. (Chris Bell photo collection.)

deep snow put a slowdown on ambitions of small claim miners, or any activity, other than hunkering down and waiting for the mining season to begin.

Even John Kendle and his barricaded family fortress appeared to be on ice until the spring melt. He was still poor, old John Kendle who had a brain *phizziitz*. Something just snapped, and it made him weird. Then spring sprung, and evidentially Kendle's brain freeze thawed back to at least semi-normality. Soon afterward, he was noted recording placer claims and going about his daily business as if nothing had happened.

Chapter Sixteen: Warrior General, Reorganized, 1899–1905

WARRIOR GENERAL REMERGES, 1899

The Warrior General Mining Company came back to life in May 1899. They reissued the exact statement that was announced to the public when they formed their company back in 1896. Obviously, less was accomplished than the early list of improvements had forecast. But they did continue to lease their mineral holdings to groups of miners and ran that ore through the same old milling equipment that the Blewett Mining and Milling Company sold them in the complete-package deal. Now they seemed to be focused on pushing those past company-generated statements beyond the boasting stage and into reality.

So finally, according to the Warrior General Mining Company, their commitment to progress as originally intended was on the move once more. The month of May passed, and the Warrior General Mining Company came up with little to back their words. Even their promotional stint failed to generate enough interest to get their publicly available company stock sold in satisfactory quantities. The Warrior General Mining Company was at the point where they needed an infusion of something straight out of Prayersville. They needed something to build up momentum in their mine-related endeavors, especially since, for the parting fact for the month of May, not one claim was recorded in the Culver Gulch-Blewett area. The Warrior General Mining Company was setting starting dates for one project or another and, then later, having to change the production and milling schedule.

Warrior General Mining Company's 20-stamp mill (1896). It was previously owned by the Blewett Mining and Milling Company. (Chris Bell photo collection.)

Of the mines most talked about in Culver Gulch that were pulling out ore, there was no monetary data to reflect that activity. Evidentially for lack of the Warrior General Mining Company mill processing any ore; it could be assumed no commercial amounts of ore were being processed, although there was ore being stockpiled.

The Pole Pick claim and Blewett Tunnel miners had an ore bin full of ore from the new workings driven during the winter. Up at the Summit Pockets area, Tunnel No. 1 was in about 80 feet and still mucking ore. Tunnel No. 2 had a mineralized ledge of ore 3 to 4 feet wide at its full length, averaging $15 in free-milling gold per ton. It was estimated there was 2,000 tons of ore in sight.

E. A. Grunden was actively working the Black Jack mine, mining high-grade ore from the Peshastin vein. At the Peshastin Creek level, across the creek (southeast) from the lower Black Jack adit, was the portal to the Golden Cherry mine tunnel. It was owned by John A. Shoudy Sr. The Golden Cherry vein was on an east extension of the same vein as the Black Jack and had its own water-powered arrastra.

Owners Thaddeus Neubauer and Peter Anderson had the Lucky Queen mine on the north edge of town, with the lower tunnel at the county road level. The two men were finding pocket gold in decomposed quartz and calcite. Anderson led an active and productive life in Blewett from 1898 until April 1905, the month he sold all his mining claim holdings and left town.

WARRIOR GENERAL CONTINUES ITS LEASE PROGRAM, 1899

The mines under ownership of the Warrior General Mining Company continued, in August, to be worked through their lease contracts. But there was no word that the mills were processing the ore. Underground development went on as usual for any miner active in and around the Culver Gulch and Blewett area claims.

There were small mine owners that had arrastras busy processing ore, and John Olden's arrastra mills was crushing ore from his digs. There was also John Shoudy's mill, and other arrastras, but how much ore was being produced and who was producing it was not being reported. There were three new claims recorded August 25, 1899.

WARRIOR GENERAL REPLACES THE OLD BLEWETT MILLING MACHINERY, 1899

In September, news was heralded about in Blewett that two railroad cars loaded with new milling equipment out of San Francisco were on their way to Leavenworth via the Great Northern Railway. Then the equipment was transported by horse-drawn wagons up the newly constructed connecting road directly to the Warrior General Mining Company at Blewett.

The company added another 18 men to prepare the mill-site foundation for installation of the updated processing machinery. These activities indicate the removal of the original 20-stamp mill for the installation of a replacement mill. Over 30 years later, Ollie Jordin would bulldoze down this mill and replace it with another updated stamp mill. There was a total of 36 men working to have everything operational for the coming mining season. Then, added to the company's joy, it was announced that a 6-foot-wide ore ledge was struck on one of the Warrior General's claims that ran an assay of $156 per ton in gold.

The Warrior General was hard at work in October. The company was trying to get things in order so their mill would be ready to start by December. At this same time, a corporation out of Chicago had a lease on the Pole Pick mine. They were sending mined ore down the tramway to ore bins at the Warrior General stamp mill in preparation for the start of the new reduction and separation system. In the meantime, the Warrior General Mining Company was in the process of building a store and a hotel.

By November, installation was under way for a cyanide plant. The company was planning to treat ore from the Culver Gulch/Blewett mines and other claims in the Peshastin Mining District. There were several arrastras (locations not identified) actively running ore since the Warrior General mill wasn't up and running, even at the loss of some gold through that old inefficient system. The situation was tolerated because many of the claim holders of smaller mines had to continue to make a living while waiting for the big milling operation to start. No claims were recorded by local miners in November.

WARRIOR GENERAL ACTIVITIES AND A NEW WAGON ROAD

With the Warrior General Mining Company appearing to be on the verge of gold production and the Chelan County folks aware of the potential for monetary gain from the mining sector, the connecting wagon road between Leavenworth and Blewett was completely finished in December 1899. This was during the time James Wilder was Blewett's postmaster.

On December 1, a new mail contract was announced, and James Wyckoff was contracted to carry the first mail in his stagecoach. Among his first passengers were Hiram Montgomery, Henry Resburg, his wife, Mrs. Resburg, along with their daughter, Kate Montgomery (in later years, Kate became Mrs. Bailey). It is interesting to note that Hiram was Kate's father, but after Hiram and Kate's mother divorced, Kate's mother married Henry Resburg. Kate soon met James Wilder's young son Roy, and they became grade school classmates, which evolved into a lifelong friendship.

As everyday mining-camp life plodded along, folks waited hopefully for an early spring. Along with the opening of the 1900 mining season would be the completed milling improvements, the overdue results of the Warrior General Mining Company's boasts of good things to come.

WARRIOR GENERAL STAMPING MILL AND CYANIDE PLANT, 1900

While the Warrior General ran the newly equipped and updated 20-stamp mill, the leasing party working the Peshastin mine was operating the cyanide plant. The crew at the cyanide plant was W. H. Resburg and Charles Wright. One man worked days, and the other worked nights. There was also a chemist and a teamster included in the mill schedule as needed. The cyanide plant was located to the north end of Blewett on the west side of Peshastin Creek. The plant was shut down and removed in 1901.

There were two old stamp mills; one was about 1,000 feet northeast of the Warrior General Mining Company mill and had a three-stamp unit. The other stamp mill was said to be located ¼ mile south of the Warrior General milling area and was the property of the Tip Top mine. A horizontal, 100-hp engine ran most of the machinery. A 12-hp upright engine was also mentioned as the power supply to the smaller machines.

In June 2013, the author and two other members, Terry and Todd Carlson, of Northwest Underground Explorations, discovered two concrete foundation blocks on a wide, flat area by the road located at the lower west end of the Golden Chariot claim, which the Tip Top mine owned at one time. One of the concrete blocks had a groove notched into it and a broken bolt pattern on top that would facilitate a type of Pelton-wheel device. This would establish the site of the aforementioned Tip Top mill location.

During the summer of 1900, the Warrior General was planning to add another 20 stamps to bring the mill to its full stamping capacity of 40 stamps. Six more concentrators were planned for a total of 12. The richer high-grade sulfide ore was sacked and most likely shipped to the Everett smelter, which operated from 1893–1910. Also, the railroad terminal at Leavenworth was closer than the Ellensburg railroad terminal. Leavenworth was also connected to Blewett by the newer, downhill wagon road headed northward, as opposed to the hard-pull going up and over Blewett Pass.

The lower-grade ore was first concentrated at the mill before shipment to the smelter. The Warrior General intended to mine 2 to 5 tons of high-grade ore daily at an average of $300 in gold per ton. These were admitted estimates.

A group of Boston businessmen was running the Warrior General Mining Company. It is noted that from that point a lot of money was being invested in mine-related improvements, with more financing announced for the coming mining season. Plus, there was more Warrior General Mining Company owned improvements in the business sector of Blewett. George W. Boggs was hired to run the updated cyanide plant.

Within a few days of a Peshastin tunnel strike announcement, the crew at the Pole Pick hit their rich deposit of free-gold-bearing white quartz. Other than these two news articles, word about Blewett mining activities was slow in reaching the outside.

By mid-June 1900, with Boggs's expertise as manager, the cyanide plant at Blewett produced gold bricks valued between $1,000 and $1,500 and began averaging one gold brick every two weeks. It was all extracted from gold-bearing sulfides that were not caught in the milling process, as it ran off into the tailings of the 20-stamp mill.

REORGANIZATION OF WARRIOR GENERAL, 1900

In 1900, Warrior General Mining Company reorganized and continued under a new company heading as the Chelan Mining and Milling Company. The Chelan Mining and Milling Company began its duties by allowing a continuation of company claim leases that were formerly controlled by the Warrior General. This did not appear to translate clearly with all the various information related to the Warrior General Mining Company to Chelan Mining Company after the reorganization. This may be the reason for the resulting confusion and lack of information regarding the Chelan Mining and Milling Company ownership. Some reports on its mining and other mine-related activities that should have been accredited to the Chelan Mining and Milling Company were errantly credited to the Warrior General. This situation may be the cause of the litigation that was to follow, involving the two mining companies, although the reasons for this confusion remain unclear.

It appears the milling method used to processes the various lease claims also changed. Although little is mentioned in outside news sources, mining in Culver Gulch was assumed to be moving along in the same manner as in the previous mining season. It was stated that George Boggs's meticulous observation of the new milling process was paramount in reclaiming a considerable amount of gold from the tailings that were set aside for the purpose of extracting gold via the newer cyanide method. This routine went on for 18 months. The reorganized Chelan Mining and Milling Company continued to run the mining operations. Then it merged its mining operations (lacking explanation) into association with the Badger State Mining Company. The name change didn't help the company, and it began plodding along in a not overly successful gold-producing mode.

About the same time that the Chelan Mining and Milling Company and Badger State Mining Company (two different companies with the same owners) were limping along with whatever mining activities was keeping them afloat financially; Thomas A. Parish (assessor for King County, Washington) organized La Rica Mining Company.

This is the 20-stamp mill about the time the Chelan Mining and Milling Company had active ownership in 1900. (Grace Browitt Elkins photo collection.)

LA RICA CONSOLIDATED MINING COMPANY, 1901-1905

General J. D. McIntyre was managing La Rica and the Badger State Mining Companies. These two companies were run separately but owned by the same investors. W. H. McKay was one of the known middlemen for the two companies.

Repairs and updating of old mining equipment were badly needed. McIntyre set out by repairing the bucket tram from the Culver mine down to the mill. Next, he had the company hotel remodeled and opened it as a boarding house for La Rica/Badger State employees.

La Rica paid its first dividends to company shareholders in February 1904. The payment amounted to 25 cents per share. The total number of the shares paid was not in the released data. The April 1904 payout was a dividend of 30 cents per share.

La Rica Consolidated Mining Company's 20-stamp mill during its ownership in 1901. (Chris Bell photo collection.)

Note: The newspaper article omitted "Consolidated" from the name, calling it La Rica Mining Company. Mining company names occasionally appear altered in title reference according to which particular newspaper reporter was identifying a mining company in the report. On two or three occasions within the Blewett-Culver Gulch mining company references, the shortened company name was later used as the official name upon relocation and claim recording, which can add to confusion during data research.

Then John McCarthy was contracted to construct a water-power plant, related to La Rica's mining activities, which replaced the steam-powered source that ran the Warrior General 20-stamp mill. It was an expensive addition, and as John's water-plant construction was getting under way, he was interrupted. It seems his brother Richard still had a wild streak in him, akin to the one that drove older brother John in his youthful years. So big brother John had to make the long trip to North Yakima and bail Richard out of jail and then return to Blewett to oversee the water-plant project.

John Stout and his son Robert were Blewett resident/miners. They received a contract to run 1,300 feet of tunnel on La Rica properties. John had two shifts of men on the job. The men running the workings were using a Burleigh drill, and they also put in a hoisting setup. John Olden, along with George Turner, was mining an ore outcrop on the Culver claim for La Rica and Badger State Mining Companies.

In May 1904, La Rica and Badger State closed down because of a misunderstanding among stockholders and their dissatisfaction with their mine manager, General McIntyre. This action included the refusal of payment on a number of company checks over several weeks. Meanwhile, McIntyre kept things moving along as he resumed his stamp-mill operation.

By July 1904, General McIntyre had 75 men working full throttle. Miners were kept busy loading the tram ore buckets with rock for the workers at the 20-stamp mill and cyanide plant. Gold-bearing rock was sent down to the company mill ore bins at the rate of about 140 tons of ore per day. The word given the stockholders was that another 20 stamps was intended to be added to the mill, raising the number to 40 stamps pounding ore. Due to low water volume by September 1904, only 10 of the 20 stamps were running. It was noted that several times in the past years (possibly to spike the promotional end for added appeal), mining companies boasted about adding 20 stamps or more to their milling process. Usually those extra stamps never materialized. Unfortunately, after a fairly good start, things began to slow down for La Rica Consolidated and Badger State Mining Companies and the Chelan Mining and Milling Company. Once again, owing to dissatisfaction with the management of La Rica and Badger State properties, Thomas Parish took charge in January 1905.

Thomas brought in mining engineer Eugene Knapp of Seattle to be his superintendent. The intent was to install air compressors and other machinery at once. Knapp examined the company property and submitted a report on his findings.

Richard Waite, a civil engineer from Seattle, was brought to La Rica Consolidated Mining Company mines to run various surveys so work at the mines could resume—only they didn't. A month later, things at La Rica Consolidated Mining Company started to take a dive. Waite returned to Seattle and took passage on a boat bound for the Alaska gold fields and started a business as an assayer and surveyor.

Meanwhile back at Blewett, La Rica Consolidated Mining and associates came up with a solution to join forces as the Washington Meteor Mining Company.

It is unfortunate that there are gaps in the data sources of mining companies such as these. Sometimes a pattern of how mining businesses react to certain economic and ore-deficient situations begins to emerge. The subtle beginnings of a slowdown in production, due to loss of ore output, was often concealed by pointing out past, high-standard gold-processing performances. They are used to dishonestly sell off a mining company that is deemed to be in a position to lose money for the company. Back-room deals are not often exposed, so the source of the problem is anybody's guess.

With that said, the mines of Culver Gulch and those near Blewett were not prone to deceive in this manner. Many of the resident miners with decent mineral holdings were long-term Blewett area residents and had a trusted reputation to back them in their personal mining property dealings.

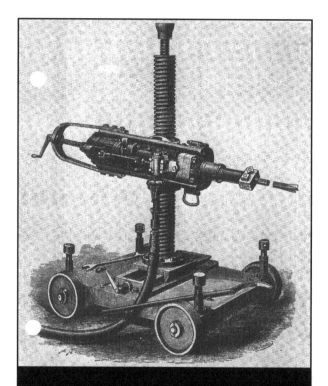

This is a Burleigh drill, as mentioned on page 136. (Photo from GEOTIMES magazine, November [1969].)

Chapter Seventeen:
Blewett Happenings, 1900-1907

FRANK REEVES SWAYS THE
HEART OF THE VOTING MINER, 1900

Frank Reeves, as a young man, was beyond his years in business knowledge. He was also instrumental in partitioning the north section of Kittitas County into the lower half of Chelan County in 1899. So with his new name recognition working for him, he ran for prosecuting attorney in the first Chelan County election during 1900. The vote would be too close to depend on just the Wenatchee District ballot count, so Frank headed to the town of Blewett for their support and the 200 miner/resident voting bloc in that precinct.

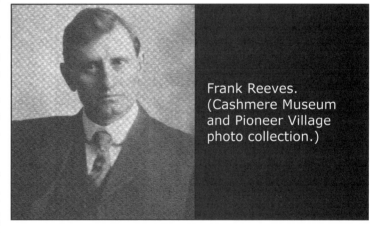

Frank Reeves. (Cashmere Museum and Pioneer Village photo collection.)

How to get it? The key to persuade those 200 voters on to Frank's side … was the beer-and-whiskey persuasion technique. Frank hired miner/rancher George Hansel to help pick up the mood musically with his fiddle.

So an invite was sent out for several days in the mining district that free food and drink were being furnished by Frank Reeves at the saloon of Frank's choice (he probably lost the vote of the other saloon owners in Blewett), and all the good old boys had to do was listen to Frank's campaign speech for a fidgety few minutes.

As expected, a large crowd of miners and other area folks showed up at the saloon on the prearranged date. The overflow crowd spilled out onto the property surrounding the establishment of liquid pleasure in what may have resembled a beer garden. George Hansel was sawing away on his fiddle as booted miners and other Blewett residents stomped their whiskey-routed gyrations on the sagging, creaking wood floor of the saloon. There they all were—singing, drinking, laughing, and dancing. Yes, life was good and was destined (according the partiers) to get even "gooder."

About this time, two soiled old miners pushed their loaded packhorse ahead of them through the swinging doors of the saloon and followed in. They made progress to the center of the room with beer kegs in sight. Things were looking good until … the floor snapped, popped, and collapsed down and into the cellar of the saloon. All drinking, music—everything and everybody in the drop zone—was funneled into the splintering maelstrom of wood, miner's bodies, and horse flesh. Anything and everything the descending bodies could grab onto in an attempt at self-preservation didn't help, but only added to the collateral damage. Then there was an unsure, totally silent pause …

Well, at least not all was lost—the bar went down too, down to the late-arriving miner duo, which momentarily redefined the meaning of room service. All anybody could account for in the way of injury were some scratches and bruises, and one wild-eyed horse with a possibly permanent, mental disability.

As the mass of displaced humanity and horse hide gathered itself and reconnoitered the situation, George Hansel's unharmed fiddle was back in action playing "Captain Jinx of the Horse Marines." The saloon was in shambles. What to do? The red schoolhouse, that's what to do. The extricated revelers headed there, set up a bar, and all crammed themselves wherever there was room. Frank Reeves gave his campaign talk, and afterward the womenfolk showed up, and dancing was the theme of the party as George's fiddle wailed away until dawn for the non-stop dancers.

Oh, yeah, and Frank got elected.

TUNNEL NO. 9, BLEWETT TUNNEL, 1900

In 1900, news came out about a strike of high-grade, gold-infused sulfide ore that was assayed from $250 to $465 in gold per ton. The assays were not picked from high-graded samples, but as an average across the surface from which they were discovered. The enriched ore was cut into while following a 5-foot-wide, true-fissure, low-grade quartz-and-talc-composition ledge that ran for 900 feet through Tunnel No. 9. To this point, the average assay in Tunnel No. 9 carried $4 per ton in free gold, plus a small amount of copper.

CULVER GULCH DEVELOPS A 300-FOOT SHAFT, 1900

This location data and year fits the physical placement of the 300-foot-deep connecting shaft that allowed accessing the multi-claim tunnel levels in Culver Gulch. The shaft was continuous from Tunnel No. 9 up to and passing through the Blewett Tunnel (located on the Culver claim) for another 80 feet to open at the surface (the Blewett Tunnel was developed extensively in 1893). Tunnel No. 6 connects through various off-set levels down to Tunnel No. 9 and thus accessed the shaft by the multi-level, connected, underground workings.

This information gives an approximate timeline as to when the 300-foot shaft was developed. Up until this data was discovered, no verified year for the development of the 300-foot shaft was available

Other data called the 900-foot tunnel a drift, and still another erroneously referred to it as a crosscut. Tunnel No. 9 was following a vein encountered on the Pole Pick claim. This is another instance where mining terms and newspaper reporting during that era can cause future fact-gathering problems.

Part of the reason for the long 900-foot tunnel was to get to depth onto a known ledge and encounter the ore body containing gold-rich sulfides. The high-grade sulfide rock inside Tunnel No. 9 was up to 16 inches wide, and ran parallel with the hanging wall.

This find was not a blind lead but a continuation of the Pole Pick vein. It surfaced to become an apex on the outcropping rock of Tunnel No. 4 and Tunnel No. 5. Tunnel No. 9 was planned to reach a point vertically under an estimated 250,000 tons of free-milling gold-bearing rock near the surface that was above the deposit of the deeper sulfide ore. The raise, a 300-foot shaft, was run upward through the sulfide ore. This is what they may have been referring to as an ore-shoot as it was blasted; the overhead ore was mucked into ore cars waiting below in Tunnel No. 9. From the ore-car loading area, it was sent out through 900-foot-long Tunnel No. 9 to the ore bin at the tram-station terminal outside the tunnel portal. Tunnel No. 9 became the haulage level for those high-grade workings. The gold-bearing rock was sent down to the company mill via the ore-bucket cable-tram system. An underground raise into the gold-bearing ore was developed near the portal of Tunnel No. 9. In the last decade, the roof of the raise has been collapsing into the tunnel workings.

The ore taken from a raise, possibly near the portal, was assayed $10 to $12 in gold per ton. At that time, it cost about $1.50 per ton to mine and $2 per ton to mill, for a total of $3.50 per ton, with gold being valued at $18.96 an ounce. The Warrior General's 20-stamp mill (the old Blewett mill site) was capable of processing 50 tons of ore per day, which made a good profit margin.

The Pole Pick mine also removed a large amount of free-milling ore in 1900. It came from a 2-foot-wide gold-bearing quartz vein that was deposited between slate and porphyry tunnel rock. The product was a gold brick valued at $2,175 from a 21-day run of ore through the Warrior General Mining Company mill. In 1900, the 20-stamp mill shipped gold bullion worth $68,000.

BLEWETT PASS MINING COMPANY, PRE-1901

The following claims were under the ownership of James Wilder until 1901. Data on recorded claims identified the Blewett Pass Mining Company claims as Amber Glee, Ivanhoe Extension, Byron G tunnel site, Byron Lode, Twins, Roy and Ray, Kennelworth, and Hazel. Variations from the above claim name list were known to be long-term mining claim holdings of James Wilder.

James favored leasing some of his various claims and then working them after the lease ran out. This pattern allowed others to develop his workings and sometimes make a profit while mining on gold-bearing quartz. This strategy made it easier for James to accesses suspected areas of ore deposits not yet cut by tunneling. Overall, Wilder got a lot more out of the lessees than they got out of him.

BLEWETT PASS MINING COMPANY 1901-1914

Some of the Blewett Pass Mining Company claims began as lease contract digs, or they were sold to mining businessman W. H. McKay. McKay was also noted as being financially involved with La Rica Consolidated Mining Company. James Wilder may have been among the partners or sufficiently shrewd to be near enough to the action to take advantage of buying in when the opportunity presented itself.

There is no data pertaining to this company's production activities, so it may have never gotten beyond the exploration or pre-development stages. W. H. McKay was president, and the company office was located in Seattle, Washington.

In 1901, there was a group of 11 claims that later made McKay's mining properties list. The company didn't come with the entire properties intact. They were added to the Blewett Pass Mining Company holdings from time to time. Those he added were the Kennelworth, a relocation of one unlisted claim, the Twin, Amber Glee, Ivanhoe Extension, Roy and Ray, Hazel, Byron G, Tunnel Site claim, Byron Lode, and the Rainbow No. 2 and Rainbow No. 3 claims. McKay also had control of a mineralized ground called the "W. H. McKay Property," identified as the Pole Pick and Pole Pick Fraction properties claims.

DAN SHASER'S BRIDGE-CROSSING ACCIDENT

Dan Shaser was returning from conducting business in Ellensburg and was one bridge away from making an entrance into Blewett. As he rode his horse onto the bridge, it collapsed. It seems repairs began, in this case, when the rotten boards of the bridge gave way and left Dan and his timber-straddling horse suspended in the air. Dan had an axe, and with great difficulty, he chopped out the bridge girders to set the steed loose from its precarious perch. Neither participant was injured in the accident.

MARKO FAMILY

About the mid-1900s, several Marko family members, including John, Robert, Matt, and Joe and Lena with their 19-year-old daughter, were noted in residence at Blewett. Joe was a machinist at the 20-stamp mill. Robert Marko was a resident/miner who had the Grandview claim. It was located west, up past the headwaters of Negro Creek. When the snow forced Robert off his dig, he turned to hauling firewood for the folks in Blewett. Matt Marko was noted as a teamster. Among one of his jobs was hauling blasting powder for the Badger State Mining Company. John

Marko was in charge of some mining interests in Blewett. He was active in the area for several years. Later he went to Alaska to manage a large mining company. He was the son-in-law of Lena Griffin. Lena was married to Edward King.

JOHN GRIFFIN

John Griffin first came to Blewett to inspect some of the Culver Gulch and other Blewett area claims about 1898. John returned later, became involved in Blewett mining activities, and by 1904, he was married to widow Lena King. Edwin C. King was Mrs. Lena King-Griffin's oldest son. Old family patriarch Joel King moved in with his Blewett resident daughter-in-law, Mrs. John (Lena King) Griffin, and granddaughter Mrs. Joseph Marko (Joel King died September 6, 1919, and is buried at the Peshastin Cemetery). John Griffin became a permanent Blewett resident in 1904, when he entered into active control of the Tip Top Mining Company and had copper claims up Negro Creek.

Around the middle of January 1905, John Griffin lost his infant son and young daughter to whooping cough. They were buried in the Odd Fellows Cemetery in Ellensburg, Washington. Within the month, John was dealt an additional burden to bear due to a severe onslaught of rheumatism. This happened as he and miner Con Bell were developing the Tip Top mine property on the west slope of Windmill Point. At this time, he was compelled to quit manual labor in the underground workings.

During the first part of May, John Griffin had a relapse of his hip problems and needed to travel over the mountains and on roads in poor condition to get to adequate care. An emergency team of compassionate friends sawed out fallen trees from the road and repaired it where needed so that John could be transported to a physician. John was laid out on bedding in the first wagon rig of the season to go over the summit at Blewett Pass. He was taken into Cle Elum where he received much-needed and extensive attention.

John's hope for improving health-wise was focused on getting well enough to endure a trip from Cle Elum to South King County, Washington, and the curative waters of the Green River Hot Springs facility. By June, John was road ready and made it to Green River Hot Springs, but he was suffering great pain resulting in very slow gain in improved health. John's illness prompted him and his family to spend the winter months of 1906 in Ellensburg.

Eventually John could get around on crutches. When he was deemed well enough, he went back to Blewett and assumed running the Tip Top Consolidated Mining Company. By October, John was functioning in his daily routine, but he was in constant pain and had lost most of the mobility of his rheumatoid leg. Hobbling about on crutches was the best he could do. It appears that he was again a driving force with the Tip Top Company at this point.

John's sciatica pain subsided one year later, and in 1907, he was on the mend. John's physical progress was going well until July of 1907. At that time, an inflammation in his hip rapidly developed. Surgery was performed at Leavenworth by Dr. George Hoxey and Dr. Felch resulting in the removal of one quart of puss from his hip area. Afterward he became very ill, which led to an infection-related death at noon, November 20, 1907. John was 48.

The manner, in which these two miners are working on the ore vein here, is similar to the way the ore was stoped from the No. 9 Tunnel in Culver Gulch. (Vic Pisoni photo collection.)

Chapter Eighteen: Washington Meteor and Alta Vista Mining Companies, 1904-1907

All Blewett's various milling facilities and most other mine-related activities were idle due to bad weather in 1904. The exception was Thomas Parish, who was scurrying around camp looking after his La Rica Consolidated and Badger State mining properties in preparation for a possible merger into the Washington Meteor Mining Company.

Various, intermittent legal conflicts took place over verification of claim-property control in the Blewett area among the La Rica Consolidated/Badger State and Warrior General mining companies in upper Culver Gulch. The owners of the stamp mill and lower mining claims in

Washington Meteor Mining Company's 20-stamp mill (1903). The tailing pile, up-slope, and to the back of the mill, is at the Meteor tunnel level. (Chris Bell photo collection.)

the gulch were also involved in the court case. Others contending for their water rights were a group associated with the stamp mill. Then there was pressure from impatient stockholders waiting for monetary results in their long-held mining-company shares.

Negotiations were entered into by the trustees of all the bickering mining companies, and the entire $2,000,000 in capital stock was set aside as treasury stock. It was divided into 2,000,000 shares at the par value of $1 each, fully paid and non-assessable, and no promoter's stock was issued. Every dollar gained from the sale of stock would be put directly into running the emerging Washington Meteor Mining Company.

Ten thousand dollars was spent improving, testing, and verifying Washington Meteor's mineral potential. Assays from the company claims were stated at values ranging from $9.21 to $39.38 in gold per ton of ore. The depositories for the company were the Washington National Bank and the Northwest Trust and Safe Deposit Company of Seattle, Washington.

The Washington Meteor Mining Company mineral claim properties listed in 1903 were: the Black Jack mine, the Key Note, Homestake, Viola, Peshastin, Sandel, Bob Tail and Bob Tail Mill Site claims, the Hummingbird, and Culver mine. The ore from Washington Meteor's underground workings were processed through the company's 20-stamp mill. There was a cyanide plant northeast of the Washington Meteor 20-stamp mill that was later converted into a horse stable.

STAMP MILL STRUCTURE AND EQUIPMENT

The Washington Meteor Mining Company boasted a 40-stamp mill building in 1903, but only 20-stamps were ever installed in any of the company mills. Washington Meteor's mill was fully equipped with both steam and water power. Four frue vanner tables, or concentrators, were listed as operational. There was a small building on the west end of the mill that held the machine shop. In the space between the machine shop and the mill was a 36-inch water pipe that drove the turbine-style Pelton wheel, located 30 feet underground. The 36-inch pipe was still visible, as of 2013, and in its original placement, south of the mill site, alongside the lower road leading into Culver Gulch. The water power was the source used to compress the air that operated the machine-powered air drills in the mine workings.

On the upper (third) floor is where the stamp cams and other top parts of the 20- stamp machinery were exposed and accessible for maintenance. They were located in the south side of the building and had ore bins on the exposed stamp-stem side of each set of four sets of five stamps each. The north end of the building was vacant, wherein 20 additional stamps could be installed.

The second story of the stamp mill contained the lower end of the stamps. The foot or hammer at the base of the stamp shaft weighed 800 pounds each. These dropping stamps crushed the ore between the foot and iron base plate. The finer ore remnants were washed through a fine steel screen and onto a 4x6-foot copper plate, heavily coated with mercury. The mercury attracted the freed gold into its thin liquid glaze on the copper plates. Then the plates were scraped clean, and the gold containing mercury amalgam went through a process that finished in a brick shape of mixed gold and silver, called bullion, that was shipped to the Tacoma smelter.

Close-up picture of the 20-stamp mill features an unknown man in the forefront and two women in the background (1905). (Chris Bell photo collection.)

This is the Washington Meteor Mining Company superintendent's residence (1903). The three men on the left are not identified. John Olden is to the far right leaning against a post. The edge of Olden's cabin appears along the left edge of the picture. Notice the wood flume in the background. It carried water from Culver Springs Creek to the 20-stamp mill. The rock outcrop, above the flume, had a hole blasted through it as part of an older water ditch system, which once served the same purpose as the newer wood flume. (Chris Bell photo collection.)

The results of the processed bullion were delivered to the US Government Mint to determine the percentages of the gold and silver values to be paid to the gold-mining company.

On the ground floor of the mill, machine-operated vanner tables concentrated particles of gold ore not caught by the mercury-surfaced copper plates. These escaping gold-bearing grains passed over the plates, down into a chute, and onto the vanner tables. There, the heavier pieces containing gold were separated and collected out of the lighter waste material. The waste contained little value and was passed on to the tailings pond below the mill.

Front center, the ore bin and, *far right*, the entrance to the Meteor tunnel (1903). (Chris Bell photo collection.)

CYANIDE BUILDING

To save sacking, hauling, and smelter charges, the Washington Meteor Mining Company had a complete chemical plant for treatment of gold-bearing sulfide concentrates and tailings accumulated in the cast-off pond area next to the stamp mill. In the cyanide process, the ore was dried and then placed in a solution of cyanide, which dissolved the gold in the same manner as water dissolves sugar. The solution containing the disseminated particles of gold passed through several small tanks containing zinc shavings. The gold suspended in the solution attached to the zinc shavings, which went through another process that removed the gold from the zinc. The solutions were recycled and used again after being reinforced with additional quantities of cyanide. The thoroughness of this process is the best method of extracting a very high percent of gold from a ton of rock. The cost of the cyanide treatment was $2.50 per ton at the Washington Meteor Mining Company mill and cyanide plant, as opposed to a charge of $20 by the smelter.

These men are inspecting the gold-bearing vein in the Peshastin tunnel (1903). (Chris Bell photo collection.)

PROMOTIONAL BOASTS

Water power replaced the former power source obtained by steam. When powered by steam, the daily expense to run the mill was $30. With the new water-powered Pelton wheel, the cost per day effected a savings of $25 overall. This included the addition of operating the new air compressor that supported the new air machine drills.

The Meteor Tunnel was run westward to tap the ore veins and massive McCarthy and Parish ore-shoot deposits, identified as those deposits connected with the workings of the Peshastin claim drifts that were mined earlier, about 100 feet above the Meteor Tunnel.

Then, an all-too-familiar mining-company promotional statement was announced. The Washington Meteor Mining Company confidentially stated that by drawing additional water from Peshastin Creek, the company would be able to increase their stamp mill capacity up to 60 or 80 more stamps. Until that point, the mill was served mainly by ditches bringing water from Culver Springs Creek. Similar to past promotional fables, there were never any ore deposits found at this time that were large enough to require a stamp mill that size.

1905

Thomas Parish emerged in April 1905 as the vice-president of the Washington Meteor Mining Company. Eugene Knapp was brought by Parish to fill the position of managing engineer. Knapp was Thomas's previous boss at La Rica Consolidated and Badger State companies. Before the year was out, Parish was gone from the company.

A new board of officers and directors was announced as follows: O. J. Hobson was president of the Washington Meteor Mining Company and general superintendent at the mines; J. M. Cramer was vice-president; C. R. Hesseltine, secretary-treasurer, and president of the Rogers-Hesseltine Company (from Seattle). Five other board members and trusties were appointed. Among the trustees was A. A. Matwick (Matwick was responsible for the plan to develop the upper and lower Matwick Tunnels that proved no advantage in an attempt to crosscut to the Peshastin vein).

BLEWETT'S "SCOTTISH EARL" AND HIS LOST GOLD COINS, 1905

The death of Thomas Douglas would be of low priority in recounting if it were not for the fact that old Tom had hidden family secrets for years, brought to light only upon his demise.

In the late 1890s, Douglas drifted into the Culver Mining Camp, the oldest mining camp in the Wenatchee Mountain Range at that time. His first mineral claims recordings appear in the Swauk Mining District in 1897.

Thomas's Peshastin Mining District claim recordings begin when he registered the Hoosier and Washoe placer claims in 1901. They were located about 1 mile above the mouth of Tronsen Creek. From time to time, he worked for other miners, but did so only to distract people from the fact that he didn't need to work at all. And when he did work, it was noted that he did so in an unenthusiastic manner.

In truth, Thomas Douglas was a member of a rich Scottish family, and although his digs made no great amount of money to speak of, he always paid in cash at

Blewett stores. Thomas had numerous subscriptions to magazines and newspapers, which included the more politically radical content of that era. He would read them hunkered down in his cabin, and nobody would see him in town for days after he received his mail-day literature. This display of his moodiness and anti-social behavior was common knowledge to the Blewett folks. He appeared to be content playing solitaire card games, drank alone, and avoided social affairs.

When he periodically left town, he headed to Leavenworth. Folks would know he was out of town because his mail piled up at the post office until he returned for it. He was never known to hitch a ride from local Blewett residents. (After Thomas's death, it was guessed that he may have gone "outside" to pick up his family-issued allowance.) From Leavenworth, he boarded a train for an unknown destination.

Douglas occasionally allowed two other eccentric, mining, bachelor characters to visit his cabin where they would drink and play cards. A revealing incident occurred on one of the boozing card-playing events in the spring of 1905. Tom was drinking heavily and got in the mood for a different twist to their routine card game. So he dragged a wooden box from under his bed, popped off the top, and displayed to the surprised and excited visitors tiers of row after row of neatly laid $5-, $10- and $20-gold coins. So the men played for several hours using the gold coins as chips. After the gaming time was over, Thomas, true to his character, carefully counted his gold coins and replaced them under the bed. The two old miners were sent off into the night holding onto thoughts of their secret, gold-chip poker game.

Normally the code of the Blewett Camp was to "mind one's own business." The story of the gold as chips in the card game got out to a few more Blewett residents selected to hear, "Don't tell anybody, but ..." The event was somewhat contained within the community by those who honored such secrets. So the whole event was purposely muddled by casting comments of doubt about said happenings. Thus was the shrouding of the story into the uncertain realm of hearsay. Plus, Thomas always carried a holstered six-shooter and was considered a willing proponent for the use of hot-leaded defensive action should the occasion present itself.

Due to his reconsideration of his prideful actions on that booze-ignited night, he thought it prudent to bury his gold stash. The habit of burying a valuable stash of any kind was common, owing to distrust in banking institutions. It usually was hidden under ground within line of sight from a doorway or window. However, Thomas was not standard in many of his actions, so who knows where he may have thought was a secure place for his gold.

One moonlit night, Thomas, open to view, was seen out and about his surrounding cabin ground and appeared to be burying something box-shaped. The strange sight was reported, at a post-mortem date, by a woman who was up that night with a sick baby. It was a night-shrouded and sight-challenging distance that separated her house from his dwelling place, but the moon-lit view of his activities was unobstructed. The woman's child needed attention, so she was drawn away from seeing any more of his compromised, gold-burying activities.

Henry Resburg was postmaster in 1905. Thomas failed to show up for his usual stacks of literature on mail day. It was assumed he was on one of his outside trips during the following weeks of his absence. After his March trip departure, nobody could recall seeing him return. Then he missed another mail day, and Postmaster Resburg was disgruntled that Thomas's pile of mail was cluttering up the limited confines of the post office mail room.

The next day, teenaged brothers Billy and Fred Burmeister went by Thomas's cabin and could see that his three-day-capacity oil lamp was lighted. The curious boys decided to look inside and saw what appeared to them as the wastefully burning lamp. Then they noticed that he was inside lying on his bed motionless and staring at them.

Billy and Fred ran back to the post office and told Postmaster Resburg about the scene and added, "He's dead, except for his eyes. They's still alive. He saw us and blinked 'em." Resburg was also Blewett's justice of the peace and called the county prosecutor, who authorized an investigation. Then Resburg went straight to Thomas's cabin, and there Thomas lay, completely paralyzed except for his eyelids. Thomas Douglas died within a few days and was buried in the Blewett Cemetery, the first adult person in the Blewett town area to die of natural causes.

Thomas's cabin was thoroughly searched, but no gold was found. However, his birth certificate was located along with detailed information explaining that he was heir to the family fortune of his father, the Earl of Angus, Scotland, and Countess Mary Douglas, Thomas's mother. This translated into all those gold coins he possessed.

Herein lies the earlier part of Thomas Douglas's story. When Thomas, the oldest Douglas and heir to the family title was 20 years old, he secretly married Scottish lass named Jennie, who was of less than noble birth. Of course, his father, James Douglas, the Earl of Angus, and his wife, Countess Mary Douglas, were quite passionate in their expressed disapproval of Thomas's actions. Thomas, the future Earl of Angus, stormed out of the castle vowing not to return until his beloved wife was accepted into the family. That didn't happen, so he and his wife sailed to the United States and disappeared ... for a while. The happenings and whereabouts of Thomas and his wife are lost to our inquiring minds, although he was eventually found passing through solo when he arrived in the Swauk and Blewett areas.

Many years later (almost in conjunction with, but still before, Thomas's demise), after the old Earl of Angus died, they declared Thomas legally dead so the next heir could be acknowledged as head of the family. That action was pursued even though the Douglas family was aware of Thomas's survival (consider the gold-coin allowances he received). Resburg's letter explaining Thomas's death arrived in the hands of the Douglas family about the same time as the "legally dead" papers for Thomas (the rejected earl-to-be) were completed.

After the snow melted off the ground in the Blewett area around Thomas's cabin, the tale of his lurking figure burying a box circulated around town, giving signal enough to cause a rush of dirt-flinging shovels that pockmarked the Douglas property. The result left small craters of a Civil War-like battlefield landscape. But, alas, no box was discovered containing gold coins.

Then a rumor went out and about town saying that there was digging that went on before the snow melted, which leads one to consider that perhaps the box of gold coins was discovered before the post-snow, gold-rush excavations. But, Thomas was the kind of guy that would have no problem exhuming and re-burying the cache of gold coins several times—just to be safe.

Thomas B. Douglas died on a Saturday, March 18, 1905, at 2:30 P.M. He was buried in the Blewett Cemetery on Sunday evening by his friends. It had been several years since anybody was buried there. The coffin was handmade locally due to the roads being blocked by slides. The service consisted of a Bible reading, prayers, and two hymns. The deserted Douglas cabin was taken over by the Hobson family.

INTO 1906

By June 1905 through June 1906, things weren't going as smoothly as the Washington Meteor Mining Company had planned, or would have folks believe. Advertisements declaring really good deals on the company's stock sales appeared on full-page advertisements within *Westerner* magazine in February, April, May, and June of 1906. Similar ads also appeared in various newspapers within Washington State. For the past few years, high gold-producing data had appeared along with boldly predicted future ore output, based on some of the more recent assays, along with other premature announcements that had not yet been proven.

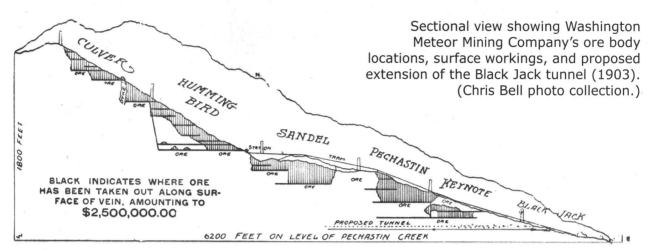

Sectional view showing Washington Meteor Mining Company's ore body locations, surface workings, and proposed extension of the Black Jack tunnel (1903). (Chris Bell photo collection.)

These ads were placed throughout the region. "Clip here, mail today" coupons were printed within the ad presentation to allow easy mail-order stock purchases. A June 1906 ad offered stock at 20 cents a share if taken at once.

At this point, in addition to the formerly described stamp mill, the company had an air compressor, and machine drills, a machine shop, two blacksmith's shops, and ore bunkers at each of their several mine sites. The aerial tram was advertised as "3,000 feet long" serving the upper workings. Building structures consisted of a hotel and boarding houses, superintendent's residence, mine company office, a complete assay plant and laboratory, a new 45x70-foot cyanide building, horse stables, wagons, schoolhouse, two stores, post office, powder house, and several small residential dwellings. A man named John McLennan was positioned as the mining superintendent.

But unsuccessfully suppressed events were unfolding that were mudding the swift waters of promotion. S. T. Riordan, a stockholder of Seattle, was suing for $36,000. This was in lieu of money he would have received for his stock investment but lost due to what he deemed misrepresentation by the Washington Meteor Mining Company. By July 1907, his stock was worthless. Details of the lawsuit's results were not forthcoming.

WASHINGTON METEOR MINING COMPANY REORGANIZED, 1907

John M. Cramer was the company president of the Washington Meteor Mining Company in May 1907, and John McLennan was noted as the company's superintendent. E. C. Limback was hired as the company mining engineer. Limback had an excellent reputation within the Northwest mining region for his efficient and reliable mining results. He had eight to 12 miners developing the Meteor Tunnel, which was acknowledged to have reached a total depth of 1,500 feet of workings. Limback drove the mining development an additional 300 feet and encountered the main fissure vein. The vein varied from 2 to 18 feet wide, and the ore was said to assay from $2.40 to $580 per ton in gold.

1906 Washington Meteor Mining Company assay office. (*Westerner* magazine, February 1906.)

C. R Hesseltine was in Blewett with an interest that went beyond his involvement as a financial agent. He was exploring the possibilities of some degree of ownership. In town, at the same time, were a new cook and another crew of men who gained employment with the Washington Meteor Mining Company.

A Washington Meteor Mining Company mill worker is weighing ore concentrates that were valued at $90 per ton in 1903. Sixty to eighty tons of ore per day was crushed by the mill to produce 4 to 6 tons of concentrates. All sacked concentrates were hauled to the railroad at Cle Elum and shipped to the Tacoma smelter. (Chris Bell photo collection.)

ALTA VISTA MINING COMPANY ORGANIZED BY THOMAS PARISH, 1906

John Ernest originally recorded the Alta Vista (Pole Pick No. 2) in 1874. The claim joined the Culver on the north and the Pole Pick No. 3 on the west. Pole Pick No. 3 was owned by the Cascade Mining Company's group of claims on the Negro Creek drainage, including the old Blinn properties. Ernest later sold the property to John A. Shoudy. During 1901, F. G. Thorp was noted working the Alta Vista under a lease contract from Shoudy. John Shoudy sold the claim to Thomas Parish in 1906.

During Washington Meteor Mining Company's various stock promotions and mine-related activities, Thomas Parish organized the Alta Vista Mining Company. He was the company president and his son, Albert Parish, was treasurer in 1907. Albert bought Will Tuttle's Blewett house for $75 and became an established Blewett resident/miner.

Claims in control of Alta Vista Mining Company and development work at this point in time were: Tunnel No. 1, 60 feet in length; Tunnel No. 2, 100 feet long with a high-grade body of gold-bearing ore; Tunnel No. 3 in 90 feet; and Tunnel No. 4 was 100 feet in length.

The Alta Vista stockholders held a meeting in Seattle on October 8, 1907. The following officers were elected: Thomas Parish, president; Edward C. Cowles, secretary; and Albert Parish, treasurer.

WASHINGTON METEOR AND ALTA VISTA MERGER, 1907

With the finalization of the merger contract in 1907, the Washington Meteor and Alta Vista Mining Companies combined their claim properties. This allowed the use of Washington Meteor Mining Company's Tunnel No. 9 as an ore-haulage level. It also gave Alta Vista access to the remainder of their deepest, rock-locked ore deposits on the Pole Pick No. 2 (Alta Vista) claim with less labor and more profit.

Alta Vista estimated from the strike and angle of the Pole Pick No. 2 vein that a crosscut tunnel from within Tunnel No. 9 would reach the vein of gold contained in the underground perimeters of their claim—and it did.

Alta Vista drifted 292 feet beyond the face of Tunnel No. 9 to the northwest corner of their surveyed underground workings that entered the Pole Pick No. 2. Then they ran a crosscut southwestward for another 200 feet and tapped the downward extension of the Pole Pick vein. It averaged $92 in gold per ton of ore. The new workings from Tunnel No. 9 and other recent Alta Vista developments totaled about 790 feet.

The Pole Pick Fraction claim is located between the Pole Pick No. 1 and Pole Pick No. 2. It is about 350 feet in elevation above Tunnel No. 9. At this point in the succession of various Pole Pick No. 1 and No. 2 ownerships, old claims maps show a different placement for the Pole Pick No.1 and No. 2. When compared to today's updated Culver Gulch claims map, some of the same claim names and original locations differed. The ore contained quartz, calcite, and talc and was densely disseminated with various pyrites. The veins varied from a stringer to 4 feet wide, and assayed from $8 to $200 in gold per ton.

Three short tunnels on the Pole Pick Fraction claim showed an oxidized quartz vein with pyrite crystals disseminated throughout the surrounding serpentine rock. A diabase dike cuts off the vein from the Eleanor (Pole Pick No. 1) workings.

In July, another contract was agreed upon. It was activated to have the Washington Meteor's mill process Alta Vista's ore. The mill was reached via an aerial ore tram from the mouth of Tunnel No. 9 to the stamp mill.

Thomas Parish relocated and recorded the Pole Pick Fraction claim October 25, 1907. The Pole Pick Fraction was established from portions of the Pole Pick No.1 and Pole Pick No. 2. The Pole Pick Fraction did not exist in 1893 because the original Pole Pick claim covered future Pole Pick Fraction ground. The first mining claim map on which the Pole Pick Fraction appeared was Charles E. Weaver's 1910 Culver Gulch map. By 1911, the various Pole Pick claims had developed 1,900 feet of crosscut and drift tunnels.

GOLD PAN-POLE PICK WORKINGS, 1907

In 1907, the Gold Pan-Pole Pick digs was developed above the Pole Pick Fraction claim. It showed a vein 4 feet wide. One hundred feet inside the Gold Pan-Pole Pick adit, calcite was found in the vein. Eight assays from the vein gave gold values of $27 per ton of ore.

Chapter Nineteen:
Blewett Mining Activity, 1910-1913

Charles Weaver researched and made a physical examination for the information about Culver Gulch and Blewett's mining claims in his report, "Geology and Ore Deposits of the Blewett Mining District," Bulletin No. 6 (1910). About the time Bulletin No. 6 was published, the Peshastin Mining District was known and referenced as the Blewett Mining District.

Weaver included a note of thanks to Blewett miner/mine owners John Olden and John McCarthy. Their information and extensive mining knowledge of Culver Gulch is reflected in Weaver's following mining claim descriptions.

Weaver also extended thanks to another miner/mine owner, Thomas A. Parish, president of the Alta Vista Mining Company. Weaver was a guest in residence with Thomas during Weaver's mining-season visit at Blewett. According to the information at this time, the town of Blewett was home to about 40 miners.

The total footage for the underground workings of the Washington Meteor Mining Company was given at over 7,000 feet, which didn't include all the raises, shafts, or open cuts. The company properties started out with the Culver claim, Bob Tail (Wye Tunnel), Hummingbird, Sandel, Peshastin, Black Jack, and Key Note (Dry Tunnel). Other claims that were added to their holdings from year to year include the Summit Pockets, Draw Tunnel, and all the numbered tunnels (Tunnel No. 1, Tunnel No. 2, etc.). The mining claims in Weaver's report have been covered on previous pages. Updated data for some of those mines is presented in the following text.

WASHINGTON METEOR MINING COMPANY LITIGATION, 1910

A complaint was filed against the Washington Meteor Mining Company in 1910. It revolved around the alleged bad-faith policy perceived by the lessees of Washington Meteor Mining Company properties. This lawsuit of considerable magnitude was started in the superior court of Chelan County. It involved the Black Jack, Peshastin, Homestake, Culver, Bob Tail (Wye Tunnel), Hummingbird, Sandel, and Viola claims. The lawsuit also included the stamp mills and other company holdings.

During the past several years leading up to the court confrontation, the Washington Meteor Mining Company owned the aforementioned properties. In the lawsuit, a group of folks holding mining stock in the company accused certain company directors of attempting to defraud stockholders. They said the directors were turning over company mining properties to other parties under the name of the Blewett Mining and Leasing Company (another source referred to them as the Blewett Mine and Leasing Company). A 5-year lease was issued to a group of men who held a large amount of Blewett Mining and Leasing Company stock. These men appeared

This miner is loading gold-bearing ore from the vein into an aerial tram bucket that was sent down to the 20-stamp mill. (Cashmere Museum and Pioneer Village photo collection.)

to be separate from the Washington Meteor Mining Company's inner-company group of officials. In the least, it was a dishonest plan by the company officials and evidently unannounced to the minimally invested stockholders. The fraud was perpetrated by city-based investors who depended on agents that appeared to be in on the illegal dealings to their mutual advantage.

The first years of the Blewett Mining and Leasing Company's activities included reprocessing tons of discarded gold-bearing sulfide ore from passed-off mill-tailing ponds in the areas. The Washington Meteor Mining Company accomplished the changeover by removing the amalgamating tables and installing three cyanide tanks with a 35-ton capacity.

Aside from the Washington Meteor claims held by the Blewett Gold Mining and Leasing Company, they added some of the workings of the Summit Pockets area. These included Tunnel No. 1 through Tunnel No. 4, located on the west side of the massive basaltic dike in the upper elevation of Culver Gulch.

A complaint against Washington Meteor stated that H. B. Rigley, one of the company directors, together with other directors, assisted in fraudulent transferring of mining claims to the Blewett Mining and Leasing Company and allowed some of the claims to go into default. This permitted the claims to be legally jumped so that the Blewett Gold Mining and Leasing Company would eventually be in control of all of the mining-related properties, including the miner-leased digs. These actions caused years of litigation and the accompanying work stoppage that crippled the mining activities of the gold-producing Culver Gulch mines involved.

During all the litigation, without explanation from the court records in Wenatchee, Washington, another unusual twist of mining-company fate occurred. A party of businessmen ran the properties and called them the Washington Gold Mines Company. This company followed the same procedure as its immediate predecessor. Then Washington Gold Mines Company was acquired via a sheriff's sale and deed to J. B. McVane to satisfy a labor dispute. J. B. Woodworth of Vancouver, British Columbia, bought the property from McVane about 1938. But, Washington Gold Mines Company thought they still owned some of the claims, and a lawsuit was thrashed out in an Olympia, Washington, court of justice. Woodworth ended up with clear title to the digs. In 1940, he made a profit of $4,000 from gold ore taken out of the Black Jack mine by miners Cliff Davenport and Anton Neubauer.

BLEWETT TUNNEL UPDATE, 1910

The Blewett Tunnel was a crosscut from the center of the gulch and ran northward on the Culver claim for about 60 feet. At that point, the 220-foot raise/shaft from Tunnel No. 9 displaced the floor of the Blewett Tunnel. It continued upward for about 80 feet to open on the surface. The adit then continued from the northward side of the open shaft to the vein, which was followed eastward.

Another known dig in the Blewett Tunnel is a raise into Tunnel No. 6, which was driven in a westerly direction on the vein. The remainder of the workings was blocked by cave-in debris. Below Tunnel No. 6 is the No. 6½, which was also run on the vein. Both are connected to one another by a raise. Tunnel No. 6 has a raise to Tunnel No. 5½ that is connected to No. 5; both followed the vein. Tunnel No. 5½ extends west where it is cut off by the diabase dike intrusion.

After 1910, the Washington Meteor Mining Company resorted to allowing the lease system of their claims for about five years, along with other mining activities taking place on their company properties.

HISTORY OF BLUE BELL (IXL) MINE UPDATE, 1910

T. John Vinton was the original locator of the IXL He recorded it August 10, 1888. It connects to the Lone Rock on the south and was joined to the Lucky Queen on the north.

According to the recorded progression of folks associated with the claim, John Burmeister relocated the IXL digs in 1890. Then he sold half interest in the mine to Walter Ferguson for $150. During that time, John was running the tunnel and lit a fuse for a giant powder charge in a double drill hole at the end of the workings. Then he went outside and waited. He heard the No. 1 hole go off, but the No. 2 charge … didn't. When John went back in to relight the fuse for the No. 2 hole, his candle went out at the point of contact. On striking a match to light the candle, an explosion simultaneously went off in the still-active No. 2 hole. Shattered rock entered his body at several places from the shoulder down to his ankles, breaking an ankle and one lower leg bone. The overall wound was said to look as if John was hit by a load of buckshot. John eventually recovered.

John did find high values in gold at his digs, but only in a few places where he encountered small pockets of the yellow metal. This was due to the fact that the vein was badly fractured, not well defined, and dislocated by a mass of serpentine rock that created enough pressure to initiate many small stringer veins.

Thaddeus Neubauer relocated the IXL, renamed it Blue Bell on January 5, 1897, and held the Blue Bell claim until 1910. John Burmeister then officially relocated it and again recorded the claim as the Blue Bell. Owner changes continued. John Burmeister is shown recording the Blue Bell once more on January 16, 1922, and Thaddeus Neubauer took the claim once again in 1934.

PROSPECT MINING AND MILLING COMPANY ESTABLISHED, 1910-1911

This is John Olden's arrastra water wheel under construction in 1903. It was located about 400 feet up from the mouth of Culver Springs Creek. John's mining partner, John Hill, is seated at the top of the water wheel. Olden sits on the bottom of the wheel with Tracy King positioned to Olden's right. (Grace Browitt Elkins photo collection.)

John Olden originally recorded the Sunset, Sunset Extension, Red Jacket, Lone Star, and Katy claims in 1907. They were located at the head of Culver Springs Creek. The Sunset Extension joined the east line of the Sunset claim. The Red Jacket claim joined the south line of the Sunset and north line of the Lone Star claim. The Lone Star area was once occupied by the old 1893 Spring Pheasant claim, on which a site called the Culver Mining Camp was located and established. Directly off the Lone Star's east claim line was the location of the Katy claim.

The ridge road on the old Spring Pheasant claim passed between a large building on the west side and two cabins on the east side. The road continued another 200 feet and ended at a small storage building. There was an ore pile on the Spring Pheasant claim, located about 150 feet northeast of the large building site.

In the 1940s, Karl Fackler pushed a bulldozer road across the Spring Pheasant claim, through the site where the large building once stood, and established a ¼-mile-long road connection to the road in the King Creek drainage area. The course it took also went through the ore pile and scattered it into the road surface and off to the east edge of the road cut. Remains of the cabin sites east of the road are presently only depressions in the ground, which require a sharp eye to detect. There was no trace of the large and smaller structures when Northwest Underground Explorations examined the remains of past mining activities in the area.

Ore mined in the pre-1910 years was processed by John Olden's two Culver Springs Creek arrastra mills. One of his mills was located about 400 feet up from the mouth of Culver Springs Creek. Olden's arrastra pit was 12 feet in diameter, 3 feet deep, and built from chunks of nearby granite outcrops that were brought to the mill site. A large 26-foot-diameter, over-shot water wheel was the power source. Water was brought from the gulch stream via a flume and ran directly over the upper surface of the water-wheel. An iron-cogged gear connection ran a smaller horizontal wheel, to which chains were commonly attached to two or three granite boulder drag-stones weighing several hundred pounds. These crushed 1 to 2 tons of ore per day into a fine powder. In 1910, when Charles Weaver was gathering information for his Bulletin No. 6 report, that particular Olden arrastra was in good running shape, but was unused.

Thanks to the rediscovery by Culver Gulch miner Dan Carlson of the Olden arrastra site, members of Northwest Underground Explorations were fortunate enough to view and photograph those recently exposed arrastra remains in 2010. The remnants at the arrastra site are the flat stones of the pit floor, the drag stones with the steel chain attachment loops, and several shafts with metal gears still connected. There are also several unidentifiable pieces of old rusty iron

This finished water wheel is another one of John Olden's three arrastras that were processing ore in 1903. Its location was not determined, although there is evidence of an arrastra site downstream from Olden's unfinished arrastra water wheel. (Chris Bell photo collection.)

lying here and there at the mill site. From year to year, depending on how much ground cover and debris the creek's flood water deposits over the old artifacts, there is an on-again, off-again chance of getting a look at them.

Due to limited mineralization and funds to pursue the ore that existed, the Prospect Mining Company focused mainly on assessment work in 1910.

HOMESTAKE MINE TO 1910

James Wilder, Olden's friend and occasional mining partner, originally recorded the Homestake claim on April 17, 1899. John Olden relocated and recorded the Homestake on November 5, 1907. The Homestake is located northwest from the mouth of Culver Springs Creek about 300 feet up an easy slope. It's about 150 feet north of the old Blewett Cemetery site and 100 feet west of the upper water ditch that once served Blewett's 20-stamp mill. John ran 165 feet of tunnel on a nearly vertically pitched quartz vein.

The walls of the tunnel were iron-stained serpentine rock that held gold-bearing calcite seams, from which John made a living. John was evidentially happy with "a little here and a little there" results. It was sufficient to keep him mining. A 1910 assay indicated a trace of gold and silver in Olden's underground workings.

LONE ROCK PROSPECT, 1910

John Olden ran an 88-foot tunnel on this claim by the time Weaver's Bulletin No. 6 was written in 1910, although no recording date was found.

The south line of the Lone Rock was joined to the north line of the Golden Cherry (Eureka) claim. The Lone Rock workings assayed a trace of gold and silver.

JOHNSON CLAIMS: APRIL FOOL, VENUS, AND DONALDSON TO 1910

Sherman Donaldson is first noted in the Blewett area on October 9, 1890 when he recorded his Last Chance lode claim, located south of the Golden Chariot (Eureka) mine. He also recorded several placer claims, and in 1897, Donaldson and mining partner W. S. Bloom were actively working the Donaldson placer on the same ground where the April Fool claim was relocated.

In 1910, the location given for the Johnson property was about ¼ mile north of the town

John Olden's Lone Rock claim portal in 1999. The height of the adit is about five feet. This requires a stooped position to access the length of the workings. There is a one-foot wide quartz vein visible on the left side of the portal. (Photo by Vic Pisoni.)

of Blewett, up a gulch where an unnamed creek flows westward off the west slope of Windmill Point. The April Fool is at the confluence of the drainage creek and Peshastin Creek. The Venus claim is joined to the east, and the Donaldson is the next claim, which is adjoined to the Venus and is on the lower slope of Windmill Point.

The April Fool claim tunnel (now caved at the portal, as are the other two adits) is 100 feet long and was driven on the vein. On the Venus claim is a 115-foot crosscut tunnel that didn't reach the vein. The 195-foot Donaldson adit trends east. Another tunnel 80 feet in length was also driven on the claim in a northeast direction. A 4-foot-wide vein of talc was cut by an open cut near the top of Windmill Point. Only a trace of gold and silver was detected in these claims' mineral assays.

BLEWETT IRON MINES, 1910

During the summer of 1910, assays were taken from iron-stained serpentine on the south side of Culver Gulch, from just above the mill and southwestward for about 1 mile to the head of Culver Springs Creek, including an area of a mountain peak named Iron Butte. Later Iron Butte was renamed Iron Mountain, which was in the northeast ¼ of Section 10 (the site of the original Iron Mountain). Today's map-named designation for Iron Mountain is directly west 1 mile, in the center of Section 9.

Sampled rock indicated that some iron ore deposits were within the margin of profit. Sixteen iron claims were located 2½ miles south of the town of Blewett. The areas included Shaser, Scotty, Tronsen, and Peshastin Creeks. Iron claims were also staked in the drainages areas of Negro and Ingalls Creeks.

Iron deposits were discovered and located in the early years, but gold was the priority mineral sought. So iron deposits were mainly in the stage of recognition and not mined.

Nelson Halvor recorded the Mountain View Iron claim on May 1888. It was located near today's patented Washington Nickel Mining and Alloys Company (established in the 1940s) in the area of the confluence of Scotty Creek and Tronsen Creek. Halvor seemingly understood the possible magnitude and value of those iron and nickel deposits.

In 1892–93, James Wilder, James Ward, and George Madden again considered the worth of the iron-ore deposits in old Iron Mountain. Their discoveries were deemed at least noteworthy by way of recording the observed iron ore. John Kendle recorded two iron claims, and Henry Weinman, one claim, in 1899. These were located near old Iron Mountain in 1910.

In 1910, road access to once-remote mining areas and distant smelters were in place to accommodate transportation needs for America's industrial iron production.

John Olden initiated interest in iron-ore-producing possibilities in the Blewett area with the observation of iron stained serpentine on six of his Iron Mountain claim tunnel walls. Furthering the interest, James Wilder's leased North Star workings showed red-stained porphyry.

Chemical tests determined the iron rock could be best treated via the cyanide process. This occurred in 1910 when the Washington Meteor Mining Company dismantled the concentrating tables in the 20-stamp mill and installed three cyanide tanks, each of 35-ton capacity. No data was found that supported the idea that the cyanide system was going to be used on iron ore. The rich iron-ore assays originated from small, limited outcrops and noted iron-stained tunnel workings, not the immense deposits needed.

1911-1913

The Blewett area, in general, took a fall from grace in the view of the local township news media. The Peshastin Mining District didn't seem to have what it takes in gold recoveries to equal the Swauk Mining District for the continuity of its big placer-gold mining successes. The auditor's office in Ellensburg shows that a noticeable flow of miners from the Peshastin Mining District vacated and were crossing southward over Blewett Pass to record new mining ground or maintain claims they had earlier established in the Swauk Mining District.

Worthwhile news coming out of the Blewett mines was non-existent for 1912 and 1913.

Chapter Twenty: Blewett Activities during World War I to 1927

STRATEGIC METAL MINERALS IN THE BLEWETT AREA, 1914

With the advent of World War I in 1914, strategic war metals were in demand. Canada went into the fray in Europe in 1914, well before the United States' latent entry in 1917, so the United States had Canada as a customer for our strategic metals ore.

Strategic metals were found in the mining districts of Washington State before the war and were known to exist in high-grade deposits. This compelled miners in the state to surge into the mountains to stake strategic metal claims.

The local Blewett miners that previously worked for the company-owned mines took up the slow days of their unemployment by making a living working the old gold-placer claims. In some cases, they continued tunneling after gold-bearing-vein rock.

As the war years continued, the demand for strategic metals ore became more urgent. When the United States entered the war, the government artificially raised the price for war ore. It was an incentive to switch from the gold placers to wartime mineral deposits at the inflated standard that the government was offering to pay.

A progression of claim recordings showed how the prospectors and miners changed by 1918, from making a living gold mining to prospecting for iron ore.

OLD BLEWETT PASS/ROAD IMPROVEMENTS (KITTITAS/SWAUK SIDES) 1915

Blewett area miner/mining engineer Joseph Warner was back for the mining season in 1915 pursuing mining-related activities. He was also there taking on the responsibility for surveying a line for the first 5-percent road-grade up the Swauk Creek side of old Blewett Pass (22 years after he had established the 7-percent road-grade then in use)

Up to this point, pack-animal transportation and teamster commerce through the pass was no problem for the locals on either side. But to the "flatlanders," it was another story. The advances in the automobile changed the requirements of roads to accommodate those less terrain-worthy mechanical beasts of burden.

During the 1914 pass-driving season, the count was 422 autos, 27 saddle horses, 24 horse-teamed wagons, and 140 pedestrians. Four people were killed in various forms of out-of-control

A car on the Blewett Pass highway crosses one of the many pre-US 97 bridges that once spanned Peshastin Creek. (George and Virginia [Davenport] Carpenter post card collection.)

Courage, good car brakes, a spare tire, and an alcohol-clear mind are what it took to negotiate the road conditions and road grade of the earliest car/truck route over the Blewett Pass highway. (George and Virginia [Davenport] Carpenter post card collection.)

vehicles with mechanically semi-suicidal, malfunctioning parts—the drivers. Some accidents were initiated by the "booze and gas don't mix" formula.

The road was completed in July 1916. But, the alcohol-fueled humans and automobile carnage continued, even with the improvements in road conditions.

BLEWETT'S LOST MINE

Back at Culver Gulch, in May 1915, there was excitement over miners T. B. Lambson and a man, identified only as Babcock, due to the discovery of a "lost" mine from 22 years previous (1894). Lambson and Babcock's good fortune resulted when Moses Bollman gave them an old map of the "lost" shaft location.

Bollman died in 1908, so he had to have given them the map before his expiration date. This indicates that Lambson and Babcock invested little time seeking the old mine, or found nothing in those intervening years of failed searches. Eventually, they found and opened the old dig.

Bollman owned the "lost mine" property about the same time Joseph Warner was building the first road up Culver Gulch to the Culver claim in the early 1890s.

Bollman gave no reason for walking away from the workings. It may have been due do to the ever-present mining nemeses—lack of funds or litigation.

The two men were clearing out debris from the old Bollman mine shaft and first came across old rusty picks, drills, hammers, and other mining equipment. After continued excavation of the shaft, they came upon the remainder of an ore vein. The ledge carried a pay streak 36 inches wide with ore values of up to $50 per ton. Warner examined the newly opened lost mine and made an offer of $80,000, which Lambson and Babcock were considering. A search into the source that submitted the "lost gold mine" story was void of any follow-up correspondence. The only evidence of a second shaft (other than the known location of the surface opening for the 300-foot workings) is shown on an old Amalgamated Gold Mines Company promotional map (Northwest Underground Explorations has yet to pin that shaft location as "found" on the group map).

CHELAN GOLD DIKE COMPANY, 1915

The Nellie A. claim was recorded on June 1, 1915 (owner unknown). It was located in such a manner that Culver Springs Creek ran through the south half of the claim and was bounded on its north claim line by the Peshastin claim. The Chelan Gold Dike Company was recorded into the record book on June 24, 1915. The company's one claim may have been an attempt to promote and sell unproven property adjoining the successful Peshastin mine. This property filed no assessment work papers and was gone from the claim records book the following year. The promoted ground overlaid that of John Olden's active claim area at the time this company appeared. If this was an effort by Olden to initiate interest for a chance to sell the claim, then this would be a legal repositioning of ground in which he already had control. This effort to promote a mine sale appears to have ended similar to Olden's failed attempt to promote and sell the Prospect Mining and Milling Company back in 1911.

GOLDEN WEDGE MINE

The first noteworthy mining news out of Blewett after World War I focused on C. G. Carey, who originally recorded the Golden Wedge claim November 24, 1919. John Olden owned it after Carey. H. A. Searles and Ernie Rubens recorded the Golden Wedge No. 1 and Golden Wedge No. 2 claims August 7, 1948. Their two-claim mine had a lower adit and an upper adit. The claims were located on the north side of Culver Springs Creek about 500 feet up from its mouth. A quartz vein varied from stringers up to 8 inches in width. The county rock was mineralized with pyrite and blebs of chalcopyrite. Assays averaged $11.20 per ton in gold, when gold was $34.71 an ounce.

A. W. PURDY'S MOONSHINE OPERATION, 1919

A. W. Purdy, an Irish immigrant miner, was first noted mining in Washington State in 1897. He had the Big Elephant group of six claims up Falls Creek in northern Chelan County.

In 1919, A. W. Purdy was a Blewett resident-miner who owned and operated a prospective gold mine in the area. But, he was arrested August 22 by Revenue Officer H. D. Merritt and Deputy Sheriff Lou Nordyke for being in possession of an illicit liquor-making still. The federal liquor Prohibition Act began November 3, 1914, in Washington State.

Purdy said he was following a white quartz vein throughout the mining season, but gold was insufficient to support his needs—it didn't pan out. Within his claim boundary was a rich abundance of spring and creek water. So being the experienced adult beverage consumer that he was (as were his friends and their friends and their friends' friends), Purdy sensed the need for a close source of the illegal elixir to accommodate him and all of the friends' needs. He got the things he needed and started cooking up a batch of red eye for what the lawmen saw as beyond the realm of reasonable medicinal use.

Purdy was arraigned before US Court Commissioner R. S. Ludington and cited with a $1,000 bond for his appearance with the US Grand Jury at Spokane, Washington. His case was dealt with in less severe terms than if it had been committed during the all-consuming Prohibition that eventually spread throughout the country.

After Purdy settled the moonshine matter with the court, he abandoned his claim. Unknown to him, the creek that ran through his claim held a gold-rich placer deposit that was discovered two years after he left the country.

But mainly …

> He was lookin' fer gold,
> as Purdy's story was told,
> but his prospect didn't pan out.
> So what should he do?
> He's got holes in his shoes,
> from which his toes could stick out.

Says he, "I'll just drink me some liquor
'cause 'tis good fer me ticker."
"Common sense," any hard drinker would say.
But he was about to run out.
This caused him to spout
a plan, to save the day.

Says he … again, "I've enough more than me will,
to build me a still
and liquor-up all of me friends.
It beats pushin' dirt
'til me poor back is hurt.
I'll try bootleggin' and see how it ends."

Then rev'nuers showed up,
put Purdy in cuffs,
nice ones that fit him just right.
The revs sampled the juice,
which set their minds loose
as they staggered into the night.

But … the law got its man,
as only they can …
No, not due to their skill
because … Purdy also got drunk,
passed out in the trunk
of the state car parked at the still.

A. W. PURDY'S OLD PLACER GROUND GETS A NEW START, 1921

In the first week of April 1921, the *Leavenworth Echo* newspaper heralded the story about gold discovered in the placer gravels in the creek that cut through A. W. Purdy's failed hard-rock quartz claim—the same ground Purdy trekked by in 1919 when he was coming and going to mine his failed hard-rock, quartz gold mine.

Many years had passed since a local newspaper had something of this "back in the day" magnitude pertaining to gold coming out of a Blewett-area placer deposit. Rough gold and nuggets were issuing out of the old Purdy claim ground, from both creek bank and stream.

Old-time prospector Bill Hurder and his associate mining partners, Dude Brown, the chief of police at Leavenworth, and three young prospectors named Irvin Mall, Charley Shoemaker, and Hinie Carson were seen around town exhibiting some fine specimens from their gold digs. One of several nuggets was oblong and weighed ¾ of an ounce, valued at $17. They recorded Purdy's old claim in their names and recovered gold in amounts that merited a response that Purdy would have approved of: "I'll drink to that."

The gold strike was made in the gravel beds of the creek, but gold was also mined above the waterline throughout the whole drainage gulch. As to the location of the rich gold-bearing ground, mum's the word. Miner Cliff Thompson noted that his claim was on the same stream, just below the old Purdy claim and not far above the Ingalls Creek fork. Even though Cliff was more inclined to talk than the other miners, he didn't give out much in the way of location specifics.

Prospector Thompson was working his claim downstream from the Purdy ground and was also doing better than making a living. He had previously worked the stream beds in that section for several years before he finally got into that downstream pay-dirt. At that point, he was getting fine gold and small nuggets. His best gold mining effort up to that date was $16 in gold for three hours work from an old bench placer up on the side of the gulch. The gold Cliff found was in pockets on old bedrock on the bench in the side of the gulch. The dig location was about 30 feet above the creek bottom. His gold-bearing bench was covered with clay, sand, gravel, and boulders to a depth of up to 15 feet. His goal was to get enough cash together so he could build a pipeline from a beaver dam 100 yards above his workings. It would generate enough water pressure to bore into the creek bank and save considerable labor. He also planned to build a yard-arm derrick to sling boulders out of the creek that were too big for him to manhandle. Below Thompson was the Wallin claim, which was being actively worked. There were several other miners quietly working claims in a tight-lipped manner. This led to speculation by the local folks that something bigger than what was publicly known had taken place.

As it turned out, the gold take was excellent for the season, and then the familiar old theme took over—the easy gold was gotten. After that, the gold didn't show well enough the following season to merit even one comment out of any newspaper.

MINERAL CLAIM RECORDINGS, 1922-1926

The list for local mineral claims in 1922 had 22 mineral claims recorded by resident miners John Burmeister, John McCarthy, Charley Striker, and Thaddeus Neubauer. There were ten claims recorded in 1923; recorded claims for 1924 were a no-show. Only five mineral claims were filed in 1925. There were ten recorded in 1926. Assessment work and making a living from gold-producing small-claims mine owners seemed to be what was taking place.

BLEWETT PASS ROAD REPORT, 1926

With the continued improvements made on the (officially named) Blewett Pass Road, motor-vehicle travel conveniences were added to the route. The town of Blewett was now a busy, pass-through addition to the new touring-car crowd. Non-death vehicle crashes and mechanical breakdowns were, in some cases, attended to by John McCarthy's mechanical skills in his commercial car-repair garage.

FIRST CENTRAL WASHINGTON MINING CONGRESS, 1927

The First Central Washington Mining Congress was a meeting of mine owners and miners. The gathering was located at Wenatchee, Washington, September 1–3, 1927. Only five of the Blewett attendees were identified in the congress participant photo.

Some of the attendees of the First Central Washington Mining Congress at Wenatchee, Washington, September 3, 1927. Those identified, front row. Left to right, first and second, are John (a.k.a. Blackie) White and Herman Whitley. They owned and mined the Black and White mine. Seventh and eighth are Charley Striker and John McCarthy. Seated at twelve is Charles Ballard. (Photo courtesy of the Davenport and Barthol families, who were former Blewett residence.)

Chapter Twenty-one:
Amalgamated Gold Mines Company

During a history summation presented by John McCarthy, he noted a man named H. B. Ridgley as a trustee for Washington Meteor in 1906. He leased some of the mining company digs and then subleased them. Ridgley was abrasive and, in some instances, objected to inner-company dealings. This was one of the reasons for the years of litigation that slowed mining production and caused other work stoppages.

Ridgley was at one point the secretary of the Blewett Mine Leasing Company and engaged in a squabble, at the same time, with the Washington Meteor Mining Company over the lease legality; this was before joining as an associate with Washington Meteor. He was assaulted verbally over many situations, and he gave back equally in defense of his challenged activities. He

Miners pose outside of the No. 9 Tunnel. An aerial tramway transferred ore from the digs and down about 3/4 mile to the 20-stamp mill at the bottom of Culver Gulch. (Cashmere Museum and Pioneer Village photo collection.)

was known to incorporate deep finger-pointing and pushing matches during his intimidating conversations. Ridgley even got into a shooting match about who had legal control over a leased mineral claim. Finally, Ridgley was arrested for second-degree assault. But the final moment came when Ridgley dropped dead from a heart attack—ending any further squabbling, at the least from his part, in the unsettling events.

Finally, a mining-business entity known as the Amalgamated Gold Mines Company was awarded, by the court, all the contested leased and subleased mining properties.

Amalgamated Gold Mines Company appeared as a leading story in the *Mining and Engineering World* magazine in April 1916 with no notable public relations advances as to their intent. From the company office in Seattle, Washington, manager C. R. Hesseltine made a generalized

Sketch layout from a prospectus for the Amalgamated Gold Mines Company and a section of the town of Blewett. Notice the surface ore tram extended between the Peshastin claim's Meteor Tunnel and the 20-stamp mill. (Chris Bell photo collection.)

announcement that they were in possession of the various old Blewett area/Culver Gulch claims and mill facilities. Hesseltine's interactions through his real-estate holding company involved him one way or another with the Washington Meteor Mining Company as far back as 1907. He was instrumental in reorganizing, by increments, two mining companies into one. He had defined himself as pursuing present opportunities and not depending on proposed projects aimed at the future, but that statement was changing and would continue to evolve even more.

Hesseltine announced that the company was in the planning stage of building a new cyanide plant for the coming summer. The old, original Blewett stamp-mill site would be brought up to date with a new and improved ore-crushing and plate-amalgamation system. The company boasted assays that contained gold found in sulfides, silver in arsenopyrite, copper in chalcopyrite, and some free gold carried in the quartz, calcite, and even some of the gangue material. The hanging-wall and foot-wall containing the ore was serpentine. Without details, it was stated that the vein was accessed by numerous tunnels at different elevations in the gulch workings. By implication, the lowest of their tunnels was the Black Jack underground workings.

By December of 1916, J. J. Lewison was on site. He was managing the Blewett Tunnel mining activities and had ordered and then received several thousand feet of lumber. The "coming mining season" was rescheduled from the summer of 1916 to the approaching season of 1917.

Unfortunately, no work on the large scale, which Amalgamated Gold Mines Company was projecting, had taken place since a report on the mines of Blewett by Charles Weaver in 1910. Some of the mining properties the company intended to put into production had been in court litigation for the past several years. They had not been cleared to the point where full-scale work could begin, so serious mining activities were put in a state of limbo.

Charles R. Hesseltine, president of Amalgamated Gold Mines Company. (Chris Bell photo collection.)

RENEWED LIFE, 1919

By the time 1919 came around, the limbo status in the Amalgamated Mining Company changed only by way of a new manager, named Arthur Brown from San Francisco. Brown concluded the static condition of the Amalgamated properties was based on the fact that past company personnel running things were not practical mining men. Men with mining-related backgrounds would be the answer to defining the new board of directors. On the first project of the 1919 mining season, Brown had a crew of 15 men working to repair the company hotel; he followed with an entire new flume to replace the old dilapidated one. After an inspection of the properties, Brown said he thought the mines were not worked out; they were just worked the wrong way.

The reorganized company and board of directors consisted of men who had the financial means to put the company on a paying basis and were willing, at this point, to spare no expense to make that happen. To prove that point, to start with, they paid off all debts and claims that were holding the company back. The remainder of the year was a flurry of activity to repair and renew as much as they could with the early money in the company coffers.

INCREASED MINING ACTIVITIES, 1920

In July 1920, Amalgamated had a total of 15 men working on the old underground developments along the Peshastin claim. The plan was to get five of the stamps in the mill working in conjunction with the amalgamating process, tables, and flotation concentrators.

Elsewhere, men were in the process of mining enough ore from the various digs to warrant milling operations on a commercial scale. The small claim owners continued to develop and sample their recorded claims from previous years.

Two ore bins are shown below the tailings pile at the Meteor Tunnel level. The ore was taken by a horse-teamed wagon down to the 20-stamp mill. (Cashmere Museum and Pioneer Village photo collection.)

ANNUAL STOCKHOLDERS MEETING, 1921

The outcome of Amalgamated Gold Mines Company's July 27, 1921, annual stockholders meeting was a new board of trustees. The trusties were Charles R. Hesseltine, president; H. S. Calhoun, vice-president; G. W. Welker, treasurer; and J. B. Reynolds, secretary.

In August 1921, mine manager I. G. Robinson of Amalgamated Gold Mines Company stated that a good strike of free gold was made. Two hundred pounds of ore was assayed at $400 per ton; some of the gold contained in the mercury amalgam collected was valued at $700, and a sample of sulfide concentrates ran as high as $192 in gold per ton.

The new strike was made in the creek-level tunnel of the Black Jack claim. The vein was 12 feet wide. The free-gold ore averaged about 2 feet in width and widened as a raise in the ore was continued upward. Several tons of the high-grade ore was ready and waiting for the creek water to rise up enough for the stamp mill to resume operating. In December, important news of any kind pertaining to Amalgamated Gold Mines Company was absent.

PROGRESS REPORT, 1922

After a period of vague news reports and other company-related omissions, a sole-bearing progress report was released January 1922. Mine Superintendent Ernest G. Riebe explained that he started the mill without having installed the cyanide plant or floatation and sliming process, which was specifically outlined in the milling operations by the company mining engineers who worked out a complete system for the superintendent. Riebe's reason for starting without the additional equipment was lack of funds to purchase them. He admitted putting the uncompleted mill in operation without further stock assessment considerations—his mistake. He was hoping to produce concentrates in sufficient quantity and value to pay for the additional equipment.

When the stockholders heard about the situation, they started questioning the wisdom of the operation. Hesseltine was quick to sidestep the confrontation. He pointed out (from his "other people's money" point of view) that disaster was bound to come to a company whose untrusting stockholders were not loyal to the management.

It was a high priority to have that floatation machine for retreatment of the coarse, iron-sulfide concentrates before they could be shipped to the Tacoma smelter. They tried running high-grade ore concentrates over the shaker-tables, which resulted in losing 40 to 50 percent of its value along with the middlings (waste material).

The other piece of machinery that was badly needed was a ball mill to grind the ore fine enough to free the gold from the quartz rock that was also mined. The requirement for the ground ore had to be at 70 percent to pass through a 100-mesh screen, and the five stamps that were operating in the mill would have handled that amount in preparation to feeding the ball mill. What the flotation needed but did not have without the added equipment was a finer-ground product. What they needed in order to get the machinery was money, of which the company was lacking. This was due to their under-estimating the costs of the initial spending spree to bring the company machinery and other mining related issues up-graded and running back in

1919. The company's slow, inefficient system was, at that time, handling the ore supply. However, there was a secondary concern with the future advent of a higher producing mill capacity. Would there be enough ore reserves available to stay in advance of the ore needed to feed a mill with a larger appetite for the gold-bearing rock? A mill producing at a greater rate and running more efficiently would need a reserve of 1,000 tons in the ore bins because shutting down the mill and waiting for ore was not an economical option.

Superintendent Riebe was not trying to make a big showing over the course of the five months he was operating the mill. He explained that he was only running ore as it was coming from exploratory prospecting and development work.

The size of the ore bodies was not a problem; they were demonstrated to be a paying deal. The slowdown was caused by lack of money in the company coffers to buy more additional equipment for that endeavor.

Hesseltine's response was to say that Amalgamated Gold Mines was contemplating putting in a flotation machine of 50 tons capacity per day. It was a type A2610 K & K flotation machine with rubber riffles to treat the gold-silver ore. Evidentially, contemplation did not meet the requirement because dissatisfied stockholders called secret meetings. They leaked out news to the public that put Amalgamated Gold Mines Company in an unsavory position. The stockholders elevated their grudges to the point of seeking legal counsel. Then investors in the company started to default on their payments of money due Amalgamated Gold Mines Company. Other stockholders refused to complete their contracts. Creditors caught wind of the company problems and jumped into the fray, demanding immediate payment from the company. Owing to the extensive litigation, post-war conditions, and other escalating obstacles, news about Amalgamated Gold Mines Company became cloaked in secrecy.

1923

There was a lack of any kind of news regarding the troubled Amalgamated Gold Mines Company in 1923. All mineral mining activity was in the form of 28 mineral-claim recordings filed by independent miners during the year. Evidently the established Blewett gold miners were satisfied with their small digs because none of them showed in the new list of recorded claims. All the names that appeared on the claims recorded in 1923 were unfamiliar to the Blewett area.

1926

In September 1926, after several years of legal battles in the courts of law, the remainder of the Amalgamated Gold Mines Company was sold. The general public was made aware that Amalgamated Gold Mines Company would be reopened soon, according to company representatives Thaddeus R. Dennis and George W. Welker from Seattle.

Somewhere in the mix of litigators were United States Mine and Metals Corp. and Washington Gold Mines Corp. A lack of background information about these two companies leaves their involvement and motives unknown. From this point on, Amalgamated Gold Mines Company went off to lick its corporate wounds and was unavailable for public inquiries.

With the story of Amalgamated Gold Mines Company laid to "unrest" in the seven levels of litigation purgatory, the genesis of the Blewett/Culver Gulch mineral-mining claim recordings continued. Ten mineral claims went on the mineral claims list in 1926, followed by 11 non-mining, cobweb-accumulating years.

1937

By the end of that decade of silence, C. R. Hesseltine had a crew of men working in the old Blewett Tunnel in July 1937. It was once owned by the Amalgamated Gold Mines Company, which was in litigation. He remained in charge of the property through its various changes in partnership.

As parting mining news from Blewett in 1937, Amalgamated Gold Mines Company was brought back to the public's attention. A summary of various Amalgamated Gold Mines activities for the past year was noted. Charles H. Hesseltine was in charge of the various changes in Amalgamated Gold Mines Company's spun-off sub-companies. It appears Hesseltine took on the responsibility, and eventually the blame, to see the litigation through to the end. Another way to view the matter was his supportive business associates pulled the rug out from under him. The litigation appears to have resolved quietly because no negative, attention-getting follow-up was found in the newspapers.

Chapter Twenty-two:
Gold Bond Mining Company

From 1934 and onward, the Gold Bond Mining Company began its sporadic mining activities throughout the Blewett area and especially among the old high-grade gold-producing claims in Culver Gulch. The company's list of relocated claims included those of the earliest mineral digs recorded by the old-time miners in 1874.

During September, October, and November of 1935, Blewett miner/mine owner Cliff Davenport was hired to advance a tunnel and block out ore deposits for Gold Bond. In June of 1935, Cliff started running footage in an upper elevation adit from the Negro Creek drainage side. It was located at the top of the ridge separating Culver Gulch from Negro Creek. The work was vaguely reported as being near the old Blewett Tunnel (once relocated by the Horace C. Henry). His crew struck some high-grade gold ore, described in what appears to be, presently, the known mapped location of the south-trending Davenport Tunnel in the Summit Pockets area.

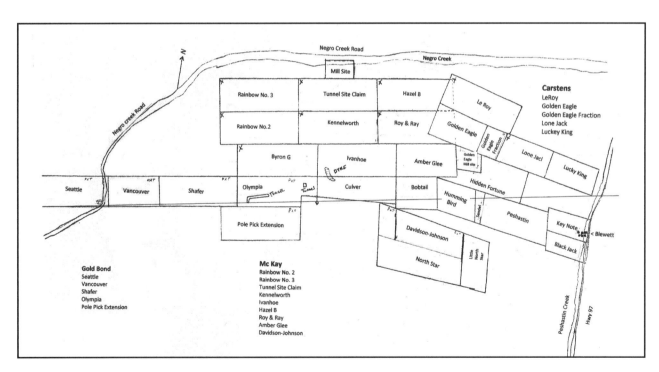

Culver Gulch and Negro Creek claims as named or renamed and located by the owners. W. H. McKay's mining claims were listed under his name from 1903 up to 1932. Chelan County sold McKay the Davison-Johnson (Pole Pick No. 1) property for unpaid back taxes. Gold Bond Mining Company was formed in 1934. Their Seattle, Vancouver, Shafer, Olympia, and Pole Pick Extension claims suggests the year for this map at around 1934. The Carstens claims may have been leased because his name was not found anywhere in data sources researched. This map is a general layout of claim locations and is not exact. (Wesley C. Engstrom map collection.)

Cliff Davenport also ran an additional 600 feet in the existing tunnel at the Vancouver claim. Eventually the Vancouver workings attained a total length of 1,200 feet. After the addition to the Vancouver adit was completed, it was also named, or referred to, as another Davenport Tunnel.

The first shipment of Gold Bond Mining Company ore was announced November 15, 1935. The company projected that 25 tons of gold ore would be sent daily to the Tacoma smelter. Company officers were J. F. Hocking of Spokane, president; Edward J. Edwards (a former Canadian mine operator) from Vancouver, British Columbia, vice-president, and Walter Shultz of Spokane. Secretary Harve M. Phipps was added to the position of mining operation director.

The legally cleared titles to the mining properties consisted of five patented claims and ten unpatented mineral properties. Some of the mines named from this group of claims, as reported in 1935, were the Pole Pick No. 1, Pole Pick Fraction No. 2, Shafer, Olympic, Pole Pick No. 3, Seattle, Vancouver, Ivanhoe, Kennelworth, and Amber Glee.

RAWHIDING SACKED ORE, 1935

The method used to transfer the ore from the upper Davenport Tunnel to the otherwise unused mill building was to rawhide the mineralized rock down the steep pack trail in Culver Gulch. High-grade ore was sacked and stored at the mine during the summer. When snowfall was of sufficient depth to accommodate the rawhiding procedure, a large bull or steer hide was placed hair side down in the snow. Up to a ton of sacked ore was put on the rawhide. Then, the sides of the hide were pulled up and laced together on the top. The resulting ore-filled, rawhide pouch looked similar to a pod or sausage shape. The summer pack trails served as snow covered "rawhide runs" during the winter.

At the beginning, transporting the ore was more difficult for the horses due to the unstable surface of the deep snow. Odd as it seems, the critters earned their oats pulling the loads downhill to the mill, where it was later transported to the Tacoma smelter. After several trips, the trail resembled a bobsled run. The developing problem on the increasingly compact and slick surface was that of control. A crude braking system was made using chains to maintain a safe speed. The method went unexplained. But, even with safety precautions, there was the occasional pack animal seen on a dead-run (maybe literally), pursued by a ton of rock—*giddy-up*!

PHIPPS TUNNEL, 1936 TO PRESENT

The Phipps Tunnel was initiated in 1936 by Gold Bond Mining Company mining operations director and company secretary, Harve Phipps.

The adit was located on the upper Negro Creek drainage, west from the top of Culver Gulch. It was a crosscut tunnel driven into the old Blinn ore vein, which was exposed near the ridge. The surface vein was exposed by a short drift (now caved in) that showed white, barren quartz 5 feet wide with a 2-inch gouge seam on either side.

The tunnel survey notes by a field geologist, Ward Carithers, states, "The Phipps Tunnel crosscuts this vein's lower half at 50 feet. For 25 feet west it has been stoped upward for 40 feet. A drift to the east extends 80 feet, and is stoped 40 feet up and 60 feet down. In a 20-foot continuation of the crosscut tunnel, an incline shaft takes the ore to the Stoner (haulage) Tunnel.

Where the crosscut intersects the vein, it is 43 inches wide and varies from 56 inches to a point where it pinches out at the face of the drift. Ore minerals seen were free gold and a little pyrite and arsenopyrite."

In 1949, the company issued a vague, generalized underground workings update. According to Gold Bond, new development consisted of several hundred feet of crosscut tunnels, drifts, and stopes (no details were given).

As of 2013, the area is under possessor claim status.

STONER TUNNEL, 1936 TO PRESENT

H. B. Stoner, a trustee of the Gold Bond Company, issued a contract to run an ore haulage tunnel to remove the mineral deposit from the mined ore in the Phipps Tunnel. The ore was taken east through a decline tunnel to a landing downslope from Tunnel No. 1. It was located on the Culver Gulch side of the ridge top. On the Stoner adit landing were an ore bin and machinery to run an aerial ore tram to the mill.

A new, Culver Gulch road was bulldozed directly over the Stoner Tunnel portal by Karl Fackler in the 1940s, which completely buried any evidence of its location. The portal area of the underground workings went lost until the year 2010. At that time, Northwest Underground Explorations member Chris Bell, accompanied by member Terry Carlson, discovered and opened the portal.

POLE PICK NO. 1 HISTORY AND ACTIVITIES

During the beginning days of mining in Culver Gulch, the Pole Pick No. 1 claim (originally the Johnson-Davidson mine) had a gold-bearing ore-lead that produced $20,000 in free gold. It was mined from its quartz-vein host by the grinding action of an arrastra.

Later, it was acquired by the Eleanor Mining Company of Chicago. Eleanor Mining Company milled about 2,000 tons in a custom mill that was owned by the Blewett-based Chelan Mining Company. That ore ran $8 per ton. The claim was surveyed for patent, which was later allowed in 1904. It was signed by President Theodore Roosevelt. The name under which it was patented was Johnson-Davidson Lode. In 1932, the property was sold for taxes by Chelan County to Kay W. McKay of Seattle. In 1935, the McKay heirs deeded it to the Gold Bond Mining Company. The physical work of cleaning out the cave-in debris and retimbering the tunnels began in 1937.

In mid-January of 1937, highway contractors Myers and Goutier had a contract to haul a minimum of 40 tons of ore daily to the Tacoma smelter. There were 24 men working the various jobs needed to accomplish the company-planned work. Due to gradual expansion, Gold Bond Mining Company reached a mining and shipping production of 30 tons per day.

Eventually, a shipment of high-grade ore in sacks, said to be worth $11,000, was ready to be transported to the Tacoma smelter.

Next on the list was a plan to tunnel deeper into the mountainside and to get the mill running to treat lower-grade ore. Consulting engineer R. K. Neil was pressing onward with a large crew of men to extend the Vancouver claim/Davenport Tunnel. The outcome of that endeavor was not the end result for reaching the original projection point. Later, Gold Bond contracted George H. Lewis of Seattle to run a 400-foot extension to the existing Davenport Tunnel, where it would reach the intended 1,000-foot point under the expected company ore bodies on the Culver Gulch side of the ridge.

Lewis struck another rich vein of ore and stoped into it. He was in 21 inches of talc (it is not known if the deposit was lens shaped or in a continuous contact zone). The assay for the find stated it carried $2,091.95 to the ton in gold. In addition, there was a quartz vein 20 inches wide in the stope with free gold showing in it. A second raise was started in hopes of following the ore rock to another rich gold deposit. The data given stated that the tunnel was in 900 feet and had 300 feet to go to reach the end of the tunnel at a final projection of 1,200 feet. It was directly under the lowest Gold Bond Mining Company workings in Culver Gulch. Lewis stopped at 900 feet.

Bulletin No. 37, "Inventory of Washington Minerals," noted that there were ore shipments for January and July of 1937 (the values were absent from the report).

Then Gold Bond assigned another contract to H. R. Brand of Bellingham to retimber the adit of the Pole Pick mine (it is joined to the Pole Pick No. 1 property) and recondition and enlarge the mill on the Pole Pick property, which Gold Bond had recently added to their extensive mine holdings. Brand and his mining associates previously had a lease on the Pole Pick mine before the Gold Bond Mining Company took legal control of it. Mining engineers described the gold-bearing vein as 1 to 4 feet wide in hard, massive quartz.

The daily output of Gold Bond's shipping ore was averaging 15 to 20 tons per day during September 1937, and there was another 100 tons of ore at the Tacoma smelter waiting to be processed. Between 1,500 and 2,000 tons of ore was blocked out at the Pole Pick property. Assays ran from $10 to $132 per ton. Gold was valued at $34.79 per ounce. The company stated that it was free from debt but was not selling mining stock at that time. Most of the stock was owned by Spokane businessmen.

1938

Snow and inclement weather delayed Gold Bond's 1938 mining season until April. When tunnel boss George Lewis got back to the company's Negro Creek level-long tunnel, his first task was to continue running the workings another 400 feet, 100 feet farther than the last report projected. During tunneling toward the 400-foot ending point, ore was cut intermittently the whole distance with two test raises developed 350 feet apart. Both stopes were in ore; one for 15 feet in length, and the other was into a 40-foot-long ore deposit. The workings ended at 1,200 feet.

The objective was a contact zone at the basalt dike where the best ore was expected. Lewis had up to 10 men working with him and was adding more machinery as needed. He also planned to build a mill on Negro Creek that season to handle the low-grade ore. When the work stopped, there was no report about reaching the basalt dike, although some rich ore was found.

The results of the ore value Gold Bond received from the Tacoma smelter for ore shipments of 1937 and the first few months in 1938 amounted to $30,000.

While George Lewis's project was taking place, H. R. Brand and his mining associates Sullivan and Carlson were assigned another contract to mine ore from the Pole Pick workings.

DAVENPORT TUNNEL STRIKES RICH ORE

Gold Bond Mining Company Vice-president E. J. Edwards was in Spokane during mid-May 1938. He gave a report and showed samples of rich gold ore from a 2-foot-wide quartz vein at the face of the previously developed Davenport Tunnel.

A contract was awarded to George Lewis in October 1938 for the construction of a tramway from one of the company tunnel portals on the Negro Creek drainage to a mill site. A 30-ton pilot mill was under consideration. The plan was to have the tram and mill up and running with ore shipments before winter set in. There was no further news of the proposed projects.

Only small claim owners appeared on the "active" list in a Blewett Mining Camp letter from Anton Neubauer to a newspaper. He was noted working his Lucky Queen and upslope Bee Queen properties. The Bee Queen was an east-trending continuation of the vein in the Lucky Queen. Other busy small-claim miners from Blewett were also noted. Bulletin No. 37 simply noted, "The Gold Bond Mining Company shipped ore in 1938."

1939—ALL QUIET

For no apparent reason, the Gold Bond Mining Company received no press about their gold ore production in 1939 or any other of their proposed mining-related projects. Evidently, they issued no press releases to explain what was talked about during the trustees' meetings. And Gold Bond was holding back their ore production for some unheralded purpose. The company was known for continued leasing of their claims and running the miners' leased property ore through the Gold Bond Mining Company mill (at the Blewett 20-stamp mill).

KARL FACKLER-POLE PICK NO. 1 CLAIM LEASE, 1940

May 1940, H. B. Stoner had a lease from Gold Bond for the Pole Pick No. 1 claim. Then Stoner subleased the Pole Pick No.1 digs to Karl Fackler. One of Karl's first projects was to run a new 1 ½ miles-long bulldozer road, under experienced miner Ollie Jordin's advice, to bring the mined

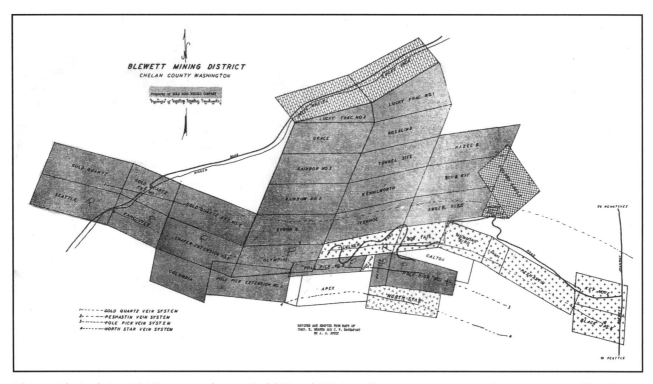

This mid- to late-1940s map shows Gold Bond Mining Company property in gray tone. The J. B. Woodworth group of seven claims is marked by a field of crosses on a white background. Woodworth's properties were previously owned by the Warrior General Mining Company. (Wesley C. Engstrom map collection.)

ore down to the ore bins at the mill. Karl also extended the Culver Gulch road up to the early Summit Pocket claims area. While scraping away the surface of the ground in the Summit Pockets area at the head of Culver Gulch, the bulldozer blade uncovered a blanket-lead deposit from 4 to 6 feet wide and to varying depths under the shallow surface of dirt and rocks. It exposed high-grade, free-milling gold quartz. Karl shipped $3,000 worth of this Summit Pockets ore to the Tacoma smelter. He then built an Allis mill on the Pole Pick claim.

The news of Karl's success got the attention of John Bradley's heirs to his estate because they believed John's old lease from W. H. McKay was still active. Litigation raised its ugly head once more, and Karl Fackler was sued by the Bradley family.

In Superior Court, Judge Fred Kemp ruled that Karl's work was requisite to maintain the mining lease under his control and that he could continue to take ore from the old Pole Pick No. 1 mine. Judge Kemp also stated that the Bradley family had showed no tendency to work the claim since 1935.

Gold Bond Mining Company showed proof of their ownership via the deed to the Pole Pick No.1. Gold Bond Vice-president E. J. Edwards explained that, before Gold Bond was cleared for them to purchase the Pole Pick No. 1 claim; they had to pay off a lien that the DuPont Company held for an unpaid blasting-powder debt against the property.

OLLIE JORDIN HELPS
KARL FACKLER MAKE A MINE

With the help of a big bulldozer, Karl and his mining crew were trying to get at the projected deposits of gold that he knew were on the Pole Pick No. 1 claim. He also needed somebody with an extensive background as a mine developer. So, close friend Ollie Jordin, a prolific gold miner from the Swauk Mining District, was invited to give Karl's latest Culver Gulch digs a look-see. Karl lured Ollie away from his Swauk gold claims with the generous offer of six dollars a day for wages at a time when two dollars per day was the going labor rate due to a depressed economy. Karl needed—and was willing to pay for—Ollie's expertise. Ollie knew how to estimate the source of mineral deposits and the most expedient way to develop underground workings to mine that gold ore. Ollie secured his Swauk mining properties with trusted overseers and left his gold deposits in his "bank" (as he called it), which were the untapped, underground gold-bearing claims near Liberty, Washington—and he headed for Blewett.

During a taped interview by Fred Kruger of Ollie's mining recollections, he gave the following account (verbatim).

Swauk Mining District miner/mine owner Ollie Jordin is on the far right with two unidentified people. (Wesley C. Engstrom photo collection.)

Well sir, I went over there, and it was the funniest scene I ever seen in my life. I'll tell ya how they was tryin' to mine that. They had a hole ya could put half this town in. They had a big bulldozer, and they'd blast all around that big hole and then clean it all out to get a 3-foot vein. Fackler said he couldn't make it pay, and what should be done to get the gold out? They had a awful rich vein too. They didn't know much about tunnelin'. I told 'em, ya get that bulldozer here, and ya need to build a road up to the tunnel. They didn't know why I told 'em to build a road up there. I was the boss, so he gave it the go-ahead. I got the road up, and I asked him for a load a timber to make a bunker. They didn't know what a bunker was. I told 'em it was to hold ore so ya could back up under it and load the loader [trailer]. We had a trailer to pull behind the dozer that would hold 19 tons. We back that under the bunker and can fill that up durin' the day. Then the next day we haul it a mile and a half down to the road.

Now we start tunnelin' and timber it up. The vein was about that wide [an unexplained gesture]. And we had to make it a little wider to work in. So I started on that vein of decomposed stuff so soft

I could run a pick in and run 300 feet of tunnel in and only used one stick a powder. That's all it took, and I kept it [the tunnel] timbered good.

Well sir, I worked for him that summer and then for months and months. We never failed to take nine tons of that ore [per day] down to the road to load. And everything was paid for, and me being paid, and it netted Fackler $100 per ton in gold. We delivered nine tons every day. A man from Wenatchee hauled the ore to the smelter for four dollars a ton. Karl started to get more and more money comin' in. Then he raised my wage. When I ended the job, I was getting $35 dollars a day. That was during World War II. That was the first work I done over there [Culver Gulch].

The reason the mine eventually stopped producing gold was due to a shortage of gas, blasting powder, and other essential items needed to mine gold; instead, they went into the war effort. Limitation Order L-208 prohibited gold and silver smelting during the war. The only ore minerals accepted were those that drove the war machine. Also, the Tacoma smelter was using its full processing facilities to expedite the war-time minerals.

Ollie recalled his way for identifying a missed shot, a failed detonation of an ore blasting hole, (verbatim):

Fackler No. 2 Tunnel. Note the tight arrangement of the timbers and laggings for the full-length of the tunnel walls. This was the adit Ollie ran using only a pick, hand tools, and one stick of explosives due to the workings passing through very unstable ground. (Photo by Vic Pisoni.)

A lots a times ya have a missed shot, and ya have a shift goin' in at night, and to keep them boys from digging' on it and hittin' it … ya laid two pieces of drill steel across the mouth a the tunnel. When they come to work that meant there was a missed shot in there. Then they'd go in there and search around 'til it was found, and they'd take it out. Otherwise, a pick could hit it and set it off. It's happened several times. I know of three got killed that way. One shot just missed … there wasn't no crossed steel at the portal, so he went in there … ya always pick down the front a yer tunnel before ya drill. He was hittin' away in there, ya know, and there was a stick a powder with a cap in it and he hit the cap with his pick and… Boom! … away she went. Killed 'em dead. If ya didn't put up a cross … that was yer last day workin' for that company. You was canned right now. They was strict after that fella got killed.

Another story Ollie told related to blasting (verbatim).

I seen some funny things there in the mines. I knew this fella runnin' a mine had this fella workin' for 'em, and he was tryin' to steal this other fella's girl from him. He thought he'd keep 'im down in the mine and give himself more of a chance to get the girl. The girl's fella didn't know a darn thing about minin'. Back then when ya go to a mine they'd give ya a whole coil a fuse … 100 feet. And the longest ya need was 4-foot to each shot. So the fella went there and drilled some kind a hole and put in his powder, cap, and fuse in that … but instead of a 4-foot piece he used it all. And it burns at a foot a minute…ya know? And golly, after a while, they says the shots must a missed. So they all went down and was eatin' supper… Bang! she went. "Hey," they asked 'im, "how much fuse did you use?" "Oh, just that coil," he says. That was 100 feet a coil.

YEAR-END NO NEWS

In the following months, Gold Bond Mining Company rode out the year with little news of their operations being released to the newspapers. The only projected Gold Bond news was the announcement for their coming election of company directors in September of 1940.

1941

J. W. Hatley was the new president of Gold Bond in March 1941. The company secretary was Harve Phipps. Karl Fackler was the company's general manager. At this time, the gold-silver ore from the old Blinn group of claims, the Wilder digs, Pole Pick No. 1, and Pole Pick were being mined on an irregular schedule. Karl Fackler continued to mine the Pole Pick No. 1 digs under lease from Gold Bond.

By July 1941, Gold Bond wanted Fackler's Pole Pick lease forfeited back to the company. Fackler resisted, and the matter ended in a court of law.

The Gold Bond Mining Company was active, but seemed unwilling to go public with their operations information at this time. So, very little information was mentioned in the newspapers about mining at Blewett. For the most part, captivating stories were focused on war and wartime-related events.

1942

Karl survived his court ordeal with Gold Bond, and he was on his leased Pole Pick No. 1 claim in 1942. The claim developments were described as two crosscuts with raises and drifts and stopes totaling several hundred feet. The ore deposits were in a main vein 1 to 4 feet wide in serpentine rock. There was mention of two subsidiary veins. The mine was said to have shipped gold ore assaying $50 to $100 per ton to the Tacoma smelter.

At this time, what became known as the Fackler No. 2 Tunnel and its stope development were the only workings on the Pole Pick No.1 vein. A 3-foot zone of faulting and quartz stringers was cut while driving the main crosscut, about 65 feet north of the main drift, and was thought to represent the Pole Pick No. 1 vein. The only other alternative was that it reversed in dip and joined the No. 2 vein above the main drift. Whether the two veins joined west along the strike was not found in the report.

Karl described a cut on the surface; it was about 150 feet west of the old caved stope, which he said exposed a 3-foot vein of quartz. It panned high in gold. At one time, some of the quartz was exposed on the dump, but the cut was filled in with caved material. Karl stated that the best area for exploring the Pole Pick veins appeared to be between the present workings and the andesite dike located to the west. He said a drift run along the Pole Pick No. 2 vein should be extended 300 feet west from the face of the drift in the main tunnel with raises up on the favorable showings. Karl suggested at least one crosscut should be driven north at the center of the new workings to check the Pole Pick No. 1 vein. If the workings were successful, a drift east on what seemed to be the Pole Pick No. 1 vein in the main crosscut might be tried. This dig would be under the ore-shoot mined by Karl in the Fackler Tunnel. If ore was found in the suggested areas he pointed out, it would be largely within the sulfide oxidized zone but should be free-milling ore of comparatively high-grade. This ore could be milled by the mine's onsite gravity mill.

1943-1944

For Karl Fackler, 1943 started out in the same manner as 1942 ended—he was mining gold ore from his leased Pole Pick No. 1 mine.

Rounding off 1943, old-time Blewett miner Thaddeus Neubauer was actively working his Lucky Queen and Bee Queen claims; J. B. Woodworth was in possession of the Black Jack mine; old-timer John McCarthy, a 39-year resident/miner at Blewett, passed away; and Ester King married Mark Hansel.

For the Blewett area mines, 1944 remained about the same. J. B. Woodworth was active with the development of his seven claims in Culver Gulch. Gold Bond Mining Company was going through the motions of active mining. Karl Fackler was busily engaged lease mining gold ore from Gold Bond's Pole Pick No. 1 mine. Cliff Davenport was making headway at the head of Negro Creek with a 75-foot tunnel and several open cuts on his Davenport iron claim.

1945

Between 1942 and 1945, while War Order L-208 was holding sway on things mine related, Blewett did not ship gold ore to the Tacoma smelter. The wartime gold production restrictions were lifted in 1945, and the Gold Bond Mining Company started making plans for a shift to begin large-scale gold operations. The smaller-production gold miners that were developing their leased Gold Bond digs had a head start in gold production. In fact they had been mining gold ore during the war and holding some of it for the day the Tacoma smelter was allowed to begin accepting gold ore shipments.

The Blewett small-claim miners kept on doing whatever it was they did during the wartime years to keep busy developing and processing their gold-bearing ore veins. Mining news from their quarter was not forthcoming for the 1945 mining season.

1947

The only entry in the *Directory of Washington Mining Operations* (1947) for claims recorded in the Blewett area was Gold Bond Mining Company. Frank Lilly was president, and F. W. Kiesling was secretary-treasurer. Lilly was first made aware of the Blewett-Culver Gulch mines through his conversations with Charles E. Marr, who introduced him to his mining engineer friend J. B. Woodworth of Vancouver, British Columbia. Woodworth suggested Lilly search out the possibilities in the Blewett area. At that time, the Pole Pick No.1 claim was noted as being actively mined. It was leased to Karl Fackler and Walter Suckling. Other small-production miners were working their claims without releasing much in the way of public notice.

1948

In 1948, Gold Bond Mining Company was still rolling along with Frank Lilly as president and F. W. Kiesling on board as secretary. The company office was in the Columbia Building at Spokane, Washington. Current production was being accomplished with Karl Fackler and Walter Suckling still working the leased Pole Pick No. 1 property.

FACKLER MINING REPORT

In 1948, Edward C. Jacobs, a mining engineer from Grass Valley, California, did a preliminary report on Karl Fackler's six leased claims and the 25-tons-per-day mill. Jacobs noted that only a small tonnage of ore was mined and shipped to the smelter at Tacoma, Washington. The smelter returns related to the high-grade gold ore shipped from the property was several tons, with values varying from $28 to $576.45 per ton. But the problem of transportation costs and ore treatment charges considerably reduced the values returned from the shipments.

The Fackler ore was friable, easily crumbled, loose rock with decomposed quartz, and some calcite. Ore exposures in the Fackler workings suggested the possibility of more than a thousand tons in sight. Quartz from some outcroppings tested on the surface above the Fackler workings showed assay values of up to $27 per ton in gold. Jacobs considered the property an unusually high-grade prospect.

1949-1951

AVONS-REESE LEASE OF THE FACKLER NO. 2 TUNNEL

Ray Avons was an experienced miner and, between 1948 and 1950, president of Calton Mining Company, located in Leavenworth, Washington. He started cleaning out old tunnels leased from the Gold Bond Mining Company on and near the Pole Pick digs. Avons, Norm Reese, and his wife were working and living together in one of the old miner cabins in upper Culver Gulch.

One of the workings was identified as the Eleanor Tunnel, but the Fackler No. 2 tunnel appeared to be the main area of mining activity (it appears Karl Fackler subleased the Pole Pick No. 1 claim to Avons). The men were running ore-car loads of mined, hand-sorted, gold-bearing rock through the jaw crusher and other equipment at the Pole Pick No.1 claim (Fackler) mill located about 100 feet north of the Fackler No. 2 portal.

The mining trio noted that during the days when they processed the ore in the mill, they were grossing about $35 to $50 from one workday shift (how many milling days this represented was not addressed). The vein they were developing swelled and pinched, so the values varied also. When considering the two- or three-way split on the gold values extracted and the lease payment plus other expenses, they may have earned only enough to cover their costs. There was mention of 60 pounds of sulfide concentrates in a 5-gallon pail that ran (assayed) about $600 per ton in gold.

The water supply they used came from a dammed tunnel (one of William Donahue's adits, located south of the Fackler digs). The water was sufficient to run the mill about three hours per day, and at night, the seeping water replaced its day-use volume behind the manmade tunnel dam. What seemed to be a brilliant start for the trio of gold-seeking folks soon faded from memory, and any follow-up information ceased pertaining to their gold-mining operation.

Mr. Calton was owner of the Calton Mining Company in 1951. He was listed as involved with mine-development work in association with the Gold Bond Mining Company. At this time, the Fackler mill was also referred to as the Avons mill.

GOLD BOND MINING COMPANY ACTIVITY

In 1949, Frank Lilly, president of the Gold Bond Mining Company, began to increase mining operations by contracting Spokane, Washington, men Harold Lewis, Larry Jeffries, and Graeme Thorne to do some development work on the Pole Pick mine (at this point, the Avon-Reese lease was still listed as the Pole Pick mine lessee of the Fackler No. 2 tunnel). There were other claims named. Among them were the Pole Pick No.1, Pole Pick No. 3, and a Pole Pick fraction claim. Gold Bond also had Richard and Will Hickock on a contract to extend the Ivanhoe workings with plans to have somebody run an extension on the Olympic workings. These renewed underground developments were meant to far exceed any past mining activities Gold Bond had undertaken.

Additional workings listed were the Phipps Tunnel development, which had begun in 1936, and the patented old Blinn claims. They were the Olympic, Pole Pick No. 3, Shafer, Vancouver, and Seattle.

The reasoning behind all the increased interest in the Culver Gulch mines was the probability of higher gold prices. But even with that prevailing thought behind the company's plans, the official purpose was to continue underground development in the hopes of gold-ore production. It seems that most of their successful mining activities were a product of the lease miners.

Last but not least, the company was debt free at this point. It had 2,335,000 shares outstanding, with the stock being non-negotiable, and there were no bonds or other fund debt. The shares were traded over the counter in the Spokane exchange with a disclaimer stating, "The foregoing report is furnished strictly as a matter of information and opinion, and is not a recommendation either to buy or sell company stock."

In July 1950, Gold Bond Mining Company reported the beginning of ore production from the Peshastin vein in the Olympia claim tunnel and made a vague reference indicating the same for the Pole Pick mine.

KARL FACKLER SELLS THE RIGHTS TO HIS MINING CLAIM LEASE

Ollie Jordin was asked to sell the Pole Pick No. 1 claim lease for Karl Fackler. Karl agreed to pay Ollie for selling the lease. As Ollie told it (verbatim):

I was to get so much if I'd sell it. I sold it to a bunch over in Seattle. I was to get $500 a month 'til I got the $2,000 for sellin' it. Well, the company that bought it went broke—fizzled out. They didn't finish payin' for the mine, and the mine went back to Fackler.

I sold it for Fackler again. I sold it to a feller named Olsen. He had this woman over in Seattle, and her sister was a millionaire … in Seattle. And every time she'd get to dabbling in mines, she'd let her have 40 or 50 thousand dollars. Well he [Olsen] got her in with him. He had plenty of money to start on. He wanted to make this deal that he wouldn't take the mine if it didn't work out in a year for him, and take the ore out. He'd get me all the men I wanted to get that ore out. So a feller went over there [Culver Gulch] named Custer. He sold 'em a mill from Seattle. They already had a mill in there, a plenty good mill. But this new mill was to be much better. Well they tore out the old mill, and started puttin' in the new one. [It is at this point that the original stamp mill ceased to exist. This became the second mill installation to occupy the present-day historic 20-stamp mill site.] It cost 'em $10,000 to get the thing set up. 'Course they had to dig a awful big hole down into the hill for it.

Well, this Olsen used to come up and get my men. I had four of 'em workin' in the mine, and he'd take one man and make him go work on the mill. Then he comes for another one. Finally I told him he hired me to get the ore out. I says, "You aren't goin' to hire any more, and I want my men back because if ya get that mill runnin' I won't have any ore for ya to run in it. So these men are goin' to get out the ore and stockpile it, or the mill will make ya a lot a nothin'."

So later we run about 50 ton a ore, and Olsen wanted me to come down to the mill and sample the mill to see wither we were savin' any gold or not. I told 'im even before I went down I knew he wasn't savin' anything. It's all goin' over it in the waste. He told me I was crazy. So, okay, I went down and showed 'im. I told 'im, "Look, I'm goin' out to the tailin's with this gold pan." It was ore right after it was crushed in the ball mill. That's where the gold all was. I went out and panned it.

He watched. I said, "Now can you tell which is which?" And there was just as much gold in one as there was in the other. I told him he wasn't savin' a nickel of his gold. I told 'im it was because the gold was goin' over and under the quicksilver. I had to take him back in and show 'im. That's the mill they sold 'im in Seattle, ya know? … That Custer.

Then old Olsen kept doin' some funny things … all the time. He drove up to the boys that was workin' for me and was tellin' 'em, "You don't pay no attention to Ollie. You work as you please." Then he'd tell me the men was workin' for me and I do as I pleased, and can 'em if I want to. I told 'im I didn't have any men I wanted to can, but I got one man that if he don't put out a little more work next shift I was gonna can 'im. That was Walter Luther. He wouldn't work at all, but I got him workin'.

And Olsen got funnier and funnier, and I told Olsen's wife he was actin' funny. So he was goin' over to Seattle for about a week to raise some more money. He told me he'd give me $500 if I filled up the hole where we took the old mill out. Custer sold him that no-good new mill—no good at all—wanted to take the new mill out and put the old mill back. He wanted me to fill up the old mill hole so I could put the old mill back. I told 'im, "No, uh-uh. You have been beat enough." So he went back, and I went and told Karl Fackler … He had that big bulldozer. I told 'im to run that dozer. He knocked over the side of the buildin' and the whole side a that hill with the loose shale rock. And we filled up that hole. It took half a day. Then we packed it down to get it ready for the old mill.

Olsen came back and asked if I done any work on the mill, and I told 'im no, not a thing. He looked and asked, "How in the world did you fill that hole that quick with a wheelbarrow?" I told 'im how we pushed it in with the dozer. He wanted to pay me $500, and I told 'im, "No, ya been beat enough." And he kept gettin' crazier and crazier. I went to his wife and told her there's something wrong with him and that he's just not right.

And when he brought my pay up for $500—the money for gettin' out the ore—when I headed to him to get my check, he broke and headed up the hill. I yelled at 'im and asked what he was doin'. He says, "You're not getting to me and beat me up. No sir, you're not." I told 'im, "Who the devil wants to beat ya up?" He said if I beat him up, I wouldn't get my check. I told 'im I wasn't goin' to beat him up. Finally I got him to come down the hill, and I got my check.

Fackler was over there, and I told 'im somethin' was wrong with Olsen. His head was not right; he is off half the time. Told 'im we should take him to Wenatchee. So we told his wife, and she said he was acting awful funny at home. So we took him in, and they X-rayed his head, and he had cancer of the brain. He had that all the time he was over here. They took 'im to Seattle and operated on 'im, and of course, he died.

When I talked to Custer, I told 'im I knew he knew the mill was no good. I asked him if that was his real name, and when he said yes, I told 'im that that was his last stand on the Blewett. We said our goodbyes, and never seen 'im anymore.

OLYMPIC, STONER, AND GOLD DUST TUNNELS, 1952

Frank Lilly was president of the Gold Bond Mining Company in 1952. At this time, the Phipps Tunnel and Stoner Tunnel were used to haul Peshastin vein ore from the Olympic claim. The ore bunker for the Olympia was at the Stoner Tunnel level. At the same level was the head of the aerial tramway. It hauled the rock down to the Suckling mill ore bunker.

Lilly vaguely described a tunnel identified as the Gold Dust Tunnel, located on the Pole Pick (No. 1?) claim. It continued to be developed during the winter months. He suggested the Gold Dust Tunnel might be opened up through a shaft or raise connected to the Eleanor Tunnel. The Eleanor workings were located 250 feet below the Gold Dust digs at the Avons (Fackler) mill level. The Avons (Fackler) mill was designated to process Gold Dust Tunnel ore.

GOLD BOND MINING COMPANY SEEKS OLD NICKEL LEDGE, 1950s

With the beginning of the Korean War in 1950, strategic metal needs encouraged the search for those needed mineralized ore-rock deposits to produce wartime metals. Lilly proposed extending a road to a nickel ledge or dike located on the north slope of Culver Gulch, northward from the Amber Glee claim.

The author and Terry Carlson went searching for the dike outcrop in 2008. An uncompleted road leads toward the nickel dike. From the end of the road, we contoured through the brush to the workings. What we found at the base of the outcropping reddish-brown, nickel dike formation were several coyote holes. These are body-size tunnel cavities that were excavated while the miner hacked into the rock in a prone or other laid-out, horizontal position on the ground. Terry inspected a few short prospect digs and one that was about 20 feet long. There was no obvious sign of nickel-enriched mineralization.

Gold Bond production reports for the season were not impressive. The company justified the situation by issuing a statement that they were curtailing gold production in favor of more development work until gold prices went up in value. Then along came the old mine-development suppressor—litigation!

1953

No news-worthy mining information appeared in 1953. The usual mining property reports showed the mines in the Blewett area were still owned by the same owners, and no new names appeared in the claims records.

1954-1958

The year 1954 was another non-event mining season for the Blewett Mining District. Nobody died, nobody was born, and evidentially, nobody got notably rich mining gold. The usual suspects showed up in the mine owner's yearly, active-claims circular.

Arthur Ellis issued another vaguely described notice that, during 1954, the company's Pole Pick mine claim was opened at a lower level located just west and a little south from the portal of Tunnel No. 9. He stated that the new crosscut tunnel to the ore vein would give a good account of itself, even at the present gold prices. Resumption of stoping in the Olympia workings was planned for later in the spring. A short tunnel would also be run to open the Ivanhoe vein at an area that assayed as favorable. Gold Bond Mining Company leased another slice of its gold-bearing property to Gold Mountain Mining Company, owned by Walter Lindgren of Seattle.

In February 1955, Gold Bond Mining Company was sending out mining information about the company. This was in hopes of attracting interested producers of stainless steel and other nickel-cobalt alloys found in its gold producing claims at Culver Gulch. It gained no response.

Things remained much the same in 1956 as they did in 1955 for mining activities in the Blewett/Culver Gulch area, meaning progress was slow.

A slight amount of gold production was accredited to the Gold Bond Mining Company in profits for 1958. Some kind of agreement was made to protect leasing miners of Gold Bond's properties from access by inquiring company stockholders. This led to letters from those who bought shares in the Gold Bond Mining Company venture. They were beginning to suspect things were not as the company prospectus reported.

ANTON NEUBAUER

Jewel Sinclair came to Blewett as a newspaper reporter for the Wenatchee World in 1958 to relocate and report about previously discovered gold-mine sites (she was named after her relative, Jewell Sinclair, who was with Captain Dewitt Clinton Ingalls in 1860 when he was accidentally shot while on his lost-gold seeking trip). While she was there, Jewel visited Anton Neubauer, who was living in a cabin about ¼ mile south of Blewett. Anton's cabin was east of Peshastin Creek and across from the original 1893 Culver mine stamp mill.

Jewel took notes as Anton reminisced about Tom Johnson's old five-stamp mill that Tom bought from the Culver Mining Company. At this time (1958), the five-stamp mill site was marked by an 8- or 10-foot-diameter mill wheel on the ground at the site. Its round wood surface supported a belt that powered the stamp-mill machinery. The structure of the big wheel was sturdy, except where moldering wood was resting on the ground.

Apparently, Jewel Sinclair's 1958 newspaper article about Blewett's mining past did not stir up new interest in Blewett mining activities or in any of the gold placer ground along Peshastin Creek. It was status quo for the undeclared activities of the Gold Bond Mining Company. The local resident/miners at Blewett were also not disposed to identify their mining activities.

At an undisclosed time in the 1960s, Anton's neighbors monitored his activities due to his advanced age. During one three-day period when Anton was less than closely watched, someone noticed that he had not appeared outside. When finally checked on, he was found lying on his cabin floor.

Apparently he had tripped and bounced his head off the cast-iron wood-burning stove and was spread out, incapacitated, on the floor. He was taken to Cashmere, where they did a patch job on him. However, it was decided he needed some rest and recuperation under the observation of the trained staff at a Cashmere convalescence home. Here, a gap in his whereabouts takes place until 1964, when Anton Neubauer expired in the Cashmere Nursing Home after being ill for several months. He was buried in the Cashmere Cemetery next to his uncle Thaddeus Neubauer.

NORTH AMERICAN EXPLORATION COMPANY, 1959

This company came leaping on to center stage with a full-blown mine promotion in 1959. W. H. Palmer of Seattle pronounced the awakening of a grand new era for the untapped gold ore still present in Culver Gulch, up Negro Creek, and near Blewett. Palmer hired W. P. Johnson from Reno, Nevada, as the consulting mining geologist for the company.

By late spring of 1959, a notice sent out by the North American Exploration Company admitted there were legal problems connected with a "few" of the old claims that were causing a delay of scheduled company plans.

The residents and miners at Blewett knew enough about this kind of promotional goings-on to be more than a little skeptical. Jewel Sinclair wrote a few well-intended but benign words to encourage people "for still having faith in old Blewett, and now perhaps after half a century of inactivity, our faith may be justified." But her words did not inspire new interest.

BLEWETT PASS AND US 97 REROUTED IN 1960

Use Metsker's maps for Kittitas County and Chelan County to follow along with the text.

Today's US 97, from the beginning turnoff point of the old Blewett Pass Road at about the confluence of Swauk Creek and Hurley Creek in the Swauk area, follows a route that was completed in 1960. It crosses over modern-day Blewett Pass (originally named Swauk Pass). It is located about 4 miles directly east, as the crow flies, from old Blewett Pass. The Washington Department of

Transportation (in 1960) corrected any confusion associated with the names by replacing Swauk Pass with the preferred Blewett Pass banner, over which today's US 97 traverses north-south.

US 97 continues down the north side of (new) Blewett Pass to a point that passes the exit route of the old Blewett Pass Road at the confluence of Tronsen Creek and Scotty Creek, where they merge into Peshastin Creek on the west side of US 97.

Original Blewett Pass, now referred to as the Old Blewett Pass highway, was eventually given a surface of asphalt. But at this point (2013), historical Old Blewett Pass highway is in a state of deterioration. Some sections of the road surface have only two narrow lanes; some appear as only one and a half lanes. Here, the shoulder on the east side (the downslope side of the road) is completely eroded away. Taking this road requires attention to where you point the vehicle and doesn't allow any wiggle room for gawking at the spectacular view across the awaiting chasm just beyond one's elbow.

RENEWED MINING ACTIVITIES, 1961

Mid-July 1961, after years of small-scale lease mining activities, mining engineer Frank Lilly reported that work contracts went to Harold C. Lewis, Larry G. Jeffries, and Graeme Thorne of Spokane, Washington. The men were hired to get the Pole Pick mine ready for ore production that was expected to last throughout the year.

Lilly also contracted Richard and Will Hickock to work in the Ivanhoe mine. He said that a contract on the Olympic claim tunnel would soon follow. New equipment was ordered on the basis of more favorable market conditions. As indicated, Gold Bond claims were being worked through 1961 and continued being worked in 1962.

BLEWETT MINING COMPANY, 1962

In 1962, Willis (Bill) R. Priestly and his father Frank. W. Priestly of Seattle, were registered as in possession of the Eleanor Tunnel and Pole Pick claims. They were mining under their Blewett Mining Company title. The company was working mainly on the Fackler Tunnel No. 1 and Fackler Tunnel No. 2. A 24-ton gravity mill was used to process their gold-bearing ore.

Listings from the *Directory of Washington Mining Operations*, 1962 noted Harold C. Lewis and Graeme Thorne as lessees of one of the Pole Pick claim properties (their unspecified lease could have been held for the Pole Pick No. 2, Pole Pick No. 3, or the Pole Pick Fraction claim).

Bill Priestly, in the lead, and Karl Fackler heading toward the old mill that processed gold-bearing ore from Fackler's leased Pole Pick No. 1 claim. (Wesley C. Engstrom photo collection.)

GOLD BOND MINING COMPANY VS. ARTHUR H. ELLIS, 1964

During 1964, back at his eastern Washington residence in Reardan, Arthur Ellis was brewing up a Superior Court complaint and then took it to Spokane for judicial action. Frank Lilly, company president, was listed as co-defendant with the Gold Bond Mining Company.

In late fall of 1962, Judge Raymond F. Kelly issued an order temporarily restraining Lilly from disposing of or secreting Gold Bond Mining Company ledgers and legal books. Lilly was directed to show cause as to why the restraining order should not be made an injunction pending a trial and why H. G. Schlomer should not be appointed temporary receiver to take charge of the company's books and records.

Ellis stated he owned 200,000 shares of Gold Bond capital stock at 5 cents par value. He believed holdings of the company contained monetary value. Ellis also said there had been no shareholders or directors meetings held since he became a shareholder in 1949. (Law provides that if no shareholders meeting has been held in 18 months, any shareholder can call a meeting upon proper notice to all shareholders.)

Nothing had changed at the start of 1964, but by March, there was a response to those holding Gold Bond Mining Company stock. Superior Court Judge William H. Williams, at Spokane, ordered Gold Bond to arrange a special meeting of shareholders. The meeting was April 23. H. G. Schlomer was appointed temporary receiver of the Gold Bond Mining Company. The stockholders put together a five-man board and discovered that Gold Bond was near being operational; ore production was to soon follow.

The new board of directors was Reardan-area wheat farmers Arthur H. Ellis and Henry Schwartz; Albert Buob, wheat farmer; H. G. Schlomer, insurance executive; and Archie Stewart. Thirty stockholders attended an arranged meeting in a Spokane auditorium.

NORTHWEST MINING VENTURES COMPANY, 1964

Bill Priestly and his father, Frank W. Priestley, formed Northwest Mining Ventures in 1964 to perform underground development on the Pole Pick No. 1. It was granted with a one-year lease from Gold Bond. They had seven men ready to mine and mill ore from a Gold Bond Mining Company property lease that Bill and his father held on the Pole Pick No. 1 and Eleanor Tunnel digs. Under a contract agreement with Frank Lilly, they were to mine a minimum of $100,000 worth of ore per year, with a 12½-percent share going to the Gold Bond Mining Company.

Arthur Ellis was subsequently elected president of the Gold Bond Mining Company, Mrs. Dorothy J. (Hesseltine) Stewart was vice-president, Mrs. Marie (Meyer) Cheney was secretary, Mrs. Arthur Ellis was assistant secretary, and Archie Stewart was treasurer. Fred E. Woeppel was the company attorney. The company books were opened for inquiry from this point forward.

1965-1969

Mid-summer 1965, Gold Bond Company signed a one-year lease with Blewett Mining Company (Northwest Mining Ventures Company was being run as a separate company by Frank and Bill Priestly, possibly for legal reasons). The purpose was to start extensive exploratory diamond drilling. The ore utilized was from bulldozed surface ore in the Summit Pockets area. The exploratory ore samples were run through the Fackler mill, which ran on a single-shift basis. Bill Priestly was in charge of the operations.

The combined *Directory of Washington Mining Operations,* Circular No. 43, for 1965 and 1966 showed no new Blewett area mining claims were recorded. That was partly due to the fact that any able-bodied Blewett miner/resident plus outside help were hired as laborers by Gold Bond.

During 1967-69, mining activities rolled along in compliance with the plans Gold Bond had set forth under its new management. At this point, Bill Priestly was exercising his mining activities through the Blewett Mining Company (any mention of Northwest Mining Ventures was not forthcoming). He was operating the 24-ton gravity mill with limited testing.

1969-1980

In October 1969, surface assays taken from the Gold Bond properties in years past showed deposits valued at 2.5 to 3.5 percent nickel. In 1970, Tibor Klobusicky, the company consulting engineer, ran a magneto metric survey to determine the scope of the nickel-bearing zone. Nothing noteworthy occurred outside the same activities noted for 1970.

Gold Bond Mining Company (1972-73) was continuing to evaluate the findings of their consulting geologist, J. Jacobson, over the assays of the past three years. Gold Bond Mining Company was in a dilemma in March 1974. In the past, Gold Bond Mining Company's seven patented and 17 unpatented claims were operated as separate mines: Alta Vista, Pole Pick No. 1, the Blinn claims, Wilder, and Golden Guinea properties. Gold Bond's consulting geologist,

Tibor Klobusicky, advised the company to revise old surface maps and open inaccessible mine portals. At this time (1974), the Gold Bond Mining Company was entering negotiations to acquire additional mineral holdings in the Blewett area and in Wallace, Idaho.

From 1975 through 1979, nothing new was added to the small-claims books for Blewett. This may have been partly due to gold prices starting to accelerate upwards, and big mining companies were coming into the Swauk and Blewett Mining Districts and claiming huge blocks of mineral land. In 1975, the price of gold per ounce was at $160.86. By 1978, it was $193.40, and in 1980, gold per ounce was at $615.00. This set the stage for all the gold-seeking actions and deals that went on in the Blewett area throughout the 1980s.

Chapter Twenty-three: Montana de Oro (MDOI) and Keradamex Enter

MONTANA DE ORO INCORPORATED, 1979

The Gold Bond Mining Company board of directors submitted a report to their company stockholders on September 7, 1979. An exploration and operating lease contract was assigned to New Mexico-based Montana de Oro Incorporated (MDOI). Thomas E. Coleman was president. At the time of the contract agreement, MDOI was working on property adjoining Gold Bond-held claims. Montana de Oro committed their company intentions to include exploratory work on Gold Bond land within the year. Montana de Oro said they had already made arrangements to obtain a 25-ton-per-day mill for use at the claims area.

ATTEMPT ADIT, 1979 TO PRESENT

The following information is a description of the 1979 mining activities on the Attempt dig, as observed by 15-year-old Tom Richardson (Tom is the present owner [2013] of the Pole Pick No. 1 claim). Young Tom happened to be on one of his many camping trips in the Blewett-Culver Gulch area. There he discovered Montana de Oro miners Karl Fackler and Bill Priestley. They

Fifteen-year-old Tom Richardson on the right, and friend Jack Ball, stand at the portal of the Attempt Tunnel. Its purpose was to crosscut into the Pole Pick vein. The project was abandoned before reaching the main vein structure. (Photo by Tom Richardson [1979].)

were directing a crew of miners who were blasting and mucking their way southward from the vicinity of the Blewett Tunnel portal area. MDOI was tunneling their way toward the Pole Pick vein. Tom gained their trust and friendship by his intense interest in the history of the mining activities in the gulch. MDOI miner Joe King told Tom that Montana de Oro had access to $2.5 million for exploration and mining.

The Attempt project was run to intersect the gold vein that was being worked at a lower elevation in the gulch at the Fackler No. 1 and Fackler No. 2 tunnels. While driving the workings, Karl Fackler and Bill Priestley's miners struck a high-grade pocket of gold. It panned out very high concentrates of fine gold from the crushed quartz ore that was found at the 60-foot point in the workings. Tom noted that the total value in gold amounted to $6,800 from that one deposit. Gold was at about $300 per ounce in 1979. The workings reached to about 75 feet, and then the digs were abandoned. There was no definite reason that Tom knew of for the work stoppage. Tom was invited to work with the miners at the Fackler workings; Karl and Bill were unaware of this.

Tom learned how to mine and was allowed to join in working the rock drill, blasting rock, and mucking out the ore. When the unsuspecting bosses were in the area, Tom stepped aside and went back to being a casual observer.

In 1993 and 1994, a Canadian company named Gold Bond Resources (no connection to Gold Bond Mining Company) leased mineral claims from Montana de Oro. One of the observations they made was that the Attempt Tunnel never reached the Pole Pick vein. The odd thing about this was that the vein was visible on the surface in the direction the Attempt workings were headed. So with this in mind, the work stoppage on the Attempt appears to be deliberate. But why? This question goes unanswered.

In the year 2000, miner/mine owner Tom Richardson took a serious stand for his belief that Culver Gulch had untapped deposits of gold waiting to be discovered. So Tom and some mining-interest backers formed Goldfinger Resources. Goldfinger purchased the patented land that held the Fackler No. 1 Tunnel and Fackler No. 2 Tunnel, along with an adit to the south of the two Fackler portals that was originally known as the Big Mouth. It is presently named the Goldfinger workings. Then there was a change of plans involving unpaid debt owed to Tom. He cancelled the debt in return for sole ownership of Goldfinger Resources. Through shareholder vote, Goldfinger's Washington State holdings were sold to Tom's "Richardson Gold Mines, Incorporated." It has evolved into Gold Mines, Incorporated (as of this date, 2013), and is owned by Tom Richardson, who is also the company president.

GOLD BOND'S CLAIMS

Gold Bond Mining Company claims included within the terms of the Montana de Oro lease were the following:

Patented Mining Claims
S. C. Davidson Lode (Pole Pick claim), Olympia, Pole Pick No. 1 (Thomas Johnson Lode), Pole Pick Extension No. 2, Seattle, Shafer Extension No. 2, and the Vancouver claim.

Unpatented Mining Claims

Amber Glee, Byron G, Columbia, Gold Quartz, Gold Quartz Extension No. 1, Gold Quartz Extension No. 2, Gold Quartz Extension No. 3, Grace, Hazel B, Ivanhoe, Kennelworth, Lucky Fraction No. 1, Lucky Fraction No. 2, Rainbow No. 2, Rainbow No. 3, Rosalind, Roy and Ray, and the Tunnel Site claim.

A report was to be forthcoming for the stockholders … "if commercial ore was developed or if something else of interest occurs." The notice was signed by Gold Bond Mining Company President Arthur H. Ellis and the board of directors.

The price of gold was at $615 an ounce in 1980 (up over $300 from 1979 prices). The race was on to stake and record mineral claims, and take advantage of the ever-rising gold prices.

In December 1980, Montana de Oro published its financial statement for 1979 and 1980. The bottom line indicated an income loss per common share of $1.99. And from here, it started skidding down the slippery slope toward litigation.

LITIGATION AGAINST MDOI, 1981

On January 30, 1981, bachelor miners Joe King and Larry Karr sued Montana de Oro and Willis (Bill) R. Priestly and Jane Doe Priestly, his wife, on complaint for wages due Joe and Larry.

Joe and Larry were signed into a written contract on May 1, 1979, to do work for Montana de Oro. But for some reason, in mid-June, the two men and the company mutually agreed to terminate the written contract and verbally agreed for the men to take $10 an hour. In addition, project manager Bill Priestly promised Joe and Larry a bonus of 1,000 shares of common stock at the end of the 1979 mining season. Priestly also promised to pay Joe and Larry 50 percent of their regular pay during the winter months (December 1979 through April 1980). Montana de Oro/Bill Priestly allegedly failed to follow through with the agreement, and litigation was begun.

By March 25, 1981, Arthur Ellis was also in contention over Montana de Oro's activities and insisting on some answers to his unheeded questions. Tom Coleman was trying to respond in as positive a way as he could, considering the minus column his work was reflecting.

Karl Fackler told Coleman he was convinced that the tunnel should be continued. The plan was to continue on the Pole Pick vein the next season because it was the most promising. The Ivanhoe claim was dropped from the work list due to very low gold assays (0 to a trace). Coleman encouraged Ellis not to send a glowing report to his stockholders because it wasn't warranted. Ellis was trying to find some good news regarding gold production, but the truth was exploration was the precursor to gold production. An impatient Ellis was told to keep the faith.

October 5, 1981, is the first indication that Bill Priestly was president of MDOI. Tom Coleman stepped down as company president. He was suffering ill health due to mercury poisoning in connection with his mining activities. He remained on the board of directors, retained all his stock options in the company, and remained under Montana de Oro's medical program for as long as the program was available.

Edgar Lawrence was the company director. Priestly's signature and position as the company president was first openly verified at the bottom of a "Hold Harmless Agreement." In the document, he wrote, as president of Montana de Oro, that he held harmless Gold Bond Mining Company from the formerly filed lien claims of the company's mechanic and material man, John Knowles. It protected Gold Bond should a foreclosure occur under the lien statutes

Knowles was going to drag Bill Priestly, Karl Fackler, and Tom Coleman into court over an outstanding debt for labor performed. The value of the debt was $8,365, plus interest at the rate of 1 percent per month from August 30, 1981 until Knowles was paid. It is interesting to note that, in the Knowles court case and that of Joe King and Larry Karr, there is no public notice of the outcomes. This may be due to settlements out of court.

POLE PICK NO. 1 PROGRESS REPORT, 1982

Bill Priestly, as president of MDOI, sent a report to Art Ellis and the company's stockholders in mid-January 1982. It stated, "The operation was closed for the winter on November 5, 1981 because of weather conditions. The new equipment was installed and we expect to have the new mill operational by early June. This new mill will have the capacity of 1,500 pounds per hour with an additional capability for handling 2,000 pounds per hour when our mine production requires it ... Our plans for 1982 include opening new sections of the Pole Pick veins. And in addition, to develop a portion of the Ivanhoe vein within the Ivanhoe and Amber Glee claims."

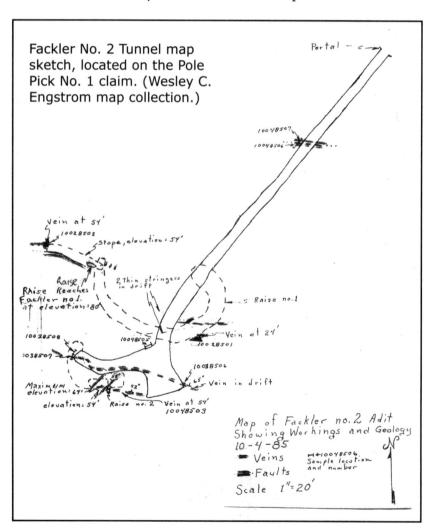

Fackler No. 2 Tunnel map sketch, located on the Pole Pick No. 1 claim. (Wesley C. Engstrom map collection.)

Assays were made at various locations on the active workings in May 1982. The company sent no material to the smelter and had only a small amount for eventual refining. Production-run testing was halted at mid-summer because of failure by an essential piece of equipment—the Ellis mill. Repairs were attempted but failed after several weeks. It was decided to enlarge the mill capacity because a totally new equipment configuration was needed. The company bought a 1-ton-per-hour Joshua Hendy ball mill from California and a rake classifier from Utah. There was an additional delay until October waiting for the pinion gear for the ball-mill drive.

All the old equipment was removed from the mill, except for the mercury plates and the shaker table. The refit and installation of the new equipment was nearing completion. In the next two months, it would be finished and ready for possessing ore.

Then work was delayed several weeks because of extreme winter weather, which necessitated extensive road and mill-site repairs. The parting words in the report describe the assays as spotty but encouraging enough to expect a successful summer operation.

By September 1982, Bill Priestly sent Art Ellis a new road gate key and the yearly proof of labor report for an anticipated visit by Ellis at the company's mine workings. Art didn't make his only planned trip for the year because of reasons unknown. But, by November, the new mill was fully charged and ready for the 1983 mining season.

Development at the Pole Pick No. 1 (Fackler No. 2 Tunnel) was driven ahead, and the Fackler No. 1 Tunnel level was run for a distance of 40 feet to the Pole Pick vein. Plans called for driving on the vein, both east and west as far as was practical before stoping ore from above. Then 16 inches of snow fell, and the temperature dropped to 5 degrees, putting the work schedule on a day-by-day basis. A scheduled independent examination of the property by a consulting geologist was rescheduled for the spring of 1983 because of the foul weather.

FOLLOW-THROUGH, 1983

During the winter months, several major mining companies contacted MDOI expressing interest in examining the property. Art Ellis and Bill Priestly followed up on the interested parties' requests. In August 1983, Montana de Oro chose to work with Canada-based Keradamex Inc.

By June 1983, Priestly wrote to Art Ellis and informed him that since the inception of their mining program's lease on July 29, 1979, Montana de Oro had diligently explored the potential of the Culver Gulch properties. The vein systems involved covered an enormous amount of ground. Priestly pointed out the need for the work to be done in an orderly, scientific manner.

The vein structures cut through several property boundaries, and not all of those claims were within Gold Bond Mining Company's control. Montana de Oro, in addition to Gold Bond's efforts to expand on the Pole Pick No. 1(Fackler digs) had also opened the old workings on the Amber Glee, Olympia, Byron G, Gold Quartz Extension No. 2, Big Dipper, the Blewett Tunnel, Tamarack, Black Cap, and the fraction claims. All the old workings were caved, and it would be costly to open them.

Company engineer, Karl Fackler, had previously mapped and sampled the old workings. It was Karl's knowledge that projected the best approach to develop the workings following the chosen direction in which the tunnels should be advanced.

Meanwhile, Keradamex (which was buying mineral claims in the Blewett area) was impressed with Fackler's findings and agreed with him on the course that the program was following.

At this point, the new 1-ton-per-hour mill proved to be a success. It produced 30 tons of low-grade ore with a recovery rate of 98.6 percent. The .06 ounces of gold per ton ore was used to balance the mill. Future value of the mined ore would depend on the production of the Pole Pick No. 1 vein from the Fackler No. 2 Tunnel.

KERADAMEX AND MONTANA DE ORO JOINT VENTURE, 1983

In August 1983, Montana de Oro and Keradamex of Toronto, Ontario, confirmed terms for a joint-venture agreement. A formal agreement was signed three months later. The properties consisted of 24 claims held directly by Montana de Oro under lease from Gold Bond Mining Company and 325 claims held by Keradamex within Kittitas and Chelan Counties.

The joint-company development was in hopes that a program of surveying and mapping, followed by diamond drilling, drifting, and crosscutting to explore ore vein systems, would prove beneficial. Keradamex had the right to quitclaim any time it chose. Montana de Oro was to keep all the maps and sample results, including rock cores.

By December of 1983, financial statements indicated Montana de Oro was suffering a lack-luster economic mining season, similar to the ones for the 1980–81 assessments. The bottom line was a $1.73 per share net income loss.

The newly elected board of directors was Willis (Bill) R. Priestly, president; Karl Fackler, vice-president; Norma Kragtrop, secretary; Lynn Priestly, treasurer; and Edgar Lawrence, director.

During that time, Montana de Oro furnished the labor and equipment to open the Meteor Tunnel for examination and sampling. The project was completed in January 1984, which kept crews of men working beyond the normal mining season.

LITIGATION, 1984

Gold Bond held a special board meeting in mid-March 1984 at Spokane, Washington. Art Ellis (age 75) was the company president and director; his wife, Lena Ellis (age 71), was secretary. Robert L. Hautala was auditor, stock-transfer agent, mining engineer consultant, and a board member.

Shortly before the Gold Bond Mining Company board meeting, a notice of intent was sent to Montana de Oro declaring forfeiture and cancellation of Montana de Oro's mining lease for the Gold Bond mineral properties according to Gold Bond. It was issued because Montana de Oro had failed to perform under the guidelines of the lease.

Montana de Oro was declared in default and had 30 days to correct the lease work failures. If they didn't comply, their company would have to surrender all 26 of the leased claims back to Gold Bond Mining Company.

Equipment used in the Pole Pick and Pole Pick No. 1 mines. The air supply tank is on the far left. It was used to pressurize the compressed air tank of the locomotive setting on the tunnel tracks. To its right, on the ground, is the fuel supply used to run the electric generator located in the far background. In the foreground are the ore mucker (with the bucket up) and a side-dump ore car. (Photo by Vic Pisoni.)

Montana de Oro's April 11 reply to Gold Bond's accusations was filed by attorney Roger A. Castelda. His response to Gold Bond refuted the threatened lease cancellation. The bottom line was … the argument went to a court of law.

Karl Fackler gave his affidavit. In it, he presented facts that from 1939 to 1979 the only work that Gold Bond Mining Company did on their claims was general assessment work and labor to make sure those claims were not abandoned or cancelled. Karl noted that out of all the 40 years of assessment work, there were only three years that Gold Bond did actual physical assessment work for themselves. The other assessment work for the other 37 years was undertaken by the Fackler family. That assessment work was paid for and performed by Fackler family members on Gold Bond Mining Company claims. Gold Bond never reimbursed Karl Fackler whatsoever for any of the assessment work undertaken and, furthermore, did not have the Fackler family's permission to utilize their assessment work for their (Gold Bond's) benefit in filing proofs of labor preformed. In fact, as regards to the patented claims, even the taxes were paid by Fackler so that Gold Bond could retain possession of the claims and not become forfeit. At one point, the Gold Bond patented property taxes were in arrears for four or five years, and Charles Fackler paid them to keep the claims from being sold at a sheriff's auction.

This makes no sense on the face of it. Obviously there was something more than what is expressed in the information at hand. However, if Gold Bond could control and knew the date when the Pole Pick No.1 became in default, they could purchase the property under a different company or person's name and evict Fackler. Fackler appeared to have perceived this possible deception and, thus, had an ulterior motive of his own for spending his time and money and taking such an extended monetary risk. Otherwise, why would he have taken these unexplained actions? Although, by handling it in this manner, Fackler did keep control of the mining activities and protect his investments and perpetuated his profits as he continued to produce gold ore.

In the affidavit, Fackler acknowledged that, had it not been for his family's money and labor, Gold Bond Mining Company claims would not have existed at the time of the pending litigation. In an Order to Show Cause for Preliminary Injunction, Judge Fred Van Bickle ordered Gold Bond Mining Company and its president, Arthur Ellis, to appear personally or by attorney on September 4, 1984, in the Superior Court at Wenatchee, Washington. A warning stated, "If you fail to appear in person or by attorney and answer this application, the relief as described herein may be granted."

Gold Bond realized they had made a mistake by bullying Montana de Oro. The court proceedings ended with Montana de Oro continuing with its previous mining activities, including their Keradamex connection.

MONTANA DE ORO AND GALAXY CRUISE LINE, 1984-1987

Montana de Oro was back in control of their leased Gold Bond claims in September 1984. The company took another mining partner into consideration in September. The company was in the process of linking Montana de Oro and Galaxy Cruse Line in Nassau, Bahamas, into a joint venture-mining agreement.

Through telephone conversations and a resulting letter of intent September 25, 1984, the two companies agreed to enter into a joint venture agreement. Galaxy Cruise Line was to provide the sum of five million dollars. The money was to be used for development, exploration, and mining operations on the claims.

These actions were followed by a lack of follow-up information, other than the fact that Keradamex and Galaxy Cruise Line were no longer associated with Montana de Oro in any other business connections.

Montana de Oro noted that the company lease from Gold Bond Mining Company terminated December 31, 1987, and it was decided that they would not continue the lease. Montana de Oro was focused on the development of the Peshastin vein system on their own claims. But MDOI and Gold Bond agreed about working together to interest major companies in investing in their respective properties.

MDOI moved their equipment from other projects down the hill to the Bob Tail claim adit. There they uncovered the Peshastin vein for a strike length of 125 feet. They were also opening the old workings.

Bill Priestly closed with the information that he was headed to New Mexico to assist with the development of the company's gold and silver project that was expected to provide funds for MDOI to continue its mineral-seeking efforts.

MDOI, 1988-2002

All company-owned mining activities appeared to be on hold from 1988 until 1997. There were no important references about the Culver Gulch mines, other than a few gulch property filings as an "in exploration" notice.

Bill Priestly left for New Mexico in 1991. Cashmere, Washington, resident Paul (Bud) Corbaley, who worked for Priestly as the company machinist, became the property gateman and caretaker. Bud and his wife, Ruby, lived in a cabin for ten years, on a remaining strip of the old Blewett Pass highway (east of US 97), located about ¼ mile south of Blewett.

Bud and his son Dan gave several of our Northwest Underground Explorations members a tour of the Culver Gulch mines in 1991. Bud died within a few years of that Culver Gulch trip, and his wife Ruby went to live with their daughter at Medical Lake.

Without knowledge of all the details, NWUE was made aware that William (Bill) Priestly, Willis Priestly's son, went into partnership with the present mineral claim owners in Culver Gulch.

Bud Corbaley was the caretaker of Bill Priestly's Culver Gulch claims in the 1990s. Bud guided a group of Northwest Underground Explorations members to and through the various gold mine workings. (Photo by Daryl Jacobson.)

In 1999, Gold Bond management determined that the future possibilities of commercial mine development of their Culver Gulch properties were remote and put all Gold Bond Mining Company's mineral claims up for sale.

Gold Bond sold their five patented mineral claims in the year 2000. They were the Shafer Extension No. 2, Pole Pick Extension No. 2, Olympic, Vancouver, and Seattle claim (the old Blinn group). As of 2002, these claims are no longer patented.

2013

Currently, all the original 1874 mineral claims once owned by MDOI are in possession of new owners. The claims range from the stamp mill at the beginning of the gulch road up to the ridge top of Culver Gulch. NWUE met the new owners of the historic Culver Gulch mines while doing

Former Blewett childhood residents Phyllis Barthol-Cramer and her cousin Joyce Davenport-Rosenberger are standing by the town of Blewett historic marker. Miner/mine owner John McCarthy and wife, Alice, lived in the log house that once stood there. (Photo by Vic Pisoni.)

research about the area. The information from that contact and resulting friendship with the miner/owners was used in the NWUE book, *Discovering Washington's Historic Mines Volume No. 2*. It covers the East Central Cascade Mountains and the Wenatchee Mountains.

BLEWETT TOWN SITE, 2013

It takes a good imagination these days while driving over Blewett Pass and by the flat, open ground of the old historic mining town site called Blewett to realize that there were and are (as of 2013) active mineral properties west of US 97 in Culver Gulch.

On the advice of consulting geologist Tibor Klobusicky, Mile Post 174 is the site of a large 200-foot-long turn-out/parking area that has on display a historic marker identifying the historic Blewett town site. The collapsed, nineteenth century, historic 20-stamp mill still maintains its deteriorating presence west of US 97, at the foot of Culver Gulch. Presently, the old mill structure is on an active mining claim, as is the road that is routed up to the top of the gulch.

During the time of Blewett's most energized ore producing activity, 20 stamps in the mill were sometimes heard thunderously pounding 24 hours a day to free the gold from the mined ore.

Note: The ground surrounding the mill site is not open to mineral collecting or metal detecting without the permission of the owner, nor is any of the other active claims along the Culver Gulch road all the way to the top of the gulch ridge.

Chapter Twenty-four: Tronsen, Shaser, Scotty, and Ruby Creeks Mineral Claims History

BEGINNING MINING ACTIVITIES, 1858 TO 2013

Captain Mortimer Robertson was prospecting the placer ground on Tronsen Creek June 17, 1858, as indicated by his field notes. He and some of his trusted men also panned for gold in the areas near the confluence areas of Scotty, Shaser, and Peshastin Creeks. In the process of their gold prospecting, pans containing up to $3 in gold dust and flake gold were taken.

Daniel Shaser came to the area years later, in1874, and prospected for gold. From 1888 through 1959, 83 mineral claims were recorded within a 1-mile radius, using the confluence of Scotty Creek and Shaser Creek as the center point. In 1891, Daniel Shaser was noted as the owner-operator of an arrastra on Shaser Creek. It is not known where it was located. On May 31, 1899, Iron Mountain claims No. 1, 2, 3, 4, 5, 6, 7, and 8 (iron ore digs) were recorded. They were owned by four men: R. F. Brown, D. G. McLean, George Persinger, and Adolph Ralf. This group of claims is in the vicinity of old Iron Mountain, located in the center of the northeast ¼ in Section 10. This is presently (2013) the unnamed peak printed as elevation about 5,200 feet. About 1 mile east is today's map-designated Iron Mountain (elevation about 5,400 feet).

In 1910, samples of iron ore from hot spots in the Blewett area included assays from Ingalls Creek, Negro Creek, Culver Springs Creek, King Creek, and the areas of Magnet, Tronsen, and Scotty and Shaser Creeks. Iron ore was known to be in those areas as early as the 1880s, but gold fever was the driving force of the early mining days in the Peshastin Mining District. The unproven, high-grade iron ore deposits remained just that—unproven.

About 1915, and the start of WWI, the need for strategic wartime minerals brought the dimly flickering memories of the Blewettites back into the iron-ore spotlight. For the next 25 years, 26 iron claims and 17 placer claims were recorded in these areas. While the rush to file and record iron claims cooled down in 1919, another event heated things up a bit. The Peshastin Lumber Company mill, located in the confluence area of Scotty and Peshastin Creeks, burned to the ground on August 15, 1919. The mill fire spread into the nearby slopes and charred the bushes and trees. Damage to the mill and ready-to-ship wood products amounted to a loss of $150,000.

The early 1940s (the beginning years of World War II) showed a renewed interest in the strategic metals claims of the Peshastin Mining District. The focal point in the Shaser Creek area was in Sections 13 and 14, the iron-ore-bearing land north of the North Fork Shaser Creek. Prospecting for iron and other strategic wartime minerals from 1940 to the mid-1940s escalated. Washington Nickel Mining and Alloys Incorporated was leading those Blewett-area claims-recording activities.

BLEWETT'S NICKEL-IRON ORE DEPOSITS, 1940

Former iron, nickel, and chromite claims recordings filed during World War I became pertinent to the mining areas around Blewett as nations friendly with the United States sought strategic metals ore for the war under way in Europe.

The nickel silicate found in the Blewett area was being seriously sought, but nothing developed from any of the strategic-ore prospects the Blewett miners found. This was due to the low-grade of the mineral deposits.

WASHINGTON NICKEL MINING AND ALLOYS—IRON PROSPECT, 1940S

Washington Nickel Mining and Alloys began developing 11 claims on the Iron prospect areas for both hematite and magnetite deposits. They occurred as small masses in peridotite, with iron content ranging from 42 to 51 percent in strategic minerals.

The 11 claims were leased to American Mineral Resources out of Detroit, Michigan. The Division of Geology then came in and mapped the area. The US Bureau of Mines sampled the ore. After the lease to American Mineral Resources was ended, Washington Nickel continued to develop the properties.

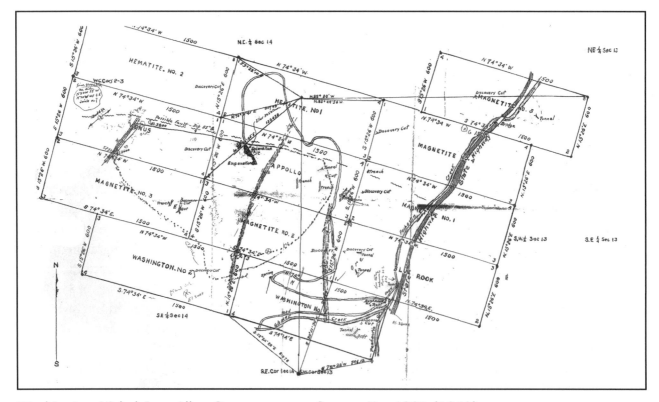

Washington Nickel-Iron Alloy Company map, Survey No. 1281 (1949).
(Bureau of Land Management.)

WASHINGTON NICKEL MINING AND ALLOYS— NICKEL PROSPECTS, 1940S AND PRESENT

In the 1940s, Washington Nickel had nine nickel claims. All assays for nickel were low, and the tonnage figures were purely estimations, based on shallow surface exposures. Wishful thinking seems to have had the upper hand. The other failure was the attempt to find ore deposits at depth through test samples taken by US Bureau of Mines.

Harry J. Hood, Washington Nickel's company president, and E. L. Davis, president of the American Alloy Steel Corporation from Detroit, Michigan, bought the iron and nickel prospects. He combined them as Washington Nickel Mining and Alloys Corporation. His idea was to extract an estimated 56,000,000 tons of nickel-chrome ore by the open-pit method. The operation never got under way. But, the mining claims were patented.

In 1942, while Washington Nickel was still poking around their properties hoping to finding new, richer, and larger mineral deposits. Murray Budge and C. C. Golding were scratching the earth for gold at the Budge claim located on the south bank of Scotty Creek near its mouth. They had a 200-foot tunnel that produced assays of $3.50 to $12 in gold-silver ore. In 1943, Washington Nickel gained possession of the Budge claim and renamed the claim Peshastin.

In 2012 and 2013, Washington Nickel started selling its properties to individuals, who have improved existing road surfaces and gated off their parcels of land. These private land holdings are posted as "No Trespassing."

RUBY CREEK MINERAL CLAIMS HISTORY

Not much happened, north of the town of Blewett, in the way of gold fever proportions on or near Ruby Creek, except during placer and hydraulic-mining activities from 1892 to 1899. Some fairly good indicators were assayed for copper, but they failed to advance into more than the prospective stage due to very limited ore deposits.

Gold, on the other hand, was always present at the confluence of Ruby Creek and Peshastin Creek. Gold-placer claims were staked from the mouth to the upper elevations of Ruby Creek and onto Windmill Point.

The following is a limited summary of the 47 claims recorded. Few held or developed claims for an extended time in Ruby Creek; prospectors/miners came for one mining season and left. Some miners would return in later years to relocate their abandoned digs. Following are claims-recording area information from 1884 to 1927. After 1927, claims recordings were all minimal attempts to double-check for any mineral deposits that may have been missed.

Thaddeus Neubauer was the first; he recorded the Ruby claim in 1884. Its vague location was given as Ruby Mountain (later named Windmill Point). After Thaddeus, came a list of names that appeared to be prospectors of a just-passing-through nature. Most of the claims were held by some of the earlier established Blewett miners, such as Jacob Somers, James Wilder, Pat Hurley, O.

S. Cloud, W. S. Bloom, Sherman Donaldson, A. W. Munden, John Heavner, John C. Johnson, E. E. Keys, H. A. Feller, C. B. Meredith, Clarence Jennings, W. R. Eisenhower, and Charles Harvey.

On June 13, 1895, it was noted that Charles Harvey and associate mining partners S. W. Elliott and H. C. Castleberry had five miners exploring their group of 13 mineral claims. The digs were on a dike that was traced eastward into the Ruby Creek-Windmill Point area's outcropping rock formations in the upper elevations of the Ruby Creek drainage. Harvey had a cabin on the creek near the properties. The zones where mineral assays showed 8 percent nickel in the ore held no traces of gold or silver.

The Ruby Creek area claims were hard-rock and placer (hydraulic) properties that ranged from the mouth of the creek all along and into its headwaters.

RUBY CREEK/WINDMILL POINT AREA

Although few in number, the 13 Windmill Point mineral claims were, in some instances, within close proximity to the headwaters claims attributed to the Ruby Creek claims. They were attempts to locate mineral deposits that were continuations of the vein structures in Culver Gulch. These hard-rock claims were located mostly on the western slopes of Windmill Point. They were recorded after the initial claims taken in the Ruby Creek area.

The Tip Top mine (located in a gully on the upper west slopes of Windmill Point) was the only gold mine east of Peshastin Creek to produce a profit over the years when the other Windmill Point claims were active. It was originally recorded by Jacob Somers in 1880. After the Tip Top started to produce gold, other prospecting activities near the mine soon followed. As for recorded claims, S. L. Cone and John E. Walters were the first to record other Windmill Point digs in 1881. In September, Cone and his mining associates recorded the Esmeralda claim east of Windmill Point ridge. It was a failed attempt to find the same vein structure that was located in the Tip Top mine, which was directly west of the Esmeralda on the western slope.

Walters was somewhere on the ridge between the Tip Top and Esmeralda with his Windmill claim. The following year, Edward Blewett recorded Walters's Windmill as his own relocation claim Windmill property. Gus Nilson followed in 1892 with his Red Jacket dig. Charley Striker took on the Esmeralda in 1896. E. E. Keys, Oliver Cloud, and John Heavner grabbed a few more mineral claims.

Chapter Twenty-five:
Negro Creek Mining History

USE THE GREEN TRAILS MAPS FOR MOUNT STUART, WA (NO. 209), AND LIBERTY, WA (NO. 210).

CHINESE MINERS IN THE PESHASTIN CREEK AND NEGRO CREEK AREA

Available data indicated that the Chinese miners camped or placer-mined Peshastin Creek. They were on their way through, from their known digs in the Swauk Mining District, to established Chinese gold-placer bars on the Wenatchee and Columbia Rivers.

Moses Bollman noted in 1880 the appearance of Chinese near the town of Blewett. There is a reference and physical evidence of them being at camp and active as miners in an area about 2½ miles up Negro Creek. A Chinese miner, Louie Hey, had the Red Tiger placer located at the 2½-mile location at Bear Creek in 1890. This was told in statements to members of Northwest Underground Explorations by Negro Creek resident/miner Jim Holderhoff. Jim's mining partner (name withheld by request) located the Chinese miner's campsite and showed him camping items that were compatible with the Celestial's way of life. And recorded claims listed at the DNR library in Olympia, Washington, verified Louie Hey's claim.

Jim told of his past mining partner who climbed a rocky slope north of Negro Creek to the base of a cliffy area located midway to the ridge top. An old, long-abandoned, and concealed Chinese mining camp was located there. It is said to be situated under the protection of an overhanging cliff boulder (a natural cave

Miner Jim Holderhoff is entering one of his mining digs near the Caldo (Lucky Strike) mine area in upper Negro Creek. (Photo by Vic Pisoni.)

structure at a middle elevation of the ridge slope). Its Chinese occupancy was confirmed by the broken remains—dish, bottle shards, and Chinese coins with square holes in the middle. This was said to be near Jim's cabin area, known as the old (1960s) Caldo mine property (originally recorded as Charley Striker's Lucky Strike mine).

Note: The Caldo claims are presently (2013) under new owners and are active mining claims.

An attempt by Jim and several of us from Northwest Underground Explorations was made to find the camp, but we did not locate it on the one trip—and have not yet. The location in which the camp was situated is within a small area, but the climb deserves a "Mountain Goat" rating for any approach taken to ascend to its outcropping rock facings. The Chinese were also known to be placer mining at the confluence of Peshastin Creek and Wenatchee River. This information was made evident in a statement by A. O. McLeod who owned the ground and removed the Celestials off the digs.

Charley Striker, as he appeared in the 1880-1890s. (Photo courtesy of the Davenport and Barthol families, who were former Blewett residents.)

MINERAL DEPOSITS

Geology of the slopes in the Negro Creek drainage and mineral veins mined in the area constitute a continuation of the ore ledges found in Culver Gulch and traced northwestward into the Negro Creek area. But, this mineral belt exposed by the deep gulches of Negro Creek is different from those of Culver Gulch in many ways, even though the two areas are only divided by a commonly shared ridge.

Data for the mining efforts engaged in, from its mouth to the headwaters of Negro Creek, are vague to non-existent during some years. So total mineral production, value-wise, is not known. Some of the ore veins in the area have a sulfide mix of gold, silver, and copper. There were limited white quartz rock veins containing cost-effective amounts of free gold, and even those were not long-lived. Ore that is essentially copper in nature is not in the quantities that rated the deposits as commercial-grade.

Nickel was often reported in mineral assays from the Negro Creek digs. It shows mostly in serpentine-peridotite associated with reddish-brown, east-west trending nickel ledges of the area. The green-tinged ore mineral of nickel is called garnierite. This fact offered hope in pursuing the mineral, and many prospectors/miners attempted to find profitable deposits. The same was said of the cinnabar (mercury-bearing) ores in the area. The richness of the ore has assayed high, but the cinnabar veins were narrow and of little commercial value.

Other rocks that contain mineralized veins are near the diabase dikes in the area. There is one diabase dike intrusion on the ridge forming the divide between Negro Creek and Ingalls Creek that has low-grade copper sulfides. Another showed evidence of nickel. These do not form in veins but, instead, show as scattered blebs in the gabbro (dike-rock) formations. As such, the gabbro rock does not hold any high hope of containing the area's source for gold.

PLACER DEPOSITS

The richest placer gold deposits were established north of the town of Blewett on Peshastin Creek, near the mouth of Negro Creek, and up Negro Creek. The gold-bearing gravel was deposited from the upward extension of the present quartz veins in the area and by erosion of the drainage system emptying into the creek. The old gravel channels follow the course of the stream banks, but are not necessarily present in the banks along today's waterways. This is due to the downward cutting drainages assisted by the upward thrust of massive regional rock movement to deposit the pebbles of quartz and country rock where they are presently found.

The placer gravels on Peshastin and Negro Creeks vary in depth-thickness and material character. The original gravel deposits in the Negro Creek drainage area was deposited on creek banks upon ancient, elevated creek-level benches. All gravel available for practical placer mining at this point in time is at present-day, lower-level deposits on Negro Creek's current bedrock.

Where the bedrock is composed of slate, many crevices and potholes have produced rich gold deposits in the past. On Negro Creek, for 2 miles above its mouth, wide gravel bars were worked by sluicing. The average depth of the gravel bars was about 5 feet. Presently, evidence of the old water-carrying sluicing ditches can be found along the north bank of the first 1½ miles of lower Negro Creek.

Note: As of 2013, it is commonly known that there are still active placer and hard-rock claims located from the mouth of Negro Creek, upstream to the Brazos claims, and beyond (2½ miles) to the Caldo claims. There is also a lack of evidence at some locations identifying which claims are active because they are poorly marked. So if the "sometimes a great notion" crosses your mind about going for the gold, it is suggested that you check the claims' recording files of the ground that is of mineral interest to you.

One of the minerals that most of today's active prospectors along Negro Creek are aware of is platinum in the gravel bars. In 1942, government geologists found native platinum about 6 miles up from the mouth of Negro Creek. Chromite was also discovered in a drainage gulch at the head of Negro Creek. The unidentified location yielded two chunks of nearly pure chromite weighing about two pounds each.

ROCKHOUNDS!

And, for rockhound-minded folks, there was a teasing bit of information presented about agate-lined geodes, whole and broken. They were found in the vicinity of the Davenport prospect (four claims) located on the north side of Negro Creek in Sections 7 and 8. Access up Negro Creek Road is approached from the locked gate at Ingalls Creek trailhead. This road is blocked by a landslide that obliterated about 600 feet of the road approaching the old Blewett Highway-Negro Creek Road bridge abutment.

The other means of entry is to wade across Peshastin Creek at the mouth of Negro Creek, or park ¾ mile south on the old stretch of Blewett Highway and walk to the mouth of the creek where a log crossing may be found about 200 feet upstream. It becomes your responsibility to determine which way you wish to access upstream. There is "backdoor" to the head of Negro Creek; it is a north-trending dirt road located beyond a locked gate in the North Shaser Creek area. The gate is located on north-trending Road 2207, the beginning of the Negro Creek-bound route. It gains elevation up to 5,200 feet on the pass at Iron Mountain. From the pass, the road descends into the headwaters of Negro Creek. Take the road approaching an area named Gold Creek Basin. The geodes were located on the slopes in Section 7.

NEGRO CREEK MINERAL CLAIMS, 1860-1896

In 1858, gold was first discovered in the placers of Peshastin Creek and Negro Creek by a party of miners returning from the Fraser River gold digs in British Columbia. They only worked the placer ground as they were moving through the area. In the late 1850s to early 1860s, prospector Antoine Etienne, for whom the creek was named, stayed around long enough to take $1,100 in gold,

Charles Splawn came along the trail following Peshastin Creek in 1860 and claimed he was the first to discover the placer gold in the creek. That may be a fact, but he did not stay long enough to imprint that activity into the minds of the miners who were active and in place on their Peshastin Creek placers at that time.

John Gubser, George Bearfield, and Alfred Henson made their presence known in 1861 as they mined their Peshastin Creek placer. By February of the next year, John Gubser, and family, was established in the Salmon River area mines. The town of Conconully is at the center of the old Salmon River mining campsite.

In 1874, Culver Gulch's three-ore vein system was picked up beyond the basaltic dike that intruded Thompson (Culver) Gulch, thrust upward, and displaced the three main east-west ore veins. Marshall Blinn followed the continuation of the Pole Pick ore vein from the west side of the dike down to and across Negro Creek. Blinn recorded the Olympic, Pole Pick No. 3, Shafer, Vancouver, and Seattle claims in April of 1880.

NORTH POLE GROUP, 1888-1904

George Persinger started developing his group of 10 claims in 1888 and expanded the group into 23 claims by 1904. His 1888 mining partners were Mike Callahan, John McKenzie, Andy Stoughton, George Kline, John Jurey, and Bill Lee. The North Pole claims were located in the center of Section 4, on the south side of Negro Creek and upstream from the Meridian claim. The North Pole No. 1 claim and two other claims were on a ledge 92 feet wide that runs north-south and outcrops to the north on the big red buttes of the Cinnabar King claim. A drift was run 90 feet on the ledge.

In 1895, about 40 tons of ore was mined at George Persinger's North Pole mine. Persinger and his associates bonded the properties to some miners. A mill test showed 8.5 percent nickel, 2.75 percent cobalt, and 2.15 percent copper.

But the roads serving Negro Creek and the other nearby mining camps were in their usual, deplorable, springtime condition. This was a yearly situation that hindered wagon transportation of incoming goods and outgoing ore until work crews made the roads useable.

E. T. Bradley of Chehalis, Washington, had claims adjoining Persinger's North Pole mining properties. He was also noted for inventing a single stamp mill weighing only 150 pounds. It was inexpensive and came in sections. He was expecting to sell them to the miners in the Peshastin Mining District. Nothing more was mentioned of its success or failure (probably due to its restrictive ore-processing abilities, somewhat limited to the status of a mortar-and-pestle ore-sample crushing device on steroids). Bradley became a well-known area miner and a Blewett resident up to 1904.

In 1894–95, there was 200 tons of high-grade North Pole ore on the dump alongside Negro Creek. In the spring of 1895, a rapid snowmelt raised the creek level to a powerful torrent that swept away half of the ore.

By 1904, development was a 125-foot cinnabar prospect shaft, with mercury running as high as 90 percent in the purer rock. The best prospect was a 90-foot shaft in gray serpentine. It produced free gold as small round particles. An assay processed at Spokane ran $1.70 in silver and $61.10 in gold per ton. By the end of 1904, about 1,700 feet of underground work had been done on the North Pole group of claims.

WAR EAGLE MINE, 1892-1900

Miner Charles Buttles and his family moved from Mullen, Idaho, where he and his father, Major John F. Buttles, worked in the Morning mine. Then they headed west to reside in Leavenworth,

War Eagle mine cookhouse in 1898. The War Eagle group of claims was located up Negro Creek. An unknown miner stands at the left. Seated to the right is gray-haired Major John F. Buttles. His brother Jay is sitting next to him. (Cashmere Museum and Pioneer Village photo collection.)

Washington. They began prospecting for coal, but it proved unsuccessful. After abandoning that project, they focused their attention on finding gold-bearing quartz deposits up Negro Creek. They came into possession of the War Eagle claim in 1892. Charles and his brother Jay built the War Eagle cabin. It had a small cook stove and a stone fireplace, glass windows, and the floors were hard-packed dirt. A meat locker was dug into the bank of the creek to a depth of about 3 feet by 4 feet high and 4 feet wide. It was timbered and then lined with metal sheets.

The War Eagle mine was taken over by Henry Rosenberg in March 1894. During the mining season, the Negro Creek mine-to-market road was extended up to the Cascade Mining Company (Blinn) properties.

By 1896, Charles Buttles was no longer mining. He was working for the owner of a general merchant store in Leavenworth. By 1903, he was the county assessor for Chelan County, and his brother Jay became a deputy assessor.

The War Eagle consisted of four claims in 1897. They were the War Eagle, Hidden Treasure, Gray Eagle, and Keystone, which was joined to the south line of the Gray Eagle. Major John F. Buttles, James Grant, and George Hood had possession of the properties.

This cabin/store site is located off of the south bank of Negro Creek, about ¾ mile upstream from its confluence with Peshastin Creek. Cedar Grove campground later occupied this area. (Photo courtesy of the Davenport and Barthol families, who were former Blewett residents.)

TIP TOP MINE, 1892

Other notable, newer digs were near the 570-foot Tip Top claim adit. These mineral claims were recorded up Gold Creek Basin, located on the upper south slopes of Three Brothers Mountain. Those recorded in the basin during 1892 were the Keystone, Bald Eagle, Chicago, Bunker Hill, plus eight more. Most of the claims were owned by notable Blewett miners: Harvey Souder, the Wilson brothers, Charley Striker, and W. L. Bernard.

OLD BLINN CLAIMS, 1892-1893

July 1892 was the scene of a reorganization effort at the Cascade Mining Company by Charles Bash and B. M. Long. Their position as major stockholders with the highest influence had them scrambling to generate more outside interest and capital. Their plan was to further develop the company's Olympic, Pole Pick No. 2, Shafer, Vancouver, and Seattle claims. In December, the old Blinn properties on Negro Creek continued with new development activity after being idle for about eight years.

In 1892, the remainder of the 53 mining claims and miners were dispersed all along Negro Creek and the creek drainage areas of the north and south slopes.

In March 1893, J. D. Lindsey made a trip to the town of Peshastin and reported that there was 22 inches of snow in the Negro Creek drainage area. In May, a quartz mill was being erected on Negro Creek near the Cascade Mining Company (Blinn) mill site.

POVERTY AND CRAP LODE, 1893

S. G. English (an England émigré) had two claims to his name, recorded on June 6, 1893. They were the Poverty placer and his Crap Lode claim (lode meaning a hard-rock dig). They were located near Blinn's old Negro Creek mill. The Poverty claim speaks for itself. It didn't pan out. The Crap Lode claim name may define the activity for digging an outhouse hole; English could have exposed a valuable mineral deposit, thus the claim's name.

UNION AND DOMINION, 1893-PRESENT

The original recording for the Union claim appeared June 1, 1893. The owner was William T. Rarey (he owned the W. T. Rarey Company in the town of Wenatchee). This property was located about ¼ mile up Bear Creek.

In 1897, these properties were bonded to Charley Striker, William T. Rarey, G. S. Marion, George Beam, James Fullwiler, Mahlon Souder, and George Ward. The Union and Dominion claims ore consisted of free-milling gold.

A few of us Northwest Underground Explorations members were guided to the Union-Dominion claims. Negro Creek miner Jim Holderhoff showed us a west-trending, 100-foot adit that followed a 1-foot-wide, white-quartz vein. At the breast of the white-quartz vein digs was a blackish, 4-inch-wide, crumbling, decomposed quartz material that looked like spit-out snuff (tobacco). Jim stated that he panned some "color" (gold) from the snuff-looking debris. NWUE was not successful in our attempt to pan any yellow metal from the snuff-stuff.

NICKEL PLATE GROUP, 1894

Word was out in February 1894 that the nickel, cobalt, and copper deposits up Negro Creek looked promising.

James Lynch and his brother John were the new owners of the Tip Top mine in Gold Creek Basin. They also had the Nickel Plate group of claims in the Falls Creek area. The Nickel Plate claims were bonded to Mr. Lang of San Francisco with a 30-day stipulation that required him to close the deal, buy the claims, or forfeit his bond. Lang had seven miners on two working shifts running underground workings to the ore deposits. The miners' findings would determine which way the sale of mining shares would go. Information on the outcome of that deal was not found.

Several Everett businessmen purchased a large block of mining claim shares from some of the Negro Creek nickel mines. The ore from the claims was used as flux in processing ore at the Everett smelter.

In April 1894, there were renewed mining activities up Negro Creek that assayed high in nickel. The excitement was related to the Riverside Smelting Company in the city of St. Louis, Missouri. Riverside Smelting Company received a high-grade nickel, cobalt, copper ore shipment from the Ontario mine owned by Martin Lewis and his mining partners, Captain J. K. Morrell, Gus Creelman, Ben Richardson, and Moses Bollman. Riverside Smelting was offering $96 per ton for Negro Creek ore—a low offer according to Lewis and Morrell, but they accepted the offer on those terms.

ONTARIO MINE, 1895

In June 1895, the Ontario mine was in control of F. A. White, E. C. Bronson, R. Springer, G. A. Neher, and H. D. Cooley. They were wealthy men owning $500,000 in company stock. They put twelve miners to work running a crosscut tunnel to tap the vein below the old underground workings. Under the owners' guidance, more plans were made for mining development that included building a smelter for treatment of nickel and cobalt ore or, as a more favorable deal for them and their company, some kind of agreement with the Everett smelter to build a reduction smelter near the mouth of Ingalls Creek.

There was 100 tons of ore at the Ontario mine ready for shipping. The Ontario ore was the result of two years of mining. Their average assay was $148 per ton in mineral values. Where exposed on the surface, a well-defined ledge was traced for 1,000 feet. A 4-foot-wide quartz vein carried $8 in gold, 3 percent nickel, and 3½ percent copper sulfides. There were four men working under the direction of Martin Lewis in an effort to accumulate another ore dump.

NEGRO CREEK CLAIMS, 1897

L. K. Hodges's book, *Mining in the Pacific Northwest*, features these updated 1897 mining claims.

WAR EAGLE

Although the War Eagle was first recorded in 1892, by 1897, Major John F. Buttles, James Grant, and George Hood were in possession of the four claim mine. The digs were bonded to the Cooperative Mining Syndicate of Seattle. They were located in the northwest ¼ of Section 2. An arrastra was located south of the Hidden Treasure claim and west of the Gray Eagle.

The Alder Grove campground was later established and joined to the War Eagle's east claim line. The 30-foot main adit was run on a gold-bearing, mineralized ledge of the War Eagle claim. The workings are located on the south side of the creek. A snub tunnel is located just above the 30-foot main adit. The War Eagle claims were abandoned by the syndicate in 1900.

NEW YORK

This group of 13 claims was owned by W. S. Newland and Henry Bernard. They were located in the Center of Section 35. Quartz deposits containing gold and silver were mined. None of the workings defined any ledge structure.

EAGLE AND IOWA

Henry "Hubble" Blinn of Leavenworth had possession of these claims located in the Northeast ¼ of Section 3, on the north side of Negro Creek. A shaft (minus any descriptions) and two tunnels assayed at $32.30 in gold per ton. Another ledge was 3½ feet wide, carrying $8 in silver and 60 percent lead per ton.

DAISY DEAN

The owners were the Donahue estate and F. H. Osgood located in the Northeast ¼ of Section 3, on the north side of Negro Creek, west of and next to the Eagle and Iowa. The richest development was one shaft of undetermined length exposing a gold-bearing ledge 3 to 4 feet wide, assayed at $32.20 in gold per ton. The ore was treated in an arrastra located on Negro Creek.

RAINIER CLAIMS

This group of 13 claims belonged to the Negro Creek Nickel and Copper Mining Company located in Sections 3 and 4, about ¾ mile up from the mouth of the creek. The property had two mill sites (type unknown). The Rainier ledge and a dike formation crossed northwest-southeast through Negro Creek. Four claims covered the dike and ledge formations. A 170-foot crosscut tunnel on the dike struck a series of five nickel-bearing veins. Gold showed at $5.20 per ton, and nickel at 2½ to 3 percent.

TAHOMA

The owner is unknown. The Tahoma joins the west side of the Rainier group. It had a 4¼-foot-wide quartz vein carrying a trace of copper, a trace of silver, and $8.20 in gold per ton on a vein that runs into the Rainier group series of claims.

MONTANA

Owner Tom Riley had a rock spur formation southwest of the Gordon claim. The rock outcrop contained free gold, silver, and nickel.

MERIDIAN

Owners George Persinger and John Lindsey had a quartz vein cutting through serpentine. It assayed about $10.50 in gold per ton. The Meridian was located on the south side of Negro Creek, across from and above the Ontario mine. A 40-foot-wide ledge of blue quartz between serpentine walls assayed at $19.50 in gold, $5 silver, and $2.50 in copper.

AMIGO

Owners Gus Guinn, William Elliott, and Charles Harvey had a 50-foot tunnel on the upper, south slope of Bear Creek, southeast across the gulch from the Union-Dominion claims. During the two hikes that Northwest Underground Explorations made to the adit, it was dry and appeared to remain that way all through the year. We saw no mineralization in the dig or on the tailings pile.

GORDON

Supreme Court Judge Gordon, W. L. Agnew, and G. E. Filley staked this dig on the west side of Bear Creek. It joins the south line of the Union-Dominion claims. Its 50-foot crosscut entered a north-south trending ledge of free gold, silver, and 40 percent nickel.

CHAMPION AND IDAHO

The owner(s) of these claims ran a crosscut tunnel 40 feet on its way toward a 4½-foot ledge. It assayed at $12 in copper per ton of ore. This dig ran east-west on the south side of Negro Creek and joined the North Pole ledge at an angle on its east side.

PERSINGER AND GRAY EAGLE

George Persinger had this claim that joined to the west line of the Union-Dominion. The sulfide ore contained assays up to $16 per ton in gold, 5 ounces in silver, and up to 32 percent in copper. A 25-foot tunnel was run on the mineralized ledge at the summit.

LEO

John and William Lynch owned this dig. It had a 60-foot crosscut that ran along a two-foot-wide vein of ore that cut the ledge. An assay showed 25 percent copper and some gold and silver.

CINNABAR KING

The owners of Cinnabar King were George Persinger, Harvey Souder, and Charley Striker. The claim joins the Everett claim on a 200-foot-wide dike formation that outcrops in a line of jagged, red cliffs on the south side of Negro Creek. Exposed minerals of red and blue quartz within serpentine walls showed traces of gold, nickel, and cinnabar.

MINING ACTIVITY 1898-1926

In 1898 and 1899, the established Negro Creek miners were mute about their mining activities. It was the beginning of an economic recession that ran a gambit of highs and lows from 1899 to 1904. From 1904, lingering uncertainty prevailed until the economic panic of 1907 set in. During these years, gold per ounce stayed around $18. Plus, the Negro Creek and Ingalls Creek copper, cobalt, and nickel deposits, once boasted about, were not the mineral success hoped for.

By 1905, R. H. "Windy" Brown, George Persinger, the Rolf brothers, and property evaluator Richard Weir went up Negro Creek in March. They were going to stay for the mining season. Their beginning activity was to help repair the weather-ravaged mine-to-market road along Negro Creek. They brought with them the rumor that a stamp mill was going to be built up Negro Creek … somewhere.

In August, John C. Johnson and John Stout were working 5 miles up Negro Creek near an area the Blewettites called the Park. The mining job they were hired for was at the Mountain Lion group of claims. Blewett miner and resident Cliff Davenport was the foreman at the mine.

Nothing of mining-news importance was noted for 1906 and 1907. In May, stagecoach activity began to pick up its pace, and for two weeks, it dropped off passengers at Blewett and up the Negro Creek road to the various mining properties. Thaddeus Neubauer and John Heavner were among those Blewett miner/residents heading up Negro Creek. They were hired by Martin Lewis, one of the owners at the Ontario mine.

The years 1908, 1909, and 1910 were no-shows for Negro Creek in the claim-recording files. There was mining activity happening in the established gold-placer claims, but activity in lode (hard-rock) claim recordings became stagnant after a prolonged period of promoting favorable ore deposits for nickel, copper, cobalt, and iron deposits that never proved out

R. H. "Windy" Brown and F. W. Losecamp were back in May for the 1911 season at their eight claims recorded as the Golden Guinea group (formerly the Francis L group of claims). The mine was about 2 miles up Negro Creek and located downstream from the old Blinn mill. It was said to be joined onto the North Pole mine property line. Negro Creek mining was mining news exempt in 1912 and 1913.

During 1914 and 1915, 21 claim recordings appeared in the record books. James Wilder and his son Ray owned 11 of those claims. Two of the claims were located on the south bank of Negro Creek, near the old Cedar Grove campground site. They were the Tunnel claim and Mill Site claim, the location of the Ivanhoe stamp mill. The Tunnel dig was 500 feet south of the Mill Site claim's south line.

Joseph Warner was back in August 1915, at the Blewett-Negro Creek area after several years' absence. He was on his new Negro Creek mining claim (name not given). He kept his hired men busy installing machinery for a new ore-processing stamp mill. The mine that he was developing had ore stoped out that was milled during the mining season.

In 1916, there was little interest in claiming new mineralized ground up Negro Creek. Charley Striker made a bold move and soloed with three claims. On September 5, he filed on the Myrtle H claim, the Myrtle H No. 2 claim, and Stehekin claim. The Stehekin was joined onto the north claim line of the Vancouver claim. The years 1917 through 1919 reported no important mining activities.

Even with the end of WWI, Blewett area miners Thaddeus Neubauer and John McCarthy continued searching for strategic wartime ore in 1920. They headed up Negro Creek. They recorded six claims on November 10, 1920. They were located upstream in the Park area. In 1921, Charley Striker claimed the Mac Sweeny claim, Mac Sweeny No. 1 claim, and the Myrtle H No. 3 claim. In 1922, there were six placer claims recorded.

As Negro Creek mining activities continued along in its secretive mode up to 1926, the Amalgamated Gold Mines Company made an announcement that it planned to reopen mining activities in their Culver Gulch properties.

Somewhat coincidentally, news burst forth of dozens of small placer prospects around Negro Creek being worked. And, a promising deposit of cinnabar (the ore rock containing mercury) was being pursued by Judge Thomas Burk of Seattle. Under Burk's management, two crosscut tunnels were run and cut into cinnabar-bearing rock.

Following the Burk discovery and announcement, there was verification that H. H. Coffey gained ownership of the (five) old Blinn claims. Coffey was actually a frontman for the Guggenheim syndicate. He was noted to have 30 years of mining business experience behind him. He was previously in the Swauk Mining District purchasing placer mining properties for his bosses. He eventually became interested in the past successes of the Culver Gulch quartz veins at Blewett. Coffey's research led him to believe there was more of the same gold riches to be had. He began further, extensive exploration of the long adit at the Negro Creek level on the Vancouver claim without alerting his syndicate boss from the East Coast.

1927-1928

H. H. Coffey was the company president and general manager in control of five patented claims: the Olympic, Shaffer, Seattle, Vancouver, and Tacoma. He filed for articles of incorporation under the name Bonanza King Mining Company.

Several ledges up to 5 feet wide had been opened up. Coffey commissioned an independent mining engineer who took several assays. A group of Seattle businessmen were endeavoring to gain control of the company. Their interest was broadened when shown assays of $171.14, $162.46, and $61.18 in gold per ton. However, Coffey's enthusiasm and wheeling and dealings didn't make any of the aforementioned plans happen. The bottom line was no sale, and the Bonanza King hype went away.

In 1928, Charley Striker and Charles Reid owned the Myrtle H claim. Striker originally recorded the mine in 1916. It was located on Negro Creek and was ignored for a time, but then Striker and Reid were back in 1928 to reopen the mine. At this point, the claim had a 160-foot adit, a 100-foot adit, and other shorter digs for a total of 700 feet of workings. There was an arrastra on the claim that was reported to be in the process of grinding out $62 in gold per ton of ore.

1929 GREAT DEPRESSION TO 1942

Miner Tom O'Shaughnessy began prospecting in the Negro Creek area in August of 1929. His intent was to secure a gold-mining claim. Encouraging news emanated from the Myrtle M mine up Negro Creek. This gave Tom the incentive to risk a mining season or two looking for gold in his own small but productive gold-bearing placer or perhaps in a hard-rock mine. His results were not declared.

During 1930 through to 1934, mineral claim recordings for Negro Creek and Ingalls Creek showed little activity. Mining partners Cliff Davenport and his son Herman, along with Anton Neubauer, recorded the Tom Thumb claim on June 6, 1933. It was located up Negro Creek. Oren Dodd, Ray Walters, and L. Dodd relocated the old abandoned Lenora quartz lode claim on Negro Creek (near the mouth of the creek in Section 36). They renamed it the Lucky Strike claim on June 26, 1933. No claims were recorded in 1934.

E. R. Marr recorded the Melva placer claim April 29, 1935. It was located 1 mile up Negro Creek. In January 1936, Mahlon Souder recorded the Tip Top claim, located up in Gold Creek Basin on the southern slope of Three Brothers Mountain.

Negro Creek saw only no-shows in mineral claim recordings from 1937 until 1942. There were always the mining activities of the hangers-on—the local, small miners on Negro Creek and, in particular, in the area of the town of Blewett and up Culver Gulch. The Great Depression of the 1930s was winding down with the advent of jobs created by US involvement in WWII. Once again, the wartime machine and associated ordinances called for mining strategic metal ore.

SHOSHONE MERCURY MINING COMPANY

Shoshone Mercury Mining Company was formed in 1929. They had 560 acres located in Section 4, on the north side of Negro Creek. The mercury (cinnabar ore) reserve was estimated to be worth $430,000. The property was at the end of a road running parallel to Negro Creek leading to the Shoshone claims. Owners G. J. Niemeyer, Z. T. Parker, and Roy Fontaine said the cinnabar ore was disseminated throughout a nickel ledge. By early 1942, their Circle claim consisted of a 135-foot adit and a small open cut.

In July 1942, the Shoshone claim was still active and remained in the ownership of Niemeyer, Parker, and Fontaine, all from Spokane, Washington. At this time, unpublished field notes by geologist Ward Carithers were written that give a close examination of what mining development had taken place to that point. Carithers ran a tunnel, traverse in the Shoshone workings. Mineral samples were taken for assay. The most interesting dig was in a surface open cut on the nickel dike that revealed a substantial high-grade showing of cinnabar; this dig was 35 feet above an adit on the north side of the creek.

IRON CLAIMS, 1942-1944

In early spring of 1942, long-time Blewett resident-miners Cliff Davenport, his son Herman, and their mining partners R. D. Ogden and G. Fern were up Negro Creek in Sections 7 and 8, on the Iron King No. 1, No. 2, and No. 3 and Iron Queen claims. These properties were developed by a short adit and several open cuts on an iron-ore prospect. On the property was a ridge of mixed conglomerate rock and iron ore, and an adit 60 feet long was run into the deposit.

In 1942, geologist Ward Carithers examined the claims and found no ore in place within the workings but noted there was hematite ore on the dump. A 1943 report by Broughton noted at that time there was 59,850 tons of iron ore exposed 42,720 tons of probable iron ore, and 435,850 tons of possible ore reserves within the Davenport claims. By 1944, the four claims were relocated and recorded by Cliff Davenport as the Davenport Prospect (four claims).

CHROMITE CLAIMS, 1942

These claims were later named the Copper Queen No. 1 and No. 2. The digs include two adits 3 and 4 feet long. The veins ranged up to 5 feet in width. Sulfide minerals of about 4 to 5 percent were noted in the vein material, with traces of gold and silver.

In the fall of 2011, two members of Northwest Underground Explorations (Kent Nelson and the author) took a scenic 8½-mile round-trip, photo-op hike up the Negro Creek headwaters to the west side of Navaho Peak. We passed through the northeast corner of Section 11, which is identified as the location of the Negro Creek Copper Queen workings. A 1904 map indicates there was a cabin in existence on or near the property.

On the claim, there was a shallow, sloughed-in, 6-foot-deep prospect shaft within sight of the trail. It showed no traces of mineralization. An extended search for the short adits was not attempted.

In 1942, Washington State Geologist Ward Carithers was examining mineral deposit claims at the headwaters of Negro Creek. In the northeast ¼ of Section 11, in the Negro Creek Copper Queen area, he picked up two pieces of nearly pure chromite float that had eroded off a (yet to be discovered) outcropping ore rock. They weighed about two pounds each. The location of the find, as written by Carithers, was:

> "Four hundred feet in elevation below the pass, and 1 mile southeast of Navaho Peak. This gully is the origin of a Negro Creek headwater tributary flowing southward to a larger V-shaped gully in which the water courses parallel to the trail that connects with Navaho Peak. The elevation of the chrome float discovery was at about 5,800 feet.
>
> I could not find any chromite ore in place [the source-deposit] or any more chromite float. This occurrence in serpentine is the first known to me in the Blewett region, and it points to the possibility of more in this region."

This Negro Creek headwaters area is also the source of the platinum found in the Negro Creek gravels.

1943-1955

The year 1943 started an information vacuum for the mining claims in the Negro Creek area and lasted (research related) until 1955. Even with the Korean War (1950–1953), there was no interest in the search for strategic metals in the Negro Creek area, and no data explained the lack of interest. Evidently, the failed prospecting searches for production amounts of wartime minerals and the imposition of the government's Limitations Order L-208 eliminated a lot of mining activities up Negro Creek.

At that time, the only vehicle access to Negro Creek road was gained by using a stretch of the old Blewett Pass highway. This section of road approached the mouth of Negro Creek from the north. Then it continued for the remainder of the Negro Creek road from the creek mouth

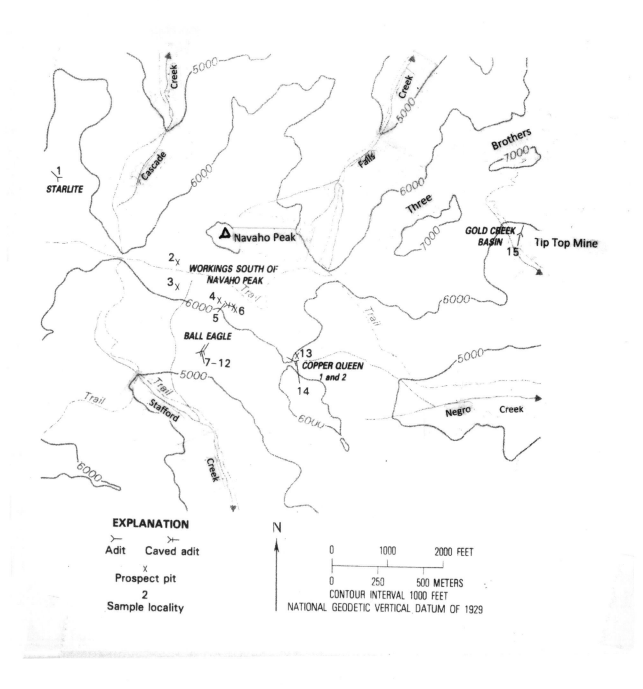

This overview map represents the Navaho Peak area mining claims.
(Alpine Lakes, Washington Geological Survey Bulletin No. 1542 [1989].)

to the upper reaches of its watercourse. About ¼ mile of that road surface no longer exists due to a landslide in the mid-1980s. Foot travel is now the only means of entry, from the mouth of Negro Creek and up to the end of the 4-mile-long creek road. The Cedar Grove campground, a destination point for picnics and camping, was established about 1 mile up from the creek mouth. The campsite was still on Chelan County maps into the early 1960s. The campsite was later abandoned and omitted from future information sources.

The gold mines in Culver Gulch and the various gold placer claims within the Peshastin Mining District appeared to be the exception. The hard-rock mines were known to produce gold by way of local miners leasing gold claims. These were held by the owners of multiple-claim mining companies, such as the Gold Bond Mining Company. The Blewett area lease-miners used the free-gold ore-processing facilities of the Gold Bond company stamp mill. There was no need for the smelting services of the Tacoma smelter.

BARKDULL MINE, 1958

Calvin Hobart Barkdull (1875-1960), a consulting hydraulic and mining engineer, took an interest in the mineral-ore content of the Negro Creek area in the 1950s. He wrote mining-related papers from 1895 (age 20) until 1958. His known mining activities ranged from California and Mexico to Skagway, Alaska, and outlying areas. Barkdull was a packer at Chilkoot Pass from 1905 to 1909. He arrived in Washington State for the remainder of his mining activities and mining-engineering career.

The location given for the Barkdull claims was 2.3 miles up from the mouth of Negro Creek in Section 3. Tunnel No. 1 (30 feet long), Tunnel No. 2 (the longest, at 280 feet in length), and No. 3 (50 feet long) are on the south side of the creek. Tunnel No. 4 and Tunnel No. 5 are on the north side. The portals at all the workings are presently caved.

GOLD CREEK BASIN CLAIMS RECORDINGS

Gold Creek Basin is a drainage tributary in upper Negro Creek.

To understand the location of these lofty claims sites, use the USGS 7.5-minute map for the Enchantment Lakes quadrant and the USGS map of the Blewett quadrant.

In Section 6 of the Enchantment Lakes map, "Adit" is printed in the upper slope of Gold Creek Basin. That 570-foot adit has never caved in at the portal or for the length of the tunnel, due to the stable rock in which it was developed. The portal is at an elevation of 6,600 feet above sea level. This mine portal was the focal point of the various, surrounding mineral claims adjoined to the Tip Top claim.

Mention of claim recordings at Gold Creek Basin began May 17, 1892, when Mahlon Souder took original possession of his Tip Top claim. And the last claim recording at Gold Creek Basin was for the Tip Top mine, made by returning old-time miner Mahlon Souder (44 years later) on January 13, 1936, during the middle of the Great Depression.

In-between Souder's two Tip Top possessions was a list of 26 Gold Creek Basin area mineral claims. Many of the names involved with the recording of the Gold Creek basin properties were recognizable, such as Mahlon Souder, Harvey Souder, Charley Striker, John C. Johnson, O. S. Cloud, Jim Gilmore, James Lynch, and John Lynch.

TIP TOP TUNNEL EXAMINATION

In 2012, a group of us from Northwest Underground Explorations examined the full length of the 570-foot adit. It showed some traces of what appeared to be silver in the form of black oxidized wall-surface exposures. There were no other identifiable minerals that could be detected in the altered peridotite rock. Perhaps Gold Creek Basin was named for occasional, minute traces of flour-gold found in the basin's drainage creek. The view from the portal of the tunnel affords a seldom-equaled panoramic photo op.

An off-trail search on the west side of the basin trail shows evidence of past mining camp locations. On one slope, several flat areas had 10x10-foot notches dug into the sloping ground in stair-step fashion indicating places where temporary or seasonal tents were set in place.

For an even more top-of-the-world panorama, continue on the trail beyond the mine portal for a steep 600-foot elevation gain. It ends on the 1-mile-long ridge connecting across the three peaks that are Three Brothers Mountain. This ridge area separates Negro Creek from Ingalls Creek. Concrete foundation anchor blocks on the ridge-top area are a reminder of days past when a fire lookout tower was stationed there. NWUE members Todd Carlson and Kent Nelson have done extensive ridge-running east of the old fire-lookout site, but no signs of mining activity were noted atop those peaks.

Tip Top mine portal in Gold Creek Basin. Standing in front of the tunnel, left to right, Northwest Underground Explorations members Kent Nelson, Todd Carlson, Bob Curtis, Jimbo Ostbye, and Vic Pisoni. Cooper, the tunnelhound, stands drooling (or is that a canine smile?) at front and center. (Photo by Kent Nelson.)

FOR THE ROCKHOUND

A government geologist report from the mid-1940s noted the presence of agate-lined geodes, whole and broken, on the north side of Negro Creek in Sections 6 and 7. This site information was not physically sought out by the author or any of the NWUE members at this time (2013). NWUE members did discover flat, layered, white calcite crystals up to 1-inch square and about ¼-inch thick in the waste tailings in front of the Tip Top claim tunnel. Also, off to the left side (northward) of the portal, look through the tailings for evidence of the blacksmith area. Poking through the charcoal will reveal very small pieces of discarded rusting steel.

FALLS CREEK AREA MINERAL CLAIMS

Use the USGS 7.5-minute map for the Enchantment Lakes Quadrangle and the Green Trails maps for Mount Stuart, WA (No. 209) and Liberty, WA (No. 210).

The Falls Creek area claims are best accessed over the same route as that to the Gold Creek Basin claims. One road ends where the Navaho Peak/Falls Creek headwaters trailhead begins.

The following claims were owned by James and John Lynch and recorded March 18, 1895: Cumberland, Iowa, Mascot, Nevada, Memphis, Ohio, St Louis, Texas, and Union claim. The following is the Nickel Plate group of claims, also owned by James and John Lynch: Nickel Plate No. 1 through No. 5. These five digs were located on the west side of Three Brothers Mountain between Falls Creek and Cascade Creek.

Two miners mining. (Linda McCune photo collection.)

Chapter Twenty-six: Lucky Strike Mine

The total for this group of claims during Charley Striker's original ownership in 1897 is not known. The mine is located in Section 4 (use the USGS 7.5-minute map of Blewett). The original mining campsite is located 2.7 miles up Negro Creek from its mouth. The campsite buildings are indicated on the USGS 7.5-minute map of Blewett by two black squares. Presently, only one cabin remains. The other creek-side building was lost to the undermining actions of yearly snow-melt flood waters eroding the foundation to the point of collapse.

The location of the upper adits is near the adit symbol with a switchback trail leading to it. The adit is printed at an elevation of about 3,800 feet.

The upper tunnel workings are those that in the past have been mistakenly identified as originally belonging to Big Antoine Etienne. He was placer mining for gold at the mouth of his name-sake location, Negro Creek. There is no evidence that Antoine was ever a hard-rock miner. All mining references about him note that he was exclusively a gold-placer miner.

LUCKY STRIKE HISTORY

CHARLEY STRIKER MUDDLES ALONG

By 1897, Charley Striker was well established as a Blewett and Negro Creek area miner. His entry onto the upper headwaters of Negro Creek was in 1890. At that time, he had two claims in the upper slopes of Gold Creek Basin. Charley was involved in several areas with mineral claims of minor value off and on until 1897. He also partnered with other men in the Union, Dominion, and Cinnabar King mines.

By 1900, he was entirely focused on developing the Lucky Strike properties. At the end of the season, Striker had a 140-foot crosscut at an elevation of 3,510 feet. It was driven eastward to intersect an ore deposit that was indicated by a mineralized surface outcrop. This mine was not timbered. Evidently he was not willing to waste time timbering to insure his safety while getting through the somewhat unstable rock and onward to those beckoning ore values.

As it turned out, it was expedient not installing adit timbers, in terms of saving time. Striker drove the crosscut tunnel along his projection of where he thought the ore vein was located. But, the crosscut was misaligned with the ore deposit in the shear zone. The less-than-functional trajectory now remains sealed in collapsed tunnel rock as a reminder that Murphy's Law is timeless. Had the crosscut been placed 40 feet higher in elevation, or 80 feet to the east, the probability of intersecting the gold-bearing ore would have been in his favor.

Striker could have continued downward with a decline crosscut for another 200 feet and intersected the mineralized shear zone, but this mathematical knowledge was beyond his academic pay-scale of experience. His practical application was to desert his failed attempt and ponder the solution to the problem while working on one or more of his several other mining claims in the Negro Creek area.

Striker remained a miner and mine owner in his vaguely noted mining activities of the following years. Nothing is recorded of his continued ownership of the Lucky Strike digs until about 1912 when he figured (possibly with outside help) the correct angle at which the gold-bearing ore deposit could be reached.

Due to certain gaps in understanding his claim-site geology during his earlier tunneling mind-set, Striker did not completely calculate the broken, misaligned nature of the rock in which the ore was located. The geological truth was that the gold on Striker's digs occurred at the intersections of the zones where irregular lenses of white quartz carried high values in free gold … enclosed in shear zones within diorite near a rhyolite contact. To say the geology of Striker's property rock structure is a convolution of earthy terms brings out the need for a simpler one-size-fits-all phrase—bad rock.

In the open cut above the upper adit, there was a series of interlacing shear zones enclosing large masses of highly fractured diorite. Some of these zones are up to 4 feet thick. Much later, field-geologist and mining-engineering reports in detailed explanation reveal a lot of these zones had to be dealt with to overcome and reach the high-grade ore.

Between 1912 and 1921, Striker tunneled at the corrected angle in a second adit at 3,590 feet in elevation. In these workings, he found encouraging specks of gold in the quartz as he ran the tunnel and did strike the intended high-grade gold-ore deposit. Then a shaft/winze (of unknown depth) was sunk on the high-grade ore. At some point, water was encountered that required a pump to de-water the flooded shaft. The purchase of the needed equipment was not appropriated for reasons known only to Striker. So a drift was run past the flooded shaft and continued along the tunnel level in gold-bearing rock.

We assume Striker was a one-man operation during this time since there was no reference to other miners and he was very secretive about his mining activities and any gold taken out. He continued with his limited mining activities by high-grading the ore, grinding the ore in his creek-level arrastra, and then panning out the gold that was crushed free of the quartz.

Charley Striker worked the Lucky Strike mine until about 1928, when he was too old to keep up with the physical demands it required. Jack McCarthy and his wife, Alice, took Striker into their home in the town of Blewett after he abandoned his cabin and claims at the Lucky Strike mine. Alice took it upon herself to nurse and care for Striker until he passed away at the age of about 66 on April 2, 1931. Striker was born in New York about 1866. He was buried at the Evergreen Memorial Park Cemetery in East Wenatchee.

KERSHNER TAKES OVER BRIEFLY

One minute bit of information was available that indicated a man named Kershner held ownership of the properties after Striker departed the scene. There was no known report of his activities, the date of his occupancy, or whatever else may have occurred under his watch.

Although the gold ore was high-grade, no record of Striker's or Kershner's gold-ore production was available, nor do we know the total in gold values taken. And after Kershner's obscured appearance, the Lucky Strike mine managed to fade into the mine-location limbo of lost mines.

THE DODDS TAKE OVER

In 1933, Oren and L. Dodd (relationship to Oren is unknown), along with Ray Walters (Oren's father-in-law), relocated the area on a quartz mining claim named Lenora. (Oren's mining background was tied to his father, James, when they lived in the Methow-Okanogan area.) They recorded it as the Lucky Strike placer claim. Its location was on the south side of Negro Creek in Section 36, which includes the beginning ½ mile of Negro Creek from its mouth upstream to the north line of Section 2. At that time, they were aware of Charley Striker's "lost" Lucky Strike property but did not have enough data to pin down the claim site. This appears to be the group's initial entry, claim-wise, into the mineralized turf of Negro Creek. After this recorded event of their presence on their Negro Creek placer, there is a long period of Dodd name-related absence in the claim record books.

CALDO MINE

In 1961, along came Oren Dodd and his newest mining associate, Ralph J. Calvert. They rediscovered the lost claims of the old Lucky Strike mine. From this point onward, the Caldo Mining Company was officially in the record book. The name "Caldo" was a combination of the beginning of each man's last name, "Cal" from Calvert and "Do" from Dodd.

Data from a 1961 report referred to four claim sites, all on the north side of the creek, but only three were plotted on the first and original Caldo Mining Company property map. They were identified as the Caldo Tunnel site. This is the site that was mentioned but, for whatever reason, was not put on the company claims property map and may have been developed later. Also a property recorded as the Mill Site claim was located from the north creek bank northward, upslope. About 20 feet above the high-water level on the Mill Site claim, an adit was later driven. The Lor'vi No. 2 mineral claim was named for Dodd's wife, Lorene V. It was the next dig up the slope. And, the Caldo No. 1 mineral, the highest claim on the upper slope, is where Striker's older digs are located.

There is at this time (2013) a caved portal on the Mill Site claim; perhaps this is the aforementioned Caldo Tunnel site at the bottom of the slope and not symbolically noted on the company map. This caved-adit entry is located immediately north (50 feet) from where the mining equipment presently sits. It is the only adit candidate found to fill in that non-symbolized map's information gap.

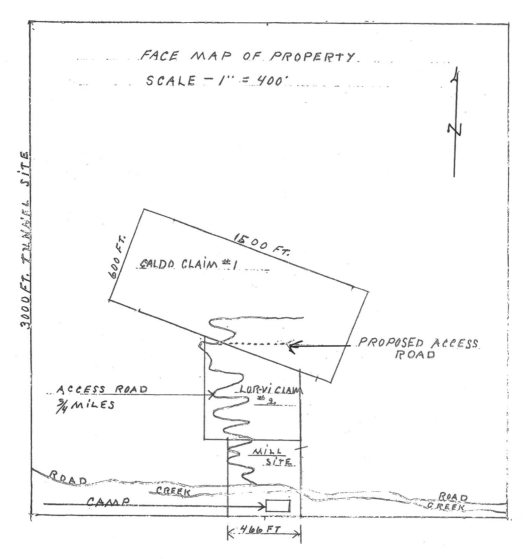

Caldo mine map. (From a company report by mining geologist L. R. Haggard.)

CALDO MINING COMPANY, 1961

In 1961, the Caldo Mining Company was incorporated by Oren Dodd as company president, Gordon Ohme as vice-president, and Ralph J. Calvert as secretary-treasurer. They were the property owners of the Caldo mine. Their previous activities compiling information about the correct location and past development of the properties were not noted.

The starting year of the original mining claims-recording and papers that proved assessment work before 1961 was not found in any of the reports related to the mine. As of that time, all the old portals to the underground workings from which the ore was taken were caved in.

The following underground Caldo Mining Company activities were supervised by an unnamed expert miner. He was most likely one of Charley Striker's close friends.

The structural underground mining developments were relocated in 1961 when the Caldo Mining Company was established. Some of Caldo's additional new improvements were a ¾-mile-long, switchback bulldozer road leading to the upper workings, a 16x24-foot all-weather cabin, a summer tent-cabin combination at the campsite on the south side of the creek, and a 6x8-foot, wood-framed, metal-covered shed, located alongside the mining equipment on the north side of Negro Creek.

Each year in the spring on the first trip up Negro Creek Road to the Caldo cabin, repair work was required to make the eroded road surface vehicle-worthy. Often one or more of the bridges spanning the creek needed replacing or repair.

As of 2013, there is no access up the remains of the old, overgrown, blocked road with numerous tree-falls, except by the hike-as-you-go method.

In the 16 months before the 1961 report came out, the Caldo Mining Company attempted to open the old workings. They stripped and ran a surface open cut, which was an area 105 feet long by 40 feet wide in the ground above the old workings. This was followed by removal of 4,500 tons of material. However, they found that as the new excavations approached and uncovered the original underground digs, the surface developments caved in. This was further due to the fractured and sheared nature of the rock. No pre-existing stopes were uncovered in the attempt, so it was not a matter of breaking through a stope. Because opening the old workings by this method could not be completed in the unstable ground, the operation was abandoned.

A different approach was begun. A crosscut was driven at a point 15 to 20 feet below the bottom of the open cut. It was on a bearing of north by 14 degrees east, for a distance of 100 feet. From there, it was continued for another 35 feet on a bearing of north by 10 degrees west. Due to the broken structure of the rock, it was necessary to set timbers and use lagging the entire length of the crosscut. This was something Striker did not do and miraculously avoided any cave-in while running his original mineral-barren crosscut. His first cuts into the rock were fresh and held strong for him. Later cuts by the Caldo Mining Company were in Striker's pre-worked area of time-weakened, deteriorated geology.

The field examination report said that ore had occurred near the intersection of the two main sets of shear zones. And, within the limited area of the workings observed, all the ore appeared to have been removed earlier during Striker's mining activities.

The good news was that the strength of the shear zones seemed to continue. This favored the possibility of locating more gold-bearing ore deposits. Several recommendations for future development were issued, but the accompanying map is more worthy than the 1,000 words.

EXPLORATIONS OF CALDO'S MINES, 1962

A search at the courthouse in Wenatchee, Washington, disclosed the names of claims located in 1962 by Oren Dodd and R. J. Calvert, which were transferred to the Caldo Mining Company. The claims were listed as Caldo Mine (Caldo Claim No.1), Caldo Tunnel Site No. 1, Lor'vi, Lor'vi No. 2, Caldo Mill Site claim, and the Transfer Instrument claim. The Lor'vi claim was soon abandoned. There was no accompanying claims map layout or location information available to explain the positioning of this (later) claims block.

During an examination at the Caldo mine property (1962) by mining engineer S. W. Zeldek, an updated observation of the mine workings and mill site was reported. He was there to advance or deny the application for the Caldo Mining Company to actively pursue gold production mining. The bottom line was Zeldek recommended that the application be denied.

After being denied permission to develop the mine for production, the Caldo Mining Company went into the exploration mode. This allowed them to continue with their mining activities without the approval of the agencies that stopped them from producing. If adequately proven by acceptable mineral discovery, the company might have been given the go-ahead by the ruling powers-that-be. As it stood in 1964, the Caldo Mining Company, under Oren Dodd as company president, was registered as "in current exploration on the old Lucky Strike claim."

CALDO MINING COMPANY FIZZLES OUT

Barney Gatzkiewicz of Seattle was the company president from 1969–1972, and the Caldo Mining Company was still listed as "under current development." Barney became an owner-partner in the company, along with Oren Dodd and Ralph Calvert.

Oren Dodd returned to his Caldo digs year after year. Finally the time came when he no longer had the physical ability to keep up with the heavy labor demands the mining operation required. Plus, all the men's hard labor that produced no gold returns must have had a negative psychological effect, as well as provided justification for curtailing further gold-mining activities. The last year of the development operation was not given, but it would have been sometime during the mid to late 1970s.

NEGRO CREEK JIM, MID-1970S TO PRESENT

Jim Holderhoff came to find gold in the Negro Creek mines and placer gravels with his father back in the early to mid-1970s. After the two men were involved with various mining claim properties for several years, Jim went solo in his attempts to find the yellow metal. Jim's dad left to attend to things on the outside. Eventually Jim settled into the one remaining Caldo mine cabin.

A few of us Northwest Underground Explorations mining history buffs met Negro Creek Jim in 2000. At this time, he was working at several different mining digs and was watchman over all the properties and equipment that the Caldo Mining Company abandoned. Jim showed us a few of the many mine adits and vein structures. Until then, at the rate we had been going, we would have had to spend several years discovering them had Jim not been our shortcut to accumulating historic Negro Creek mining information.

Each year, Jim resided on the old Caldo grounds from spring snowmelt until the fall snow storms drove him out to his wintering-down hotel room in Wenatchee, Washington. Jim stopped returning to his old mining digs in 2010 at the age of 71.

All the Caldo Mining Company properties and mining equipment, once under the possession of Jim and his predecessors, are again under renewed relocation claim ownership as of 2013.

Chapter Twenty-seven: Ingalls Creek Mineral Claims

Ingalls Creek was named for Captain Dewitt Clinton Ingalls. He became the regional legend by way of his "lost gold" story. See Chapter Two, *Captain Ingalls's Lost Gold*.

1860s-1880s

From the 1860s to the 1880s, the area on Peshastin Creek, north and south from the mouth of Ingalls Creek, was actively placer mined from year to year. At a location 1 mile to the north of Ingalls Creek, densely grouped claims were being mined on and near Danda Hill, which is not identified on modern maps.

Past placer mining activities in the Ingalls Creek area was evident in the 1860s and 1870s. A group dominated by 25 Oregon placer miners coming southward from the gold field at Rock Creek in British Columbia made a stop there. The Oregonians then decided to extend their stay near or at the mouth of Ingalls Creek. They placer mined for gold, starting from the mouth of Ingalls Creek and progressed up its watercourse.

Prominent among the group was Dr. F. G. Kellogg. He stayed in the Ingalls Creek and Negro Creek area and accumulated several placer and hard-rock mineral properties. All his hard-rock claims had ore values in gold and iron. Kellogg actively mined well into the early 1900s.

1880s

The following mineral claims began in the early 1880s. Miners with a more permanent miner/resident mind-set began recording their claims in 1884. The first was Walter Bull. He was about 6 miles up Ingalls Creek. His Excelsior claim was up Falls Creek. The other Ingalls Creek area claims owners were some familiar Culver Gulch/Blewett area miner/mine owners. Among the more steadfast miner/residents of the Blewett area were John A. Shoudy, James Lockwood, W. H. Tillman, Walter Bull, John Lyons, G. W. Parish, Harvey Souder, George Persinger, William Elliott, Howard Walters, John Hansel, M. R. Newberry, W. T. Racy, S. G. English, Robert Mortimer, John Carse, John Heavner, Adeline Hansel, and John Nelson.

Old-time miner John Nelson was noted to have once worked the same placer ground with Captain Ingalls at an undisclosed time and location. Tom Nelson, John's brother, was one of the miners involved in a running gun battle against a war party of avenging Wenatchi tribesmen in 1858. The leader of their miner contingent was Mortimer Robertson.

COBALT (COBALT CITY), 1890s

The increasing mining activities at all levels, including several different kinds of mineral origins, generated a lot of optimism. At this point, consideration of a town site at the mouth of Ingalls Creek, intended specifically to serve the Ingalls Creek and Negro Creek miner population, was in the talking stage.

In April 1895, resident/miner Ernest B. Wheat, a founder of the town of Cobalt, sent communication to the local newspapers indicating that an unofficial plat for the town of Cobalt was being laid on a wide flat area on the north side of the creek at its mouth. Some file notes referred to the town site as Cobalt City. Buildings went up in an area that was an unnamed mining camp located where the new center for operations (the Cobalt site) would be a shared focal point for the Ingalls Creek and Negro Creek miners to do whatever mining-related business they required. A reduction plant was planned, and a 12-mile branch railroad line up Peshastin Creek was being requested from the Great Northern Railway to haul ore from the area mines.

This town site named Cobalt existed at the same time as another mining camp located ¼ mile north of Hansel Creek (originally named Bonanza Creek). It was noted in 1895 as the Ingalls Camp. The Ingalls Camp was said to be on the Red Butte No. 4 claim. This was located near the center of Section 24, T23N and R17E, where the present Ingalls Creek road bridge crosses over Peshastin Creek.

The early discoveries of gold, silver, copper, nickel, cinnabar, and cobalt up Negro Creek and Ingalls Creek put dollar signs in the miners' eyes. A spin-off to these reports was talk about construction of a proposed smelter at the town of Leavenworth, Washington. It would process the projected, large amounts of the nickel and cobalt ore said to be in the mineral deposits of the Peshastin Mining District. It would also process any of the same kinds of ore that would be found up in the Icicle River mines. Then secondary to the Leavenworth smelter, a reduction works at the Cobalt City site on the expanse of flat land was under consideration. There was no road from Negro Creek to the town of Blewett at this time; only a pack trail served as the connecting byway.

In 1895, a total of 16 Ingalls Creek miners recorded mineral claims. Most were placer claims spread from the creek mouth up to the Falls Creek area.

MONARCH, 1895

The dig that got a lot of attention was the Monarch claim. Miner J. E. Reynolds located this dig near the mouth of Ingalls Creek. A 15-foot adit contained gold that could be seen in the ore with the naked eye. This very vague description of the claim location gives no indication whether it was north, south, east, or west of the creek mouth.

CLAIMS NORTH OF INGALLS CREEK

DANDA HILL

The low-grade mineral deposits on Danda Hill (not on present-day maps) and the surrounding area were first recorded in 1889. They were located about 1 mile north from the confluence of Ingalls Creek and Peshastin Creek. No defining points in the information told where the exact mining claims' locations could be found. A total of nine quartz claims were sought from 1889 until 1894, none of importance value-wise.

BONANZA (HANSEL) CREEK

Bonanza Creek has been renamed Hansel Creek (its present designation). Sixteen claims were recorded from 1890 until 1897. Most of the digs were placer claims that were spread from the mouth of Hansel Creek and upstream for about 1 mile. Of the two hard-rock digs, the first was the Alto claim (1892), owned by Lester Turner. It was located 2 miles upstream above the mouth of Bonanza Creek and ¼ mile up the north slope from the creek. The second and most active mine was the Sunnyside (three) claims. The owner in 1897 was Frank Duval. Vague information put these three claims trending east to west in the lower center of Section 23.

Chapter Twenty-eight :
Clifford Pennington Davenport
Family and Barthol Family

The following stories are about Blewett miner/resident Clifford Davenport (June 26, 1879–September 25, 1958) and relatives, the Barthol family. Their Blewett experiences portray the greater picture of permanent miners and their families and friends when they lived and worked during the gold-producing years and the gold-lean years in the Peshastin Mining District.

Clifford Pennington Davenport. (Photo courtesy of the Davenport and Barthol families, who were former Blewett residents.)

It often happens when historic research approaches the wall of known, available sources that information unexpectedly pops up to meet one face-to-face. Such is evidenced by Phyllis Barthol-Cramer and the book written by her mother, Dorothy Davenport-Barthol, *They Kept the Faith* (copyright 2002). Phyllis' cousin Virginia Davenport-Carpenter deserves kudos, along with her cousin Joyce Davenport- Rosenberger for *My Memories of Blewett*, Joyce's authored family documentation and photos. Their combined remembrances have contributed personal information and corrected many of the suppositions that have, under less focused authorization, been errantly woven into the fabric of Peshastin/Blewett Mining District history.

My first contact with Phyllis came through Doctor Charles Ballard, Phyllis's cousin. I met Charles when our paths crossed in researching common historic subject matter. Truly, it's a small world, as our connection enabled me to fill in many gaps in Blewett's history in this book.

Charles's deceased great uncle, Charles Ballard, was once the owner of the Mammoth mine (Slate Creek area) and Azurite mine (near Azurite Peak). These mining properties were the mutual interests that led from research to friendship and continuing communication. When I broached the subject of Blewett's mining history, Charles was quick to inform me that his cousin Phyllis Barthol-Cramer lived in the mining town of Blewett for the first

Annie Goodwin Davenport. (Photo courtesy of the Davenport and Barthol families, who were former Blewett residents.)

five years of her childhood. What resulted after several meetings with Phyllis are written in the following enriched additions to Blewett's history.

The Barthol family lived together with John and Alice McCarthy. With all their individual perspectives as Blewett residents, they have enhanced the story of the mining history in the Peshastin Mining District as a whole.

Big-production mine owners and miners and high-grade gold-ore mining claims had their shining moments in the Peshastin Mining District. The town of historic Blewett retains the name of Edward and William Blewett, two of those mining businessmen who made their mark and received a portion of the gold profit. They eventually left the natural surroundings at Blewett that produced a mineral industry.

Clifford Davenport stayed. He and his family, relatives, and friends are examples of the firm foundation of Blewett mining and mine-related living.

Cliff said that the town of Blewett had a 21-room hotel, an assay office, post office (the mail came from Leavenworth), a store, school, and a peak population of around 500 in the surrounding mining-district camps. Cliff owned mines and knew or worked with most of the long-term, well-established miners and mine owners in the Blewett area mines. He saw them come and eventually go. Yet he and his family members endured into the waning years of the 1940s as Culver Gulch and the Blewett mines gave way to the entrance of an escalating, more modern corporate America. In the end, Blewett, the town, morphed into a mom-and-pop kind of mining entity before bowing out of existence as a main player in the gold-producing market.

CLIFFORD DAVENPORT'S JOURNEY TO BLEWETT

Clifford Davenport was one of many outstanding resident miners in the town of Blewett in the Peshastin (Blewett) Mining District. But Cliff's colorful past starts with his family's departure from Delta, Pennsylvania, in 1888, when he was nine years old, his brother Rankin was twelve, and sister Nina was three. They were brought west by his pastor/missionary father, David Davenport, and his wife, Sarah. The family's destination was westward through the spacious Washington Territory and on to Sumner, Washington.

The Ballard family of Slaughter (Auburn), Washington, was there en masse to greet them: Levi Ballard (founder of Auburn, Washington) with his wife, Mary, and sons, Irving, William, Charles, Hazard, Leon, and Arthur. Clifford and Arthur were cousins and remained friends throughout their lives.

Cliff left home when he was 18 years old to explore the world with a full-blown interest in geology. William Rankin, Cliff's grandfather, helped inspire the youth by his valuable rock and mineral collection. So with high hopes, Cliff entered the active Arizona mining districts around Tombstone, Bisbee, and Jerome. He worked at the copper mine in Jerome, which was owned by the Douglas family (Jerome is now an outstanding ghost-town tourist attraction). From Jerome, Arizona, he went to California where he was involved in more mining activity. In San Francisco, he went underground; it was a tour of a different kind, where he saw in opium dens the drug's deplorable and destructive effects on the human body.

In 1899, Cliff was back in Washington State and, in 1900, was once again inspired by conversations about the mines of Monte Cristo in Snohomish County. His past experience as a miner quickly got him hired by one of the mining companies.

What he wasn't told was that there would be drug addicts and alcoholics hired on as miners as they recovered from their liquor and drug-induced demons. He became aware of all this after the long trip and night arrival into Monte Cristo. While he was in his bed, lodged among the tweaking, restless group, he soon got up and asked the attendant in charge what was going on and was told the facts. Cliff spent the rest of the dark hours wide awake waiting for daybreak. Such was his dislike for the situation that he hiked 4 miles from the mining town of Monte Cristo to Barlow Pass and eventually made his way to Everett, Washington.

In 1901, after working on a farm at Plain, Washington, located north of Leavenworth, Cliff acted on the information that the mines around the town of Blewett were active. He hoofed it south to check out jobs as a miner. The fact that past and present production at the Blewett mine claim had produced and shipped gold bullion worth $68,000 may have been a factor in his decision making. The Warrior General Mining Company stamp mill (the Blewett 20-stamp mill) was noted for recently producing a gold brick worth $2,175 from a 21-day run of Pole Pick mined ore. The scene Cliff came upon when he got to Blewett was one boasting several huge water wheels that powered arrastras grinding the free gold from the mined ore (the arrastra locations were not explained).

Also at that time, Cliff recalled James Wilder and D. W. Locke had the Golden Eagle mine. The Warrior General Mining Company and Blewett Pass Mining Company were in operation. Other miners were working their mines: W. E. Miller had the Hindoo claim; F. G. Thorpe had the Alta claim; John Van Pell had the Van Pell claim (near the Black Jack mine); George W. Watson, the Key Note claim (1901); Geo. Persinger, the Iron Mt. No. 2; J. K. Robinson, the Culver claim; E. M. Carr, the Rustler claim; John W. McCarthy, the Pioneer claim; and the Eleanor Mining Company was mining on the Pole Pick No. 1 claim. Also, John Olden, John Ernest, Johnny Johnson, Thaddeus Neubauer, and his nephew Anton had active claims.

The permanent, small sombrero-shaped, historic arrastra presently imprinted into the bedrock alongside Peshastin Creek was noted. Cliff was told of this arrastra being actively used as far back as 1881. Cliff noted the activity at the Golden Eagle claim stamp mill site. It was located up Culver Gulch, west of the company-run 20-stamp mill.

Note: As of 2013, the 20-stamp mill structure stands as a less than skeletal historic reminder of past mining activities. The stamp mill still displays rusting mining artifacts on the mill site's surface. The mill buildings have been victim to board snatchers and passers-by. Later miners in need of lumber for their mining projects took what they needed. Add to that list the removal of the machinery, concentrating tables, and other useful mining gear, and you see what the end result is today.

MARRIED LIFE FOR CLIFF

In 1901, after Cliff got established at Blewett, he met Annie Goodwin and her divorced mother, Alice Goodwin. They had come up from Portland, Oregon, to visit Henry Resburg, Alice's half-brother and Blewett's postmaster. Cliff also contracted to work for other miners in the Culver Gulch and Negro Creek area. Twenty-three-year-old Cliff took a fancy to Annie Goodwin, and on August 4, 1902, they were married at Blewett. Lucy Wilder, the wife of multiple-mine-claim owner James Wilder, baked the wedding cake. Cliff was working in the mines around Blewett when he and Annie became the parents of Viola Uretta Davenport on July 13, 1904. The child later died of meningitis.

In September of 1904, the Clifford Davenport family moved out of the house they resided in, and Robert Steiner moved into it. The reason for the move may have been that the Davenports would be spending some time in Georgetown (now a community in south Seattle) with Cliff's father and his family. While they were away, the homes of Mrs. Castle and W. H. Resburg (where the telephone office was located) caught fire. The residence next to

Standing under the Blewett 20-stamp mill roof, left to right: Thaddeus Neubauer, one of the Marko clan, and Cliff Davenport in his younger years. (Photo courtesy of the Davenport and Barthol families, who were former Blewett residents.)

them was occupied by John and Alice McCarthy (the former Alice Goodwin, Annie's mother, and a.k.a. Grandma Carty or Aunty Carty, depending on the individual's relationship to Alice). The fire was dowsed with water, which saved the structure. Fortunately, most of the household goods of the burnt houses were rescued.

MOUNTAIN LION MINE FATALITY

Cliff's next mining job was a contract to drive a tunnel on the Mountain Lion claim at the eastern base of Three Brothers Mountain in the headwaters area of Negro Creek. Mr. Keith from Spokane, Washington, was one of the owners. Cliff built a log cabin for a residence, about 1903 or 1904, while working at the Mountain Lion mine. The cabin was located 100 feet west of the southernmost fork of Negro Creek, on an open, flat meadow, referred to as the Park. It was southward from the mine and located about 5 miles from the mouth of Negro Creek. The Davenport cabin still stands there today, uninhabitable and moldering into the ground. At the time Cliff was living there, no trail entered into the area, only blazed trees to mark the way parallel to Negro Creek. Annie was by Cliff's side, and even though she was a city girl when she came to the area, she fast became a "woods woman," accustomed to the cabin's dirt floor and no windows. When the door had to be closed during the daylight hours, the inner darkness required candlelight.

An experienced English miner named John Stout was working with Cliff. Information dated August 1905 places John Stout and John C. Johnson as workers on the Mountain Lion claim. John Stout, his wife, and three-year-old daughter were in the Mountain Lion camp with Cliff and Annie.

Stout had a stubborn attitude that soon proved fatal. Refusing to practice proper caution, he would use a dangerously short fuse to blast tunnel rock. Cliff soon put a stop to the practice, or so he thought. Cliff was always safety minded; especially because help was not close at hand should a mining mishap occur. Later, Cliff caught Stout in a tunnel ready to blast several pre-drilled holes. Stout was using short fuses, and after some heated conversation, Stout got Cliff to leave the workings, and Stout went back in to light the fuse. Short on reason, Stout fired up his short detonation fuse and proved Cliff right and Stout would soon prove himself dead wrong. Cliff knew what had happened right away when the blast went off before Stout reached the tunnel portal. Needing help, Cliff started searching for some sheepherders that had left the Park by his cabin area after a few days of grazing their herd. One of the herders went back with Cliff, and they made a stretcher and packed Stout's rock-shredded body back to the town of Blewett.

From there, he was hauled to a doctor in Leavenworth where Stout soon died. Annie was stuck between a rock and a hard place with the totally hysterically Mrs. Stout, and her daughter. Annie took control of the situation and, carrying the little girl on her hip, led the two back to Blewett with only tree blazes to guide her. With glazed eyes, Mrs. Stout remarked from time to time along the way that she was sure they were lost, although Annie knew, even without the tree blazes, they could follow the creek down to the main road. It was a tough trip for Annie; her hip was out of joint for a week from carrying the child. Added to that, her shoes and stockings had been ruined.

Mrs. Stout was flat broke after paying for her husband's funeral, so Cliff, being the class-act human being that he was, gave Mrs. Stout all the money he had. Thus she and her daughter had funds to get them back to their relatives in Philadelphia with extra money to live on for a time.

Cliff and his family returned from the Park and their Mountain Lion mine cabin to Blewett in 1905. They moved back into the house that John Stout's son Robert, also a miner, once occupied.

CLIFF DAVENPORT AS TELEPHONE COMPANY LINEMAN

Cliff was back at Blewett working for a while in the mines, followed by a job as a lineman for a telephone company. He was the only man assigned to the job of repairing the lines running east-west over the mountains in all weather conditions and on call 24 hours a day. In freezing weather, he had to keep moving constantly to keep from getting hypothermia while out trouble-shooting telephone-line problems. In his homemade snowshoes, he sometimes found that he could walk up to the cross-arms of the telephone poles due to the height of the snowdrifts. During one overnight repair job, he could see the reflection of eyes in the dark outer perimeters of the glow from the campfire. In the next morning's light, he saw the tracks of a cougar that had been tracking him and then observing him throughout the night.

Cliff's newly gained knowledge as a lineman put him in touch with how to make batteries. They were used to lay a communications line between the residence at Blewett and the Golden Eagle mill and assay office, and the mines. He installed telephones at all the various mining company workings up Culver Gulch and down to the assay office down in Blewett.

After the family stayed at Clifford's parent's home in Georgetown, Annie got over a bout of pneumonia. The Davenport family returned to Blewett where Cliff was back on the job for the telephone company. They took up residence again in the abandoned Stout home.

ALICE MCCARTHY (GRANDMA CARTY)

Alice Viola Hedrick was born May 1, 1862, in Springfield, Illinois. The Hedrick family moved to Washington in 1875 and settled on a homestead 12 miles north of Vancouver, Washington. A few miles south, Alice had a very stable nursing job in Portland, Oregon. Her successful career was a reflection of her depth of medical knowledge and professionalism.

Young Alice was first married to Samuel Phillip Goodwin, whom she later divorced. Alice and Samuel had a daughter, Annie. In 1901, Alice and Annie visited Blewett where Alice met John (Jack) W. McCarthy, a Blewett area miner and businessman who had arrived in 1880. Love entered, and Alice left her nursing career, all for a man and a natural environment that better fulfilled her interests in life. She and John married in 1904. Although John had an intense taste for liquor products, Alice weaned him off the juice and on to a steady diet of wholesome family living.

According to Joyce Davenport-Rosenberger (whose family moved into John and Alice's house to take care of John in 1939 when Joyce was seven), John always took good care of Alice through thick and thin times. One of John's oddities was his aversion to bathing regularly, but he seemed to believe that gargling often with Listerine mouthwash was a balancing factor, which, for some folks who lived in near-presence of him, was not an acceptable fix. One might wonder if Alice got him over that problem too.

Young Alice Viola Hedrick married Samuel Phillip Goodwin. Later after their divorce, she married John McCarthy in Blewett. (Photo courtesy of the Davenport and Barthol families, who were former Blewett residents.)

Blewett didn't have a doctor, but Alice McCarthy more than sufficed with her medical background. The Blewett mining community was very fortunate to have her there for the many babies she delivered and to help heal life's common illnesses and injuries. The nearest medical doctor was Dr. George Washington Hoxey, a contract doctor for the Great Northern Railway in Leavenworth. Dr. Hoxey would come to Blewett by horseback or horse and buggy to tend to the more serious mining accidents and illnesses. When the Blewett area was snowed in, the doctor gave Alice medical instructions over the telephone.

A rash plagued the Blewett area folks during one summer. Alice called Dr. George Hoxey in Leavenworth. Dr. Hoxey knew that the rash was caused by an east wind coming from the wheat fields, which carried irritating microbes of some kind. He instructed Alice to prepare an ointment made of sulfur and lard. The concoction worked, and the rash went away.

Samuel Phillip Goodwin was Alice Viola Hedrick's first husband. He served in the US Army as an aide to General O. O. Howard during the 1877 Nez Perce Indian War. Goodwin received a federal citation of honor for his service in the conflict. (Photo courtesy of the Davenport and Barthol families, who were former Blewett residents.)

Alice was instrumental in advancing Blewett socially and in material needs. When an organ was needed for the Sunday school that she started in the schoolhouse, she helped buy one. In 1904, Alice brought a lot of lilac plants and flowers from Oregon. Those tall lilac bushes that she planted by the front porch of their house are still present today (2013), next to the historical monument. They are on the oval-shaped flat spot on which the center of old Blewett town site was once located. The year highway US 97 was improved and straightened to omit the curve at the middle of town, the lilac bushes remained, but on the opposite side of the new road.

JOHN AND ALICE MCCARTHY'S LOG HOUSE

After John married Alice, he constructed a two-story log house. He hand cut and flattened the boards with a broad-axe and chinked the spaces in-between with mortar. John

"Ellensburg and Wenatchee Stage" is featured on the car door, a rather bold statement for a travel arrangement with no horses in sight. The vehicle is parked in front of the McCarthy home. Alice McCarthy is wearing the white dress. (Photo courtesy of the Davenport and Barthol Families, who were former Blewett residents.)

built the log house on the west side of the main road on the old Blewett Pass highway. He and Alice had the first and, for a while, only telephone in Blewett that was connected to the towns of Leavenworth, Wenatchee, Ellensburg, and Cle Elum.

Near the back door at the McCarthy home was John's workshop. In the interior of the building was stored a variety of mining tools, carbide headlamps, and Cliff Davenport's mortar and pestle and gold pan.

Joyce Davenport recalled as a youngster going to John McCarthy's workshop to look at a container of gold dust that Cliff had processed. He had stashed it away in a hiding place that she knew about. Upon taking the jar to the porch to view the golden contents, Joyce accidentally spilled some of the gold. Recovering the entire spill was not an option because it fell through the cracks in the wood floor.

Across the road from the McCarthy residence was John's blacksmith shop and eventually an auto repair garage was added. There was a pit in the floor from which the underside of cars and trucks could be worked. At the side of the building was the blacksmith area. A big 4-foot-long bellows was hung over a steel box that held charcoal to heat metal to the extremely high temperature needed so that it could be pounded to form tools, sharpen drill bits, etc.

Peshastin Creek coursed by the back of the McCarthy log house, and there was a waterfall, which cascaded down from a flume on the hillside near the McCarthy home. The front of the house faced east and was located off the west side of the highway. On their property next to the house on some road frontage was a family-run store, and later, a gas pump was added.

DANGEROUS ROAD CONDITIONS

Joyce remembered Juna Smith, a schoolteacher who was boarding at the McCarthy home. She also recalled the McCarthy's' good friends, Bert and Molly Goff, who lived directly across the road from the McCarthy house. Bert was the local school bus driver.

On one occasion, a speeding gas tanker truck didn't make it through the sharp turn at the center of town. It flipped onto its side on the bridge and then slid off in an upside-down position into Peshastin Creek in front of the McCarthy house. The driver died, crushed under the wreckage. Hundreds of gallons of gas spilled into Peshastin Creek, and a lot of fish died.

When the original two-lane highway was built over Blewett Pass, the McCarthy home was always open to stranded travelers. The house had an upstairs with extra beds and a lighted heater for warmth. On the dining room table were a pie, fresh bread, along with butter and jam, and a full pot of coffee, ready to be heated. Alice would find out who the new run of grateful overnighters were in the morning after she would come downstairs. According to some of the stories these visitors told, being able to come in from snowing, raining, or bone-chilling weather had saved more than one life.

REROUTING US 97 AND DISMANTLING THE MCCARTHY HOME

Herman Rankin Davenport, Phyllis's uncle, wrote an eight-page letter with various, first-person Blewett remembrances. Herman recalled the dismantling of the old two-story log house that John McCarthy built. The house was in the middle of town at the end of a bend in the road, smack-dab in the way of the straight new, line-of-sight route (present US 97) that was completed in the 1960s. John died in 1943, so he wasn't around at the time of the new, rerouted US 97 Blewett Pass building activities. Today's Blewett Pass on US 97 was formerly Swauk Pass. Swauk Pass, which is now recognized as Blewett Pass on today's maps, is located 4 miles east of old Blewett Pass.

When the new highway was constructed through the Blewett town site, the McCarthy house was saved via controlled demolition. The logs and other structural sections were disassembled and numbered. They were reassembled as portions of other small historical-style cabins at the outside Pioneer Village section of the Cashmere Historical Society's Willis Carey Museum in Cashmere, Washington. Herman stated that many of the McCarthy household and personal articles are also on display at the Pioneer Village (although these items are not identified as such). John still had his fancy buggy manufacturing tools with him at Blewett, so perhaps they are also on display among the outdoor horse-drawn wagon and buggy items on the museum property.

The old assayer's office at Blewett, dated from the late 1870s, was taken apart piece by piece and reassembled at the outdoor Pioneer Village grounds. The indoor and outdoor displays of Chelan County history are equal in quality to that of those the author has seen in other highly praised museum facilities and historic outdoor displays in the United States.

GIVING TO OTHERS

The mail for the Blewett folks came to the McCarthy home, and Alice had an area where the mail was pigeonholed for town residents by name. In those days, Secretary of State Bella Reeves lived in Wenatchee, Washington. She would always stop by to visit Alice on her way over Blewett Pass to the state capitol in Olympia, Washington.

Alice put her Christian beliefs into loving action. As mentioned earlier in this book, Charley Striker, miner and friend of the McCarthys, became too old to live alone at his Lucky Strike

This is the log house that Jack McCarthy built. Standing left to right: Raymond Barthol, Alice McCarthy, Annie Davenport , and Russell Barthol. The stamp mill roof is in the background in the upper right. (Photo courtesy of the Davenport and Barthol families, who were former Blewett residents.)

Alice Viola McCarthy. (Photo courtesy of the Davenport and Barthol families, who were former Blewett residents.)

Looking north through Blewett. The McCarthy house is on the left foreground. The Blewett historical town site kiosk now stands where the building was located. The hotel is north, in partial view behind the McCarthy home. (Photo courtesy of the Davenport and Barthol families, who were former Blewett residents.)

claim cabin, located up Negro Creek. He abandoned the property and headed to Blewett. In agreement with Jack, Alice took it upon herself to nurse and care for Charley until he passed away. Charley had no money and no way to compensate her for his care, but that didn't matter. In Alice's understanding of being Christ-like, Charles's appreciation was pay enough for her.

Things or money didn't measure Alice's life, but her "love thy neighbor" generosity did. And as to following that spiritual guide in life, she and her family were never lacking in daily needs, even during the 1930s economic depression. Alice made it a point, if she could, to give a gift of some sort to any friend visiting. Once all she had available was an onion that she gave to a woman. As small as the gift seemed, it was that onion the woman used when she made meat loaf that night. When newcomers took up residence at Blewett, Alice would visit them with a list of household items for them to choose. Most of the goods were left behind by folks who moved out of town, and the items were given to Alice for future distribution.

BLACK AND WHITE MINING COMPANY, 1936

Early in 1936, John McCarthy's mining friends, one-eyed John (a.k.a. Blackie) White and Herman Whitley, got serious about recording claims. After several years of prospecting, they put together the Black and White Mining Company. Blackie was the company president, and John was one of several trustees.

On January 11, 1936, White, Whitley, and the company board of trustees saw fit to record nine claims. They were the Black Bird, Diamond Dick, Jumbo, Blue Bird, Jumbo Extension, Snow Bird No. 1, Snow Bird No. 2, Snow Bird No, 3, Tip Top Extension claims, and on July 5, 1936, they added a tenth dig, the Blue Bell No. 2.

Some of the known digs on their claims were a vertical shaft and three adits that totaled about 850 feet of workings, including tunnels, stopes, and raises.

Their cabin and company buildings were on the east edge of the Blewett Pass highway, 200 feet south of the Golden Cherry mine. The lower part of White and Whitley's cabin was excavated and constructed halfway into the hillside. The claims were laid from the cabin, end to end up along and past the southern claim boundary of the Tip Top mine, and eastward toward Windmill Point ridge. Information, without details, stated that the Black and White Mining Company processed its ore using a diesel engine to power a jaw crusher and ball mill. The equipment was later dismantled and shipped to Spokane, Washington.

Left to right: Annie Davenport, Anna Burmeister, Alice McCarthy, and Herman Davenport. They are sitting alongside the McCarthy house. (Photo courtesy of the Davenport and Barthol families, who were former Blewett residents.)

MINER JOHN MCCARTHY IN LATER YEARS

In 1936, 80-year-old John "Old Jack" McCarthy was on a mission (according to him) to drive his final tunnel. The adit was going to be driven on one of his iron claims located up in the Scotty Creek area. He believed there was rich gold in contacts that ran alongside or under the iron deposits. Further information on this proposed mining project was not forthcoming and may not have happened.

McCarthy stated that he had developed nearly 100 tunnels within the Blewett Mining District in his 54 years of running underground workings that totaled about 7 miles. John estimated that he made three small fortunes working the Blewett mines. At one point, McCarthy said he mined gold ore for the sum of $200 to $300 in gold daily for several weeks from the earthy innards of just one dig. John maintained that, had the mining performed in the district been more scientific, a great deal more gold would have come out of the Blewett area digs. By comparison, he said the better gold properties were "mismanaged and looted," rather than operated in an honest and more cost-effective manner (the fast-money attitude sometimes being a deterrent to higher yields over a longer time).

Left to right: Ann Homer (Alice McCarthy's sister), Gus Homer (Ann's husband), Alice McCarthy, and John McCarthy. (Photo courtesy of the Davenport and Barthol families, who were former Blewett residents.)

John McCarthy died in 1943, after over 39 years of living and mining in the Blewett area. Alice passed away November 3, 1945, after 83 sterling years of living a scripture-based life. She is buried at the family plot in the Wilson Bridge Cemetery near Vancouver, Washington.

BARTHOL FAMILY BLEWETT EXPERIENCE

In 1933, the Blewett area company-owned mines were struggling to stay busy enough to operate. Yet Phyllis's Grandma Katherine Barthol, a widow, came from Ohio to Blewett in that year with her grown-up children, including Russell Barthol (Phyllis's father), who was 25 years old (this was before Phyllis was born). Russell's brother Raymond was 30. Raymond lived to be 102 years old. He died in 2006.

After arriving in town, the family cleaned up some of the unused rooms at the abandoned hotel in Blewett and resided there. The hotel building was in a partial state of disrepair. Repairs were made to gaping holes in the upper room floors and wallpaper that was hanging down in strips.

In 1935, during the Depression, the Barthol family moved to Seattle thinking jobs would be easier to find. The move soon proved the job-search in a good sized city was not a good idea. The family moved back to Blewett where they found a way to make a living and settled in for the remainder of the year. Raymond worked in the mines.

Shortly after the Barthol family moved to Seattle, Herman, Phyllis's mother's brother and his wife Anna, and their daughter, Joyce Barthol, moved into the hotel. One day, after they were well established as a household, the wood stove in the hotel's large living room overheated and caused a fire. The suffocating smoke drove the occupants outside, except for Herman's 14-year-old dog Rex. Unfortunately, Rex was overcome by the smoke and died.

About this time, the family bought the Red Apple fruit stand, located east of Cashmere. Russell Barthol met and married Dorothy Davenport in 1937, and in March of the following year, Phyllis was born. The next year, 1939, Russell and Dorothy divorced. Dorothy went to a business college in Wenatchee, and Phyllis lived with her grandparents, Clifford and Annie Davenport, in the town of Blewett from 1938 to 1944, until she was the age of five.

The Davenport home was located ¼ mile south of Blewett, up on a presently remaining, 200-foot stretch of the old historic Blewett highway east of US 97. Anton Neubauer lived next door to the Davenport residence. When US 97 was routed past that original stretch of road, Anton's home and the Davenport house were demolished to straighten this section, which left the present, 200 feet of road. The north end of this remaining road stops short of the old upper tunnel to the Golden Cherry mine. This area is where an earlier mining camp was first set up. Later, the Blewett town site was located about ¼ mile farther north and across, or east, from Culver Gulch.

The Barthol family, *left to right:* unknown man, Ester Barthol, Raymond Barthol, Phyllis Barthol-Cramer's great uncle Charley Shultz, Kathrine Shultz- Barthol, Mildred Shultz, Amelia Shultz-Shopp, Aunt Molly Shultz-Shopp, and Russell Barthol. (Photo courtesy of the Davenport and Barthol families, who were former Blewett residents.)

BLEWETT RESIDENTS

Dorothy told of her dad, Clifford Davenport, speaking about some of the residents that lived in camp during his Blewett days. In town was a woman who was a busybody and a gossip, and on the other side of the moral compass was a Good Samaritan woman with a large family. The downside for the kindly lady was that her husband would go to the town of Leavenworth or one of the other nearby watering holes and hit the hard stuff. He often caught a ride back to Blewett on a produce wagon. But he always managed to find his way home. His concerned wife would go out to view the incoming grocery items only to find her husband spilling out onto the ground in a drunken stupor. She would ask, "Is he dead?" The usual response was, "Yeah, dead drunk," With the help of the grocery peddlers, he was put in bed to sleep it off. Then the day came when he no longer took to quaffing the old red-eye inducing liquor. It seems that the saintly lady's keeping of the faith had rubbed off on him.

Adults, *left to right:* Cliff and Annie Davenport, Alice McCarthy, Dorothy Barthol, Herman and Anna Davenport, and Mrs. Pease (the pastor's wife). Children, *left to right:* Phyllis Barthol and Virginia and Joyce Davenport. (Photo courtesy of the Davenport and Barthol families, who were former Blewett residents.)

The family of Russell Barthol (Phyllis Barthol's dad) is featured in this group picture (note the Pierce Arrow car in the background). *Left to right:* Cliff Davenport (in the hat), unnamed man, Mildred Barthol, Annie Davenport, Anton Neubauer, Kathreen Shultz -Barthol, unnamed man, Alice McCarthy, and Ester Barthol. The woman and two children in the front are not named. (Photo courtesy of the Davenport and Barthol families, who were former Blewett residents.)

In 1904, the Marko family came to Blewett as miners and for other mine-related jobs. In January, the postmaster was Mr. Taylor.

W. H. Resburg was made postmaster in February. Resburg had a side business selling a medicinal elixir called Puget Sound Bitters, which caught on fast due to its high percentage of alcohol. The locals considered this magical brew a substitute for whiskey. This was a timely occurrence, because in April, the road between Ingalls Creek and Blewett was blocked by a landslide for almost a month.

About this same time, Mrs. Richardson came to Blewett to teach at the school. Mrs. Mary McCardle followed her in 1906, and in 1907, Miss Harris came to Blewett to teach.

BLEWETT'S BIRTH EXPLOSION

Cliff Davenport and his extended family members were one of the mainstays at the turn of the century in the town of Blewett. On May 17, 1907, their newborn son Herman Rankin Davenport was added to the population. About two years later, on August 9, 1909, another baby son, Norman Goodwin Davenport, arrived. Alice (Grandma Carty) was there participating in her midwife capacity. On February 16, 1913, Dorothy Mae Davenport was born in Leavenworth with Dr. George Hoxey delivering her in the Peak Hotel. Mae Gilson was a Blewett miner's wife and a very good friend of the family, thus Dorothy's middle name. Mae's husband worked with Cliff in the mines around Blewett.

Two of the Blewett bachelor-miners that came to see baby Dorothy were Charley Striker and Thaddeus Neubauer. Striker was an ex-jeweler turned miner. He gave Dorothy an infant-size gold bracelet. Neubauer presented her with a baby bonnet. In her pleasant childhood days in the mining town of Blewett, Dorothy got to know the two men as friends.

BLEWETT MINING ACTIVITIES

During 1907–1908, Washington Meteor Mining Company claims were being leased by the Blewett Mining and Leasing Company. They then leased those properties to the Alta Vista Mining Company, located in Culver Gulch. Alta Vista Mining Company struck a rich ore vein in a raise of Tunnel No. 9. It assayed $92 in gold per ton.

In the unexplained mix of leased and subleased mining properties in Culver Gulch, the owners of the Golden Eagle obtained a lease on the North Star claim. When the lease was up, John McCarthy took a lease on the North Star. He drove two tunnels that intercepted the mineralized vein. The lower tunnel was in 62 feet, exposing a vein of ore 2 feet wide. The upper tunnel (40 feet above) was 258 feet long. At the face of the 258-foot adit, a raise followed the vein upward for 20 feet.

Due to John's efforts, he discovered concentrations of high-grade gold ore that was reputed to have assayed up to $1,200 per ton in gold. At that time, gold was valued at about $20 an ounce. McCarthy built a mill up Culver Gulch that had a tramway from the mine to a mill. The mill was powered by a Corliss engine with two large flywheels, one on each side of the engine. The engine's fuel was alcohol.

While John McCarthy was on his North Star property, Green Kinney appeared, uninvited, at the tunnel site. Evidently John didn't care much for Green. John uninvited Green and told him to get off the North Star claim. Green responded by coming toward John with a small axe in his hand. John perceived malicious intent to do bodily harm upon him and made a move that sent Green tumbling downslope. Green Kenney went to town and contacted Sheriff J. E. Ferguson. The sheriff issued a warrant for McCarthy's arrest. The follow-up was the apprehension of McCarthy. A court date was set. The result was John McCarthy's actions against Green's malicious trespass were justified with a "not guilty" verdict.

During 1908, the Golden Eagle mine was under lease possession of M. F. Peak and son. They had a permanent residence in Leavenworth and owned the Peak Hotel. John McCarthy gave them the option to buy 200,000 shares of Golden Eagle stock. The shares were controlled by property owner McCarthy. If Peak was interested in buying the mine, the selling price was $37,000. If Peak accepted, then $3,750 was due within 30 days, $10,000 in 90 days, and the remaining sum in 6 months. Their first stamp- mill/cyanide-process cleanup of the season produced 11 ounces of gold.

Peak bought the mine and then sold it to Supreme Court Judge W. W. Brock from Everett, Washington. John McCarthy then became the company president and general manager. At first, the Golden Eagle six-stamp mill was run by steam and then later converted to electricity. L. Thurmond was running the mill.

BACHELORS AT BLEWETT

Mining towns always had bachelors within their population, and Blewett had a lot of them, including sourdough miners from Alaska.

One night there was a fire at John Olden's log cabin west of where the old Black Jack mine bridge crossed Peshastin Creek. Two single men, miner/mine owners John Olden and John Heavner lived there. As Cliff Davenport and several men arrived at the scene with water buckets to help quench the blaze, an agitated and inebriated John Heavner was outside yelling that John Olden was still inside the house and had to be rescued. As the volume in fire and smoke increased, it also ramped up his agitated state of mind and shouting. Heavner yelled about Olden, "He's in there and burning to hell!" The fire was far beyond any help the men could render, and the structure burned to the ground.

While the bewildered group of men stood staring into the charred building remains, a dark form came crawling up from the direction of the creek bank and out from under the bushes. It was blurry-eyed ("*Heeere's Johnny*") Olden hugging a whiskey jug. To Heavner's relief and joy at the sight of the jug (first) and Olden (second); Heavner stated, "What great presence of mind!"

And as it goes …

Blewett school teacher Juna Smith and Thaddeus Neubauer. (Photo courtesy of the Davenport and Barthol families, who were former Blewett residents.)

John O. had the knack, come flood, fire, or attack, to save his distilled concoction.
Due to his thirst, preservation came first; his scruples inclined toward this caution.
With presence of mind, John was always on time, for libations at any engagement.
He could quaff large amounts; as regards all accounts, this covered about any arrangement.
Drinking friends would admire that he never did tire of the juice that put John at odds
In regard to clear mind … John sometimes declined, giving alcohol spirits the nod.

It could be supposed that at the time of this inferno event, the two Johns were still "grief drinking" to the death of their very long-time miner-friend John C. Johnson (not to be confused with Tom Johnson's younger brother John A. Johnson). In December 1915, as John C. Johnson slept after a night of hard drinking, he was burned to death in an arson fire at the Overland

Hotel in Leavenworth. Considering the two Johns' fire-events, perhaps their state of emoting was connected to Johnson's death.

Heavner and the Johnson clan were close friends and mining partners for over 20 years. John Olden was often included in their mining deals and hard-drink doings as long-time mining associates. In the past, when Johnson was alive, the three men partook of the adult nectar as if they believed that alcohol, like formaldehyde, could add considerable years to one's body.

Not surprising, fire water, miraculously minus an inferno such as the one that snuffed out Johnson, prescribed the ending for 69-year-old John Heavner. In May 1916, Heavner had been despondent and drinking heavily for several days. He drank himself into such a stupor that he passed out. In collapsing onto the floor of his cabin, Heavner fell from a chair and, in the process, knocked over a lighted oil lamp. For whatever reason, it went out, and a flaming pyre to equal Johnson's unscheduled cremation was avoided. The word going around Blewett was that Heavner deliberately drank himself to death. He was buried next to his long-time friend, John C. Johnson, as he had requested.

CLIFFORD DAVENPORT AND FAMILY

FIREWORKS AFTER THE FOURTH

July 4, 1914, was accentuated with Blewett's first fireworks display that impressed all, especially the youngsters. The following October, brothers seven-year-old Herman and five-year-old Norman Davenport wandered up and beyond their play area. As they explored up a trail from their playground, they came upon a mine tunnel with an unlocked door. The curious boys stepped just inside the portal and found carbide miner lamps, matches, and a small box of blasting caps. Recalling July and the joy of the fireworks, plus understanding the capacity of the caps to "go bang," the two brothers commenced to duplicate the July celebration. With blasting caps in hand, they proceeded to light the fuses and throw them one at a time into the tunnel. They would then dash away with glee behind a tree and wait for the bang. They did this several times. As young Norman lit one, it went off in his hand, severely damaging it and also blowing a hole into his side. Herman was running with his back to the blast. He received some bruises

Youngsters Norman Davenport with his older brother Herman, prior to the accident that took Norman's life. (Photo courtesy of the Davenport and Barthol families, who were former Blewett residents.)

from the incidental debris but escaped permanent harm. Seeing that Norman was bleeding, Herman carried Norman for quite a distance back to the house.

When Annie saw her son's condition, she immediately summoned Cliff, who quickly gathered a wagon and horses. Cliff took Norman 14 miles to Dr. Hoxey in Leavenworth. On that ride, Annie feared Norman wouldn't live and prayed for him and consoled him the whole trip. Unfortunately, Norman lost a lot of blood and died shortly after they got to Leavenworth. He was taken to the Cashmere Cemetery and buried beside his sister Viola.

Shock and the burden of guilt for not securing the tunnel portal settled on the old miner who owned the claim. Cliff regretted that he was not aware of the mining activity at that tunnel. Annie felt the anguish of thinking she should have monitored the boys more closely. The whole mining community felt the melancholy effect of the tragedy, and Herman carried the weight of that tragedy the rest of his life. To help overcome their grief, the family moved to Seattle on the advice of Dr. Hoxey.

In 1914, Cliff was 34 years old and thin of build, but due to his experience with mine timbering, he got a job at a Seattle tunnel site. That tunnel is now buried under the streets of Seattle and is part of the city's historic underground tour. Later, during World War I, Cliff was a timekeeper at a Puget Sound-based shipyard. Cliff's next job was working for a timber company near Cle Elum, Washington, while maintaining his family home in Seattle.

MOVE BACK TO BLEWETT AREA

In 1920, Cliff moved his family back to Blewett where they lived with Grandma Carty and John (McCarthy) in their two-story log house. Cliff found work doing assessment work in the mines around Blewett.

By this time, miner/mine owner John Burmeister had several claims including the Black Jack, in which Cliff worked. In 1921, there was no school in Blewett, so to accommodate the children, the Davenports moved to the town of Peshastin, Washington. Dorothy was in the third grade, and Herman was in the ninth grade. For several years, Cliff continued to do assessment work during the summer months in the mines around Blewett. While living at Grandma Carty's house, Cliff was available for jobs opening up some of the tunnels and running additional footage to the workings that the Amalgamated Gold Mines Company had leased during 1920 to 1923. When the mining claims he worked on closed for the winter, he found other employment. The family lived in Peshastin until 1930, the year Dorothy graduated from high school.

FAMILY TALENTS

Cliff taught Dorothy how to play the violin, and Herman was taught to play the mandolin. The duo was popular entertainment at the various community gatherings. Later, both of them were members of the Wenatchee Valley Orchestra.

Cliff Davenport was a talented man of many abilities, which he put to work at Blewett. One of his projects was an electric system that was run by waterpower. Using water from Peshastin Creek, he ran a water flume behind Grandma Carty's house and used a Pelton wheel that ran

Left to right:
Dorothy Davenport-
Barthol (Phyllis's'
mother), Cliff, and
Annie Davenport.
(Photo courtesy of
the Davenport and
Barthol families, who
were former Blewett
residents.)

an electric generator. Cliff wired each room for lights that had no off or on switches, and could not be turned off unless the Pelton wheel was disabled. The old wood stove that often heated an old cast-iron clothes iron was retired and replaced with the easier-to-handle electric version.

Blewett resident/miner Jim Smoot replaced Cliff's Pelton wheel, water power source with an old abandoned gas-run electric generator that they repaired.

Another story related to Peshastin Creek near the Smoot house was the event when 25 trout were caught in one hour.

The Smoot family had a garage with a gas pump next to the Blewett Pass highway. It was basically a "gas and soda pop" stop when Orange Crush beverage was a big hit. The historic stone arrastra near the Smoot house was a focal point where children met to play in and around Peshastin Creek.

POLE PICK NO.1 MINE STORY

Cliff Davenport told an interesting story about the Pole Pick No. 1 claim and two men, Jim Smoot and another miner, Jack, who had a lease on it. The two focused their work on the two tunnels. Jim mined in the upper adit, and Jack had the other. The upper dig was 50 feet above Jack's lower tunnel. After a while, Jim struck a high-grade deposit of gold-bearing rock. Jim swore a friend to secrecy and confided in him by displaying a lunch pail full of the gold-rich quartz ore, which brought Jim $200 in pocket money. Jim reminded the confidant that "mum's the word." Jim's reasoning for not sharing with Jack was that what Jim mined solo in that upper tunnel was his.

About the same time, Jack also cut into gold on the same vein system in the lower tunnel. Jack told Jim's confidant on the day he visited Jack's rich gold find that it was one of the best leads he ever dug on. They went through the familiar bantering routine of confided secrecy, and then Jack showed him his lunch bucket full of gold-bearing quartz. It turned out to be worth close to $300.

Unfortunately, Jim's friend wasn't experienced at mumming the mouth. He torpedoed his promises to both men and told Jack that Jim, too, had been successful at his upper digs. To the momentary dismay of Jim and Jack, the truth was known. But to Jim's and Jack's credit, they patched things up and closed down their operations for the day to celebrate their good fortune, minus the presence of their mutual non-mumming friend.

CLIFF'S MINING ACTIVITY

THE DAVENPORT TUNNELS

During the 1930 mining season, Cliff was contracted to drive a tunnel on a patented claim (privately owned) high up the gulch in the Culver drainage side of the ridge between Negro Creek and Culver Gulch. It was in the area where the gold-enriched white quartz of the Summit Pockets was previously mined. The original, five, patented Blinn claims of the 1800s begin there and run down the Negro Creek drainage slope to and across Negro Creek. Even though the claim belonged to someone else, a current mineral-property map of Culver Gulch underground workings shows the Davenport Tunnel remains named the same to this day.

Businessmen from Spokane, Washington, were leasing this particular claim during the 1930s. Their interest in the gold-bearing, white quartz at the Davenport Tunnel location could have been aroused by an old Summit Pocket area assay report. In the past, it ran as high as $10,000 per ton in the yellow metal.

Charles R. Hesseltine, president of Amalgamated Gold Mines Company was another industrious man advancing tunnels in Culver Gulch. J. F. Hocking, president of the Gold Bond Mining Company, did the same.

Hocking contracted Cliff Davenport to block out and run tunnels on the Gold Bond Mining Company properties. Two of the contracts were the Davenport Tunnel in the Summit Pockets area that Hocking may have personally leased. Later, Cliff worked in the long tunnel at the Negro Creek level, the other Davenport Tunnel.

By the end of the summer of 1931, Cliff had his crew of miners run the Davenport Tunnel near the Summit Pockets area to the first encounter with a deposit of gold-bearing ore. At $35 per ounce, it was cost effective to ship the rock to the Tacoma smelter for processing. The *Wenatchee Daily News* announced the event as a big gold strike at the Blewett mines, which created a lot of interest within the other news media around the Northwest. This, in turn, created a new flow of money that was invested in the featured mining companies at Blewett.

Gold ore continued to be mined throughout the winter. It contained enough copper in the ore to pay for the smelting costs. It was transferred by pack animals down Culver Gulch and shipped by trucks to the Tacoma smelter.

During the next summer, a professor of geology and a group of his students from the University of Washington dropped by Blewett unexpectedly. They were waiting for Cliff to come down the steep trail from the tunnel. Even though Cliff had put in a long day at the mine, he brought them back up to the tunnel (a one-hour hike, one way). He showed them the different rock formations, how the workings were timbered, how the rock was blasted, the manner in which dull drill steels were sharpened, and other mine-related subjects. Cliff stated that, in the early days of mining the Summit Pockets, there was one rich pocket deposit that assayed at $65,000 per ton, but there was only a few hundred pounds in the pocket.

Cliff was highly educated and applied his knowledge of higher mathematics to help direct running tunnels. This newer, gold-producing activity in the Blewett Mining District brought in curious mining engineers from places throughout the northwestern states, Mexico, and South Africa.

One day, the credibility of the mine owners came into question. Cliff realized his bosses, who were leasing the claim, were playing the promotion game. They were not as interested in getting the gold out of the mine as they were in getting more money out of mining stock investors due to the high-grade ore.

Cliff, being an honest man, knew that there was enough ore being produced to pay the miners and him, buy needed mining-related items, and make the company investors an enticing profit, of which they were receiving little. At this point, Cliff took it upon himself to handle the dishonesty of the matter by drifting away from the gold-bearing vein of ore in the Davenport Tunnel near the Summit Pockets. When Cliff's bosses heard of the unfortunate turn of events, his contract for developing the workings was ended. After a while, the dishonest lease/owner promoters discontinued stock sales and lurked off into the board meeting room to concoct other moneymaking ventures.

THE OLD JAMES WILDER CLAIMS

In June 1931, Cliff was in possession of the old Wilder claims under lease and bond. He had a small crew of men working several months for him, which resulted in a noticeable discovery of high-grade gold ore. Until Cliff's 1931 mining activities, no extensive mining was done on the Wilder claims.

Samples were taken from the 5-foot-wide, gold-bearing vein (most likely a pocket deposit within the vein). E. A. Wingate took the samples of ore to Leavenworth and spread the word around that it was the richest he ever saw. Other local, old mining men heralded their opinion that it could be worth several thousand dollars to the ton. At this point, no follow-up to the story could be located.

Cliff Davenport was not the type of man to go around making that kind of misleading, exaggerated statement. It is suspected other less-honest men had an ulterior motive of some sort. Perhaps they wanted to promote mined-out claim property near Cliff's gold discovery area so they could take unfair advantage of the close proximity to Cliff's workings. This kind of legal but unscrupulous action was not uncommon throughout mining history. Even in today's many-faceted mining dealings, it is buyer beware.

1932

In May of 1932, Cliff got another contract to run some more footage in tunnels up in the slopes of the Negro Creek drainage. One of these tunnels was on the Vancouver claim. It was referred to as one of the Davenport tunnels. This main tunnel is the one that has the 6-foot-wide vein of white quartz showing at the creek-level portal on the property. At that time, it was driven to a point 600-plus feet southeast on the vein. The proposed projection of the tunnel was to head under the vein on the Olympic claim.

Davenport ran his new stretch of the tunnel. Gold Bond Mining Company then had work extended on the vein by contracts, first, with George H. Lewis and, then later, with Cliff Davenport one more time. The last drift made on the quartz ledge was developed following the curve of the vein. This went more to the south-southeast, away from its original, intended point, under the Olympic claim. Instead, it was intended to run toward and under the Culver mine's vein structure.

MOUNTAIN LION MINE HIRES CLIFF

Another contract that Cliff accepted was for developing some tunnel workings for the owners of the Mountain Lion mine. It was located about 4 or 5 miles upstream from the mouth of Negro Creek (while Northwest Underground Explorations has searched for this tunnel and located unidentified adits, as of 2013, none has been verified as the Mountain Lion workings). Davenport built a tent house that had a wood floor and wood sides to accommodate his stay while developing the Mountain Lion. The roof was canvas. The two men he hired to help run the tunnels lived in an old log cabin up the road above the tent house. The road at that time ended about 1 mile farther up the creek from their dwellings.

Cliff's son, Herman, came to work at the mine and to recuperate after he contracted chemical poisoning while spraying apple orchards in the Chelan area. While Herman was at the Mountain Lion mining, his daughter Joyce was born August 4, 1932. Dr. Hoxey from Leavenworth was delayed, so 90-year-old midwife Grandma Carty was there to deliver Joyce, just as she did in many other similar situations.

The four men continued working to extend a tunnel on the claim. Meanwhile, Cliff built another cabin farther up the road on the creek. Cliff's wife, Annie, did the cooking and daughter

Cliff Davenport (white shirt and hard hat) poses with an unidentified man at the portal of the Mountain Lion Mine. (Photo courtesy of the Davenport and Barthol families, who were former Blewett residents.)

Cliff and Herman Davenport and Anton Neubauer began actively reopening old abandoned gold mines with varying results. This scene gives an idea of the conditions they had to deal with. (Linda McCune photo collection.)

Dorothy did the baking. Joyce was being cared for back at Grandma Carty's house. That winter, they were snowed in for three months at the Negro Creek cabin. However, they had a sufficient stock of wood, food, and other household items to see them through to springtime. During the next summer and fall, there were many folks that made the trip up Negro Creek to enjoy camping. Among them were men who went into the tunnel to see the progress of Davenport's contracted dig.

One night in the cabin at Negro Creek, 16-year-old Dorothy was awakened by a sound in the kitchen. With her room next to it and her door open, she saw a box of matches in flames on a shelf. She immediately jumped into action and dowsed the flaming box in a nearby bucket of water. The commotion brought Cliff and Annie to the scene. They decided that a mouse chewing on the matchbox caused the blaze. And they gave thanks that their God who never sleeps was there to protect them.

MOUNTAIN LION MINE OWNERS VS. CLIFF DAVENPORT

Cliff worked these digs for several years, and toward the end of the project, the owners of the Mountain Lion came up short on cash for his miners' payroll. Cliff paid the men the remainder owed them out of his pocket and did so assuming the owners would come through with the owed payroll—and they did not. So Cliff put a lien on the owner's property and sent the squabble to a court of justice, hoping this would force them to pay the debt owed him. It was the Great Depression years, and a failing economy wasn't the only thing derailed and slow to recover. It appears the court system was not always on track either.

Meanwhile, the three members of the Davenport family remained at the isolated cabin up Negro Creek. They were protecting their interest at the lien-hold property because of the situation created by the dishonest owners of the now inactive mining property. There they waited. It came to the point when they had enough food for breakfast, and that was it. Because the Davenport family was faith-based, they resorted to prayer, and the result was a knock at the door as the last light of the day was fading.

It was about 4 miles downstream to the Blewett highway, and they had heard no advance sounds of a car or even an inquiry of "hello in the cabin" by the approaching party. When Cliff opened the door, there stood a man with a pack on his back. The first words out of the lost stranger asked about his location, and then he stated that he had a hunting partner on the trail behind him who would soon arrive.

It seems the duo had begun their hunting hike from the west side of a low ridge in the Wenatchee Mountain Range and took a wrong turn on their hike that ended much farther east than they had intended. Cliff told the hunter to follow the road down Negro Creek to the main highway, take a right, and go two miles to the town of Blewett, where there was a gas station. Commercial trucking rigs stopped there, allowing for a good chance the two men could catch a ride back to Cle Elum. After a "thanks," the man turned and headed down the road.

A few minutes later there was a knock at the door again. This time it was both men. They had decided the hike to Blewett was a long way to haul their heavily packs, and they asked Cliff if he would mind if they left the contents at the cabin for the family to have and use. It must have looked like two cornucopias to the Davenports as about 100 pounds of food spilled out of the packs onto the table. There was a 10-pound sack of flour, followed by a ham, canned milk, canned fruit, vegetables, cookies, and more. It ended with thanks exchanged. It brought to the Davenports' minds the passage in Scripture about "encountering angels unaware" because nobody remembered seeing any hunting rifles. And, yep, there was a joyful appreciation in the Davenports' belief that God knows and supplies their needs.

Cliff took the advice of his attorney to retain possession of the claim and stayed on at the cabin alone for a while. He also stayed in close contact with the rest of the family residing in the town of Blewett. During one of those lonely nights, Cliff heard a car stop in front of the cabin, followed by a beckoning holler. Cliff went outside to see who was there, thinking it was somebody of a friendly persuasion. He couldn't have been more wrong. The indicator was a shot that rang out from the direction of the car. He was in front of the window with the lantern light silhouetting him into a perfect target. His immediate response was to drop flat, down out of sight into the darkness along the ground, and lie motionless. The car sped away leaving Cliff to ponder whether the shot was an attempt on his life or a serious move to scare him off of the property. After a sleepless night, Cliff, in hot-footed fashion, headed down Negro Creek and south to Blewett.

Cliff phoned his attorney in Wenatchee and reported the shooting incident. The result was a court hearing that was attended by over 100 of his friends wanting to testify in his behalf. The evidence available was greatly in favor of Cliff and his debt-compensation lien. It was obvious by the actions of the judge that Davenport's story didn't sway him to consider his plea. The judge did not allow Cliff or his attorney to state their case, nor did the judge let any of the witnesses testify in Cliff's behalf. After reading the affidavits, the judge interpreted the case and decided the man and woman who owned the mine were victims of laborers that pressed unfounded charges against the innocent owners.

Everybody at the presentation and judgment were shocked at the miscarriage of justice, except for the owners. Later, when Cliff had a chance to talk to the mine owners' attorney, the attorney expressed his surprise at winning the case and stated that he didn't think the owners would win against the labor lien. Cliff's attorney was privy to the fact that the judge was bribed and stated as much to Cliff. Cliff chose not to go on with further court action against the mine owners.

GOLD ON BLACK JACK CLAIM SLOPE, 1935

In 1935, Cliff Davenport, his son, Herman, and Raymond Barthol, along with their friend Anton Neubauer began clearing out caved-in portals on abandoned Blewett-area mine claims. They were searching for signs of gold left behind. They were clearing the caved portal on the lowest Black Jack workings during the 1939 mining season. It is located just above the flood line near Peshastin Creek level. This is a long adit, but there was no sign of minable ore left in sight.

On the slope, higher above the creek-level tunnel was an open cut with some red spots on the walls. Some of the red rock was knocked off, and Herman took it down to Peshastin Creek and panned for gold. The results in the pan reflected a good prospect, showing in a strong line of free gold.

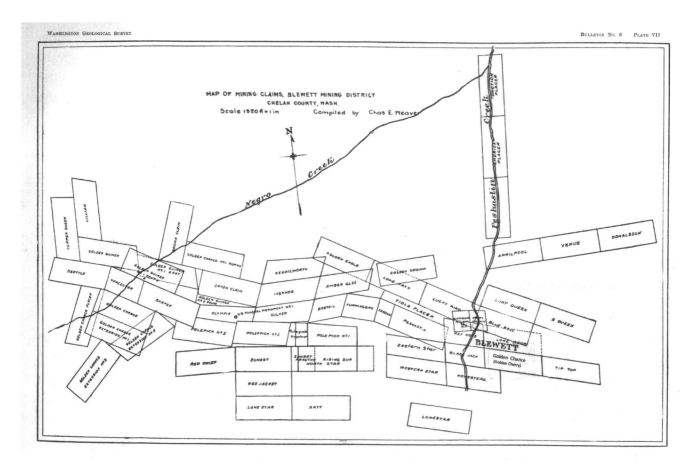

This map represents the mines of Culver Gulch and Blewett area during the time Cliff Davenport was relocating old gold-mine properties. There are some claim name changes that do not match with other maps that various mining companies circulated throughout Blewett's mining history. (Map by Charles E. Weaver; Bulletin No.6 [1910].)

The claim belonged to J. B. Woodworth of Vancouver, British Columbia. As it turned out, he also had cleared the title through a Superior Court decision from C. R. Hesseltine to the old Blewett workings and Black Jack claims in 1939.

Cliff got in touch with Woodworth and cleared the way for him and Herman to go to the Chelan County Courthouse and refile on the Black Jack claim, although Woodworth was still the primary partner. The men had to report to him about how things were developing in the new upper-slope workings. Woodworth and his wife came to Blewett for a stay at the hotel during the renewed Black Jack mining activity.

Cliff, Herman, and Anton drove farther into the hill where the elevated, outcropping gold ore was found. They assayed as they continued the workings until they struck high-grade, gold-bearing ore. A lightweight bucket tramway was built from the elevated tunnel opening on the slope down to an ore bin and truck-loading platform alongside the Blewett highway. From there, heavy-duty trucks hauled the gold ore to the Tacoma smelter. Within three months, they cleared over $4,000 after the smelting and transportation costs were deducted. That was a huge amount of money for a small-mine owner operating during the Depression years (gold was at $35 an ounce).

BARTHOL/DAVENPORT CLANS ON THE MOVE

Earlier, in 1932 during the Depression, the Barthol family moved in, cleaned, and restored several rooms of the 21-room Blewett hotel. Three years later, in 1935, they left Blewett, went to Seattle in search of work, and then to British Columbia.

In 1937, Dorothy Davenport married Russell Barthol, and they returned to Blewett. On March 18, 1938, Phyllis Eileen Barthol was born in Blewett to Russell and Dorothy Barthol.

The next child born was to Herman and Anna Davenport. Virginia Louise Davenport (Phyllis's cousin) was born on June 3, 1938. Again, the Davenport family increased Blewett's population by one on February 26, 1942, when Joyce and Virginia's sister Sandra Lucille was born.

About ¼ mile south of the McCarthy house, Cliff built a house for his family, which now included Russell and Dorothy's young daughter Phyllis. Her parents were divorced: Russell went to San Diego and worked for Ryan Aircraft Company, and. Dorothy lived and worked in Wenatchee.

After two years, Cliff, Annie, and Phyllis moved to Wenatchee and stayed with Dorothy and her family. From their residence in Wenatchee, when Phyllis was five years old, the four of them moved to Auburn, Washington, in November of 1944.

The Barthol home, located south of Blewett, was in the family's possession for several years after. They would stay at that former residence while visiting or vacationing at Blewett. Phyllis willingly reminisces with folks about her Blewett days and the friendships that were established with its mining community.

ARTHUR C. BALLARD VISITS BLEWETT, 1940

In mid-September 1940, as Arthur Ballard and Cecil Ward returned from an inspection to Arthur's Mammoth mine property and to repair vandalized wood structures at his Azurite mine in the Slate Creek Mining District, they stopped to visit Arthur's cousin Cliff Davenport and other relatives and friends in Blewett.

In Blewett, Arthur took Cecile to see the old stone arrastra that was carved and honed into the creek-side rock structure. Arthur stated that it had been there for 65 or 70 years.

Cliff Davenport was out and about resetting the stakes and corner-marking posts on a group of old, original 1870s claims that were under new ownership with clear title by Mr. Woodworth of Vancouver, British Columbia. Cliff was the only man in Blewett at this time that was physically capable to scramble the steep slopes in Culver Gulch and who knew where the correct 1870s claims boundaries were. His other goings-on during Arthur's visit were removing the remaining personal effects not yet stolen from his son Herman Davenport's vacated log cabin in Blewett. Herman's and Grandma Carty's belongings were moved to Cliff's house, about ¼ mile up the road (south) of town, where the Davenport family, Barthol family, and bachelor Anton Neubauer's dwellings were located.

Arthur mentioned that the machinery from two of the stamp mills once used to process Blewett-area ore was being used at mining properties in Alaska. He also noted a quaint building that in the past was a store and post office, and a log house that held the latest assay office was still standing.

People were starting to drift back into Blewett. One man in possession of a claim and a Doodlebug (an electronic gold-finding contraption) employed Cliff's help in locating the tunnel of his newly purchased mining claim. The tunnel was originally dug to very tight dimensions. The gossipy reasoning for the miner's small tunnel was to keep his shrewish, domineering wife from following him into the digs (silence is golden). An underground dig such as this may have required the use of a wheelbarrow.

Anton Neubauer, Cliff Davenport's neighbor, pointed out to Arthur the beaver activity near Blewett. It annoyed him that the beaver chewed down trees up to 10 inches in diameter on a regular basis. Anton took to painting tar around the trees he didn't want downed by the critters. Although he did make one concession to the beavers; when he cut down trees needed for firewood or other uses, he let the beavers chew off the branches and carry them away, saving Anton from the added labor of pruning them.

Such were the activities in the Blewett area on Arthur Ballard's visit.

BLEWETT GOLD MINING STALLS DUE TO WWII

The main core of miners in the Swauk and Peshastin Mining Districts during WWII consisted of old-timers, some of whom had seen action in WWI. There was also a contingent of prospectors/miners solidly entrenched, in one way or another, up at their Negro Creek and Ingalls Creek claims. Thaddeus Neubauer deeded his Lucky Queen gold quartz mining claim to his nephew Anton Neubauer on July 30, 1941.

During World War II from 1942–1945, the Tacoma smelter stopped taking non-strategic, precious metal ore. That meant the gold-bearing sulfide ore that the miners at Blewett mined was not being processed. This ended Blewett's business of gold mining on a larger scale. Although there was renewed interest in the old Blewett Mining District for possible iron, copper, nickel, cobalt, and other strategic wartime metal bearing ores, none were found in large enough deposits to be considered important.

THE END

Clifford and Annie Davenport were in Auburn when 79-year-old Cliff passed away September 25, 1958. Annie passed away at age 87 on October 1, 1969. They kept the faith and were instrumental in establishing important historical contributions wherever they lived.

Cliff and Annie Davenport. (Photo courtesy of the Davenport and Barthol families, who were former Blewett residents.)

BLEWETT HISTORIC TOWN SITE, 2013

A historic monument, with commemorative plaque and a reader board displaying mine-related photos stands in the middle of a large, flat, oval-shaped turnout. Signs stating "Historic Site Ahead" are posted at Mile Post 174 on US 97. Directly across from the entry road to the old historic Blewett town site is the remains of the 20-stamp mill. It is nearing the end of its scenic value as, year by year, more of the wood structure falls to the ground and rots alongside previously recognizable wooden features.

Another remaining historic site that will outlast anyone reading this book is the stone arrastra that was worn into solid rock from decades of use. It is located along the east side of Peshastin Creek just above water level. To reach the arrastra site takes caution because it is quick (but not safe or easy) to access by crossing US 97 from the southernmost end of the oval parking area, south of the Blewett historic reader board. This information is not a recommendation. This is only to let folks know where the area of the arrastra site is located. Should anybody reading this decide to go there, the responsibility of picking the route to the arrastra is entirely up to the individual. You are your own liability if you make a bad choice.

GLOSSARY

adit A horizontal mine tunnel from the surface by which a mine is entered, including its drifts, crosscut, and inclines that is developed to varying length.

aerial tramway A suspended cable carrying ore buckets from mine ore bin to a milling facility.

agate A form of cryptocrystalline (hidden crystal) quartz.

alluvium A loose mix of soil, sand, silt, and gravel that has been washed down to lower ground.

amalgam A lump of mercury that has absorbed gold particulates from black sand or other crushed base rock.

andesite A reddish type of lava.

argentiferous Containing silver.

arkose/arkosic A type of sedimentary rock (containing 25 percent or more of feldspars) resulting from rapid disintegration of granite or gneiss with no alteration by weathering, as in arkosic sandstone.

arrastra/arrastre A mining device that is a 12-foot-diameter pit, 3 feet deep and built of granite rock that was hauled to the mill site from nearby rock outcrops. The power to drive this system is a 26-foot-diameter overshot water wheel by way of a stream of water directed in a flume and over the wheel. The water wheel, in turn, operates a shaft and gear setup that is attached with chains to drag stones (granite boulders weighing about half a ton or more). These stones crush the ore into powder. Then mercury is used to extract the gold from the mixture.

arsenopyrite A mineral containing iron, arsenic, and sulfur.

assay Chemical analysis of an ore to determine what metals it contains.

assessment work Minimum amount of work required by the US government as proof that a mine is not lying idle; required only on unpatented mineral claims.

auriferous Containing gold.

azurite An ore of copper that displays a bright blue color.

bad ground An area of unstable rock or such in a mine tunnel or in any other mining development area that needs timbering.

ball mill A rotating grinding machine that uses steel balls to crush gold-bearing rock.

barring down Using a long handled prying bar to loosen and drop cracked rock overhead or on a rock wall for mine safety reasons.

basalt Dark-colored igneous rock that is fine grained in texture.

batholith A large mass of igneous rock, sometimes miles across.

bench placer This is a placer in an ancient stream deposit that can occur up to 300 feet above present creeks or streams.

bleb A small mass of material contained within a matrix.

Bleichert tram A type of aerial tramway that was patented by Theodore Otto and Adolph Bleichert in Germany in 1876. It used stationary cable from which ore buckets were hung and transported. A second traction cable was connected to each ore bucket as required to move it along the stationary cable.

blind vein A vein usually discovered when crosscut-tunneling to the main ore vein.

blocking out Boring tunnels or other activities that define the extent of an ore body. This is usually done before committing to ore mining production.

bond An agreement, similar to mine leasing, whereby a bonder must pay to lease a claim, must make certain improvements, and might share in proceeds.

bornite Peacock-colored copper ore.

breast of the tunnel The end or blasting face of a tunnel.

breccia Rock broken into fragments and naturally re-cemented into a solid form of rock.

breccia pipe A pipe formed of pyroclastic, breccia rock that has welled up from pressure below. Diamonds and other minerals can sometimes be in the mix.

bucket tram An aerial system using one or more buckets to haul ore to a downhill ore bunker and having a haul-back line.

bullion A combination of mostly gold solidified with silver; usually in brick form.

bull wheel The wheel that powers (or guides in a gravity system) a tramway cable.

buzz worm Rattlesnake.

calcite A mineral composed of calcium carbonate, which sometimes forms crystals.

carbonaceous Containing carbon in its organic or inorganic structure.

Celestials Nickname for western frontier Chinese miners. The term refers to "people of the sky" or something similar from a Chinese legend.

chalcedony Rock containing a mixture of crystalline and hydrated silica showing a cryptocrystalline structure.

chalcopyrite A mineral containing iron, copper, and sulfur.

Chilean mill An arrastra that uses large steel wheels to crush ore, as opposed to the rock-grinding action of the all-stone type.

chromite Ore rock containing chrome, iron, and oxygen.

cinnabar A mercury sulfide, brick-red in color.

cirque An elevated valley that is located at the head of a glacial area; often has a shallow lake within a natural containment area.

classifier A grid or screen that separates the various size ore material as it passes through the mill system.

concentrator A mill plant that separates the heaver ore rock form the gangue (waste) rock.

conglomerate Various small rocks naturally cemented together to form a hardened geological area or boulders to smaller rocks.

contact zone An area that has been altered geologically by contact between country rock and igneous intrusion.

contouring Walking along the side of a slope while maintaining the same elevation.

core drilling Also called hollow drilling; drilling using a hollow-stem diamond drilling bit that allows rock samples to be withdrawn from hundreds of feet inside a massive rock formation.

country rock Rock that was originally in place when igneous rock intruded into the area under great pressure through cracks and fissures.

coyote holing Drilling a narrow body-size hole in order to sight check for minerals; also developed when needing an area to deposit a blasting charge into mineralized rock.

cribbing A form of shoring the top and/or sides of a tunnel or other unstable underground workings against rock fall or loose rock debris.

crosscut tunnel A tunnel that is not run on the vein but is driven to intersect the vein.

crusher A unit of equipment used to reduce mined ore to a smaller size to accommodate following milling procedures (as in a machine called a "jaw crusher").

cyanide treatment A plant operation that uses a potassium cyanide or some other cyanide mix to dissolve gold from mined ore rock.

decline tunnel A tunnel that descends downward rather than horizontally.

diabase A dark-colored igneous rock of gabbro origin.

dike A rock formation created when volcanic magma intrudes vertically through to the ground, and is exposed as a protruding outcropping when the surrounding county rock weathers away.

diorite An igneous rock similar to granite, but lacking quartz.

dip The vertical angle that a mineralized vein makes with the earth's surface.

doré bar A bullion mix of purified gold and silver. The minerals are separated at a refinery plant.

drift A tunnel run on an ore vein.

druse Very fine crystals covering quartz rock (called drusy quartz); also called "sugar" quartz.

fault zone An area where rock has been fractured by geologic pressure, thus causing sections of it to slip or thrust up, over, or in opposite directions to each other.

felsite Igneous rock similar to granite; gray to pinkish in color.

fissure vein A vein where hydrothermal fluids are thrust from deep within the earth upward in cracks of displaced rocks.

float Vein rock that has weathered from a higher elevation and fallen down to the slopes below.

flume A ditch/channel or wood trough used to direct water to a desired location.

flux Material added to molten ore to facilitate melting; used at an ore smelter. It reduces the temperature of the melt and combines with impurities to form discarded material.

fool's gold The mineral iron pyrite, which appears as gold to the untrained eye.

foot wall The lower wall of a slanted tunnel or stope.

fraction claim A claim smaller than the allowable 20-acre-sized full claim.

free gold Gold that can be produced by directly crushing it free from its host rock and amalgamation without roasting. No cyanide treatment is needed as it is in the processing of gold-bearing sulfide ore.

free milling An ore deposit that can be processed by crushing the desired minerals (gold and silver) free from the rock, as opposed to chemically treating the ore.

Frue vanner A table that shakes; part of the milling system that separates the waste material from the valuable minerals.

gabbro A type of igneous rock that consist mostly of feldspar.

galena The principal ore of lead; consists of lead and sulfur.

gangue The waste material in the vein that has no value.

geode A mineral nodule that can have crystals contained in its hollow core.

giant monitor A large nozzle that directs a highly pressurized stream of water to hydraulically wash mineralized ground into a gold-separating riffle box, called a "long tom."

giant powder A mixture of nitroglycerine and black powder that is formed into sticks for blasting hard rock.

glory hole An opening on the surface that develops when the stoped-out ore area beneath breaks through to the surface.

gneiss A high-grade metamorphic rock that is course-grained and banded.

gossan Also called iron cap; a deposit formed of iron minerals on the surface by exposed iron-bearing veins.

gouge Soft decomposing material sometimes found between a mineral vein and the hanging wall or foot wall of a tunnel.

granetic rock Rocks that look like granite.

granodiorite An igneous rock similar to granite.

greenstone Rock that contains a high percentage of chlorite or other green minerals.

grizzly A course screen that separates chunks of ore that are too large for the crusher.

grubstake Money or goods given to a prospector who may discover a mineral prospect and, in exchange for the grubstake, shares the mineral claim profits.

Hallidie aerial tram A type of aerial tram, similar to a ski lift, in which the supporting cable and moving cable are the same.

hanging valley A smaller valley located at a higher elevation than the immediate entrance valley; sometimes on a side slope or at the end of the main valley. It is usually created by glacial action.

hanging wall The upper slope of a tunnel wall.

haulage tunnel The horizontal adit level through which loaded ore cars haul mined rock to the ore bunker outside the underground workings.

hematite The primary ore of iron; consists of iron and oxygen.

high-grading (1) Hand selecting ore sent to the mill. (2) Stealing gold from a mine when the boss is not looking.

hogback ridge A main ridge at a higher elevation, which stands out as spiny in appearance, unlike the usual, more rounded neighboring mountain ridges.

hydrothermal A way in which mineral solutions in water, under pressure and heat, are elevated through rock fissures to form mineral veins. Hot springs are hydrothermal.

igneous rock Rock that was once molten and has cooled to a solid mass.

incline tunnel A tunnel that ascends at an angle other than vertical.

intrusive rock Volcanic rock that has forced its way into the cracks of country rock.

iron cap See gossan.

jasper A red form of agate.

jaw crusher A piece of ore milling equipment with fixed iron plates that move to and from one another; thus crushing the ore (sizing it down) and allowing it to drop down to the next milling procedure.

lagging Wood planks used between tunnel timbers in unstable ground as siding to prevent loose rock on the walls of the tunnel from collapsing inward and onto the ore car tracks.

larder A personal or camp's food supply.

ledge An ore vein that is horizontal.

lens/lenticular An mineralized ore body, within a quartz vein or other type of vein, shaped thick in the middle and tapering down to points at the top and bottom.

load A mass of ore that is embedded in country rock, as in hard-rock mining.

long tom A wood trough, 10 to 15 feet long by 2 feet wide, placed at a grade to move water along swiftly. It sometimes had a metal bottom with sieve holes punched into it. There were wood slats secured to the bottom for the remaining length of the trough to make the water turbulent. Thus the light gravel, dirt, and sand washed away while the heaver gold dropped rapidly in-between the riffles. One man shoveled the gold bearing material into the long tom. It took at least 6 men to run a long tom efficiently. The dirt was removed from the long tom at the end of a run and paned for the gold. The long tom came in to use in 1848.

mafic Silicate minerals that are based in iron and/or magnesium.

magnetite Ore containing iron and oxygen; often magnetized (also called lodestone).

magnetometer A device that finds magnetic fields.

malachite A mineral that contains copper, carbon, oxygen, and water, which forms an intensely green mineral stain by way of copper being leached via seeping water onto the surface of nearby rock.

metamorphic rock Rock that has been altered from its original form by heat, pressure, and other events.

mill site A 5-acre claim or plot of land set aside for the construction of an ore-processing mill.

mine claim A 20-acre plot of land that the miner has the rights to the minerals therein.

mine dump The unwanted rock dumped from the tunnel of a mine.

muck/mucking The material blasted within the mine to be hauled out and processed.

native metals Metal, such as gold, silver, or copper, that is naturally reduced in a geologic process to a solid metal state (such as a gold nugget); unlike raw ore that has to be milled to reach high-grade purity.

olivine A silicate with magnesium, iron, and manganese; with or without calcium.

ore Minerals or rock that contain valuable metal.

ore chute A wooden chute that is used to send ore from an upper tunnel down to a lower haulage tunnel.

ore shoot A vertical or near-vertical concentrated deposit of ore.

outcrop An area where a mineral vein reaches the surface.

overshot water wheel A louvered wheel on which water is run over the top by a pipe, allowing the water's weight to rotate it.

oxidized zone Mineral containing zones near or on the surface of the ground, exposed to the air, and in an oxidized condition.

patented claim Land owned by an individual, not the government. The owner must pay taxes on it.

pegmatite A contact zone of rock where molten rock comes in contact with cool country rock leaving large crystals within the fused melt zone.

Pelton wheel A cast-iron wheel with dished cups that rotates at high speed when water through a nozzle is directed at them. This, in turn, generates power by a belt to the desired piece of equipment.

penstock A pipe or trough that directs water to power a water wheel or hydraulic mining equipment, called a "Giant Monitor" (high-powered water nozzle).

peridotite A fine-to-course ultrabasic igneous rock containing olivine and other elements; often a greenish color.

Placer/placer claim Water-born or glacial deposits of gravel or sand containing minerals, such as gold and platinum.

plat A map layout of a town's streets, lots, etc.

pluton Various size rock-mass regions created when magma intrudes into country rock from far below the earth's surface.

poke A leather pouch or bag with a drawstring around the opening to cinch tight and seal in a miner's gold dust, gold flakes, or gold nuggets.

porphyry Igneous rock that contains orthoclase feldspar as the main mineral.

portal Entrance to a tunnel/adit.

prospect A mining claim where mineral values are originally discovered and developed for assay.

pyrite Minerals containing iron and sulfur; common in fool's gold.

quartz Silicon oxide containing silicon and oxygen; found in beach sand. Quartz veins are an indicator for possible gold deposits.

quicksilver Common name for mercury.

raise In mining, a shaft that is bored upward from a horizontal tunnel.

retort A piece of equipment using heated water and a distilling system to separate gold from a conglomeration of a gold-mercury amalgam.

roasting Heating ores below their melting point to drive off unwanted elements.

rod mill Similar to a ball mill, but uses iron rods to crush the ore rock.

rhyolite Extrusive igneous rock; similar to granite.

scheelite Calcium tungstate; a major ore of tungsten.

schist Metamorphic rock with grains that have been altered by enormous pressure into flat platelets arranged along the same plane.

scree Course to medium rock debris found at the base of a cliff face.

section On a map, one square mile.

sedimentary Formed from sediment.

serpentine Hydrous magnesium silicate minerals; colors range from light-green to black.

shaft A vertical mine development driven down from the surface.

shear zone A zone where two underground rock facings slide past each other.

shoring Heavy wood beams used in a tunnel or stope to hold rock in place (wood plank lagging is often used in the process).

silica A mineral containing silicon and water (basic in sand and arkosic sandstone).

sill An igneous intrusion that is flat and roughly horizontal.

single jacking Holding and hammering a chisel into mine rock.

slate Low-grade metamorphic rock.

smelter An ore melting plant where metal is extracted from the rock.

snub tunnel A tunnel of 20 feet or less.

stamp mill Where ore is crushed under pressure of heavy metal stamps.

stibnite Antimony sulfide; an ore of antimony.

stope An excavation from which the ore has been extracted, either from above or below a tunnel level in a series of steps.

strike The angle of an ore vein in association with true, or magnetic, north.

stringer A very thin vein of ore.

stull A very thick timber wedged between the hanging wall and the foot wall; often used in narrow, angular ore rock stopes.

sulfide/sulfide ore Any mineral in which sulfur is a major component.

surface tram An ore car system that carries ore over the ground on tracks.

tailing pile The pile of waste rock that remains after the milling or smelting process is finished.

talc A hydrous magnesium silicate; very soft material.

talus Broken rock that accumulates on the slope of a steep mountain or cliff.

tramway A system using aerial cables with cars or buckets to carry ore and supplies.

underhand stope A stope driven downward, below a tunnel floor to tap into ore.

unpatented claim A possessor claim that is legal to mine, but is not private property.

vein The mineralized concentration deposited between two blocks of country rock.

vug Rock containing holes of various sizes, often filled with crystals.

winze A vertical shaft that is bored downward from a tunnel.

wood-stave pipe A pipe made of two hollow halves of wood held together in a wire wrapping.

REFERENCES

African American Experience Database, www.africanexperience.com

Amalgamated Gold Mines Company Progress Report, self-Published, January 15, 1922.

American Geological Institute. *Dictionary of Geological Terms*. Garden City, New York: Doubleday & Company, 1957.

Anderson, Eva G. *Pioneers of North Central Washington*. 1966; self-Published, reprinted in 1980.

Anema, Jay A. *Nickel Deposits on Negro Creek, Chelan County, Washington*. University of Washington, Seattle, Washington 1955

Ballard family private collection, courtesy of Dr. Charles Ballard of Tarzana, CA.

Barthol, Dorothy Davenport. *They Kept the Faith* Self-published. 2002

Bergren, Carl J. *Pioneers of Peshastin* Self-Published. No date.

Briley, Ann. *Lonely Pedestrian: Francis Marion Streamer*. Fairfield, WA: Ye Galleon Press, 1986.

Broughton W. A. *Blewett-Cle Elum Iron Ore Zone, Chelan and Kittitas Counties, Washington*, Report No. 12. Division of Geology. Olympia, Washington; state printing plant.1944

Cameron, J. F. *Personal Experiences in the Early Days of the Bureau of Public Roads* (From non-dated file).

Cashmere Record. Various 1920–1922.

Chelan County Mining Records, Claims and Names Book 1882 to 1936.

Claimant: Name, dates, and Mining Location. Kittitas County Auditor's Office, Ellensburg, Washington; volumes 1880–1938.

Cle Elum Echo. Various.

Cle Elum Tribune. 1891–1892.

Davenport-Rosenberger, Joyce. *My Memories of Blewett* Personal, unpublished collection of the author.

Derkey Robert E., Nancy L. Joseph, and Raymond Lasmanis. "Metal Mines of Washington – Preliminary Report 1990," Open File Report 90-18.

Ellensburg Capitol. 1893–1902.

Ellensburg Dawn. Various.

Ellensburg Localizer. 1889–1894.

Ellensburg Record. Various.

Ellis, Arthur. Gold Bond Mining Company Stockholders Report 1982.

Ellis, Arthur, president of Gold Bond Mining Company; various letters written to Montana de Oro, Inc. (Wesley C. Engstrom collection)

Engstrom, Wesley C. *Follow the Gold Road 1873-1903: News Articles about the Swauk and Peshastin Gold Camps*. Self-Published.

Engstrom, Wesley C. and Mary Lou Dills. *Whispers from the Grave: Stories of the Evens Family Settlers on Swauk Prairie*. Self-published, 2013.

Fort Lewis Military Museum records, 1840-1960s.

Glover, Sheldon L. "Origin and Occurrence of Gem Stones in Washington," Report of Investigations No. 16, Washington State Dept. of Conservation and Development, 1949.

Green, Steven R. "1944 Directory of Washington Mining Operations," Information Circular No. 9. Washington State Dept. of Conservation and Development, 1944.

Green, Steven R., and Ward Carithers. "Directory of Washington Mining Operations 1945," Information Circular No. 11.Washington State Dept. of Conservation and Development, 1945.

Haggard, L. R. Caldo Mining Company Blewett Mining District, Chelan County, November 1961.

Handbook of Mining Details Compiled from the Engineering and Mining Journal by the Editorial Staff. London: McGraw-Hill Book Company, 1912.

Hill, Thomas B., and J. W. Melrose. "Preliminary Report on Strategic Metals in Washington." Washington State Division of Mines and Mining, March 1940.

"History, People, and Cases of the Washington State Supreme Court," a joint venture of the Oyez Project/Thomas S. Foley Institute, Washington State University.

Hodges, L. K., ed. *Mining in the Pacific Northwest: a complete review of the mineral resources of Washington and British Columbia*. Seattle, WA: Seattle Post-Intelligencer, 1897.

Huntting, M. T. "Inventory of Washington Minerals Part 2," Metallic Minerals. Washington Division of Mines and Geology Bulletin 37, v. 1, 1956.

Huntting, Marshall T. *Gold in Washington*, Division of Mines and Geology, 1955.

Huntting, Marshall T. "Inventory of Mineral Properties in Chelan County, Washington," Bulletin No. 9, Washington State Dept. of Conservation and Development, 1943.

Illustrated History of Klickitat, Yakima, and Kittitas Counties with an Outline of the Early History of the State of Washington. Chicago: Interstate Publishing, 1904.

Johnston, W. P. "North American Exploration Company Geological Mining Report," Blewett Mining District. August 14, 1958.

Kittitas Wua-Wau. Vol. 1, Issue No. 2, 1883.

Kowalewski, Michael. *Gold Rush: A Literary Exploration*. Berkeley, CA: Heyday Books, 1997.

Leavenworth Echo. Various.

Mine, Quarry and Metallurgical Record of the United States, Canada, and Mexico. The Chicago, IL: Mine and Quarry News Bureau, 1897.

"Mineral Resources of the Alpine Lakes Study Area and Additions, Chelan, King, and

Kittitas Counties, Washington." U S Geological Survey Bulletin 1542.

Mining and Engineering. 1922-1923.

Mining Journal. 1937, 1939, 1940, and 1941.

Mining Truth. September 1926 through 1928.

Moen, Wayne S. "Silver Occurrences of Washington," Bulletin No. 68, Washington State Dept. of Natural Resources, 1976.

Moen, Wayne S. "The Mineral Industry of Washington—Highlights of its Development, 1853-1980," Information Circular 74. Washington State Department of Natural Resources, 1982.

Northwest Mining. 1939.

Okanogan County Historical Museum, Map Collection 1867-1903

Patty, Ernest N. *The Metal Mines of Washington* (Washington Geological Survey Bulletin, no. 23). Olympia, WA: F. M. Lamborn, 1921.

Reynolds, Burton Mark. *Geology and Ore Deposits of the Amalgamated Gold Mines. Blewett, Washington.* Seattle, WA: University of Washington, 1923.

Scheuerman, Richard D. *The Wenatchi Indians: Guardians of the Valley.* Fairfield, WA: Ye Galleon Press, 1982.

Shedd, Solon, Olaf P. Jenkins, and Hershel H. Cooper. "Iron Ores, Fuels and Fluxes of Washington," Geological Series Bulletin No. 27. Washington State Dept. of Conservation and Development, 1922.

Smith, Leta May. *The End of the Trail.* Hicksville, NY: Exposition Press, 1976.

Spargo, Darlene, and Judy Artley Sandbloom, eds. *Pioneer Dreams*: History of Washington Territorial Pioneers. 2004.

Spokane Daily Chronicle. Various.

Steele, Richard F. *Illustrated History of Stevens, Ferry, Okanogan, and Chelan Counties, State of Washington.* Spokane, WA: Western Historical Publishing Company, 1904.

Streamer, Francis M. *The Streamer Letters.* Seattle, WA: Seattle Public Library, Main. Branch microfilms.

Trotter, F. I., and F. H. and J. R. Loutzenhiser, eds. *Told by the Pioneers, Volume Three: Tales of Frontier Life as Told by Those Who Remember the Days of the Territory and Early Statehood of Washington.* Olympia (?), WA: WPA, 1938.

United States Bureau of Indian Affairs. Birth Records for western Washington Indian tribes, 1815.

University of Washington Geology Department Staff, revised by Vaughn E. Livingston Jr. *A Geological Trip along Snoqualmie, Swauk, and Stevens Pass Highways*, Information Circular No. 38. Washington State Department of Conservation, 1963.

Vaux, Walter G. *Barkdull Mine* (Negro Creek) Chelan County, Vol. 15, page 25 unpublished report 1958.

Washington Geological Newsletter, v. 10, no. 1; January 1982.

Washington Historical Quarterly Starting at Volume One, October 1906 through Vol. 26,

Washington State Library's collection of Daniel Y. Meschter's manuscripts, 1979–1980.

Washington University State Historical Society, information from 1935.

Weaver, Charles E. "Geology and Ore Deposits of the Blewett Mining District" Washington Geological Survey, Bulletin No. 6, 1910.

Wenatchee World. Various.

Yakima Record Newspaper, Various.

Zeldek, S. W. "Caldo Mine Report, Chelan County, Washington." US Bureau of Mines, May 24, 1962.

Blewett Gold Maps

Blewett area, Negro Creek, and Ingalls Creek nickel deposit areas; shown as an overview map in areas identified as A, B, C, and D. Kroll Map Company, Seattle, Washington.

Blewett Mining District, Chelan County, Washington, by J. J. Jutzy, revised and adapted from maps of Charles E. Weaver and Clifford P. Davenport. This map shows four groups of claims that are color coded: (1) Gold Quartz vein system, (2) Peshastin vein system, (3) Pole Pick vein system, and (4) North Star vein system. Property of Gold Bond Mining Company; not dated (Wesley C. Engstrom collection). Culver Gulch and Negro Creek claims are shown here.

Calvin H. Barkdull Properties Negro Creek Claims, Chelan County, Washington, by W. W. Vaux; March 1958.

Chelan County Metskers map: Metskers Map Company, Seattle, Washington.

Culver Gulch mines and main adit locations (no formal title was given for the map). Drafted by Don Booth and Associates, Leavenworth, Washington (October 10, 1983)

Geological Survey Bulletin No. 154, Alpine Lakes, Washington, US Geological Survey and US Bureau of Mines 1989, page 211.

Negro Creek and Culver Gulch mining claims, near Blewett, Washington, are featured. Shown and named are the mineral properties under the control of the Gold Bond Mining Company (4 claims), McKay (10 claims), and the Carsten's digs (Wesley C. Engstrom collection).

Peshastin and Negro Creek Mining District, Kittitas County, by Alex M. Reynolds, US Deputy Surveyor, Seattle, Washington (1893).

Pole Pick No. 1 Mine, Fackler No. 2 Adit underground workings map (Wesley C. Engstrom collection).

USGS 7.5-minute map of the Blewett Quadrangle.

USGS 7.5-minute map of the Enchantment Lakes Quadrangle.

Washington Meteor Mining Company, Alta Vista Mining Company, and Eleanor Mining Company property maps of mining claims and underground workings in Culver Gulch, Blewett, Washington. Surveyed by Charles E. Weaver and C. R. Feltke and combined with mining surveys formerly made by J. L. McPherson and Alex M. Reynolds. Bulletin No. 6 by Charles E. Weaver.

INDEX